WILLIAM J. BAUMOL PRINCETON UNIVERSITY

With a Contribution by
RALPH TURVEY LONDON SCHOOL OF ECONOMICS

The Macmillan Company
Collier-Macmillan Limited, London

Economic Dynamics
AN INTRODUCTION

Economic Dynamics

AN INTRODUCTION

THIRD EDITION

Second Printing, 1971

Library of Congress catalog card number: 76-84434

THE MACMILLAN COMPANY
866 THIRD AVENUE, NEW YORK, NEW YORK 10022
COLLIER-MACMILLAN CANADA, LTD., TORONTO, ONTARIO

Printed in the United States of America

TO OUR PARENTS

Preface to Third Edition

New editions are normally more obese than their predecessors, and severe self-restraint on the part of the author is usually required to keep the increase to a reasonable magnitude. I am therefore pleased to be able to report that only two chapters have been added in the current version.

No book on dynamics can with good reason ignore the tremendous outburst of writing on growth theory that has in the last decade captured more than one of our leading journals. Chapter Seventeen is designed to provide a very elementary guide to some of the mainstreams in this body of literature. It is intended to be less technical and less demanding than the available expository writings on the subject.

The other new chapter provides some illustrative applications of dynamic analysis. The ideas in Chapter Eighteen are largely my own because, despite my earnest attempt to act the disinterested observer, the examples they offered seemed particularly apt. Nevertheless, for this choice I am prepared to offer suitable apology.

W. J. B.

Princeton, N.J.

Preface to Second Edition

I must begin by correcting a fundamental omission from the Preface to the First Edition, where the extent of my debt to Ralph Turvey was scarcely indicated. The first person plural was used throughout the book not in the sense of the editorial *we* but with the expectation that Turvey would be listed as co-author. I shall not venture to speculate whether his categorical refusal represented excessive modesty or an act of judicious criticism.

Most of the revision of this manuscript has consisted of addition rather than emendation. The additions have largely been mathematical in subject matter in an attempt to provide introductions to subjects such as numerical computation in higher-order systems (Chapter Twelve), nonlinear equations (Chapter Thirteen), and simultaneous difference and differential equation systems (Chapters Fifteen and Sixteen). After much hesitation I have decided not to include any discussion of transfer functions, Nyquist diagrams, Laplace transforms, or any of the other weapons in the electrical engineer's armory which have played so important a part in recent English work, particularly that of Professor Phillips. In this decision I was heavily influenced by the fact that Professor Allen has recently provided us with such excellent introductory material to several of these areas. Moreover, most of what can be accomplished by these techniques can also be done with the aid of the methods described in this volume and in a manner which, while it may not always be as efficient computationally, is usually more easily grasped in principle since the theory makes little use of such subjects as the functions of a complex variable. There even seems to be some evidence that the engineers themselves are returning to these more pedestrian techniques.

I should like to express my very sincere gratitude to Richard

Quandt and Kenneth Longman for their careful reading of the new material which appears in this edition, to Frank Hahn and Robert Kuenne for their very helpful comments, and to the many kind readers who sent me letters commenting on various portions of the book or pointing out its errors. Through their help there has been a substantial reduction in the number of mistakes, though I cannot be so sanguine as to doubt that many still remain. For these I can only apologize and protest that I have labored long in my efforts to remove them.

Very great, too, is my gratitude to the Ford Foundation, whose grant to the Princeton University Department of Economics and Sociology helped me to complete the manuscript. Thanks are also due to the Centre Nationale de la Recherche Scientifique and to *Econometrica* for permitting me to include portions of two earlier papers in Chapter Thirteen of this book. Finally, I should like to express my appreciation to my research assistants Neale M. Albert and William K. Scheirer for their painstaking help, and to Mrs. Catherine B. Brown for her beautiful typing of a difficult manuscript.

W. J. B.

Princeton, N.J.

Preface to First Edition

This book is largely based on a series of lectures which I gave at the London School of Economics in the two academic years 1947–1949. The very pleasant atmosphere provided by many good friends and the stimulating intellectual activity were highly conducive to productive effort, some of which is, I trust, manifest in this volume.

As in many things, my first debt is to Professor Lionel Robbins who originally suggested the subject of these lectures. Ralph Turvey of the London School of Economics, whose profound acquaintance with the Swedish literature is, I think, well known, wrote most of Chapter Eight and the Appendix to Chapter Five, and in addition made his influence felt throughout the volume. Much of his contribution is based on work completely unavailable to those who, like myself, find the Scandinavian languages a closed book.

In addition I must mention the invaluable suggestions and criticisms of many friends and students. I particularly remember the contributions of David Finch, now at the International Monetary Fund, Jan Graaff of St. John's College, Cambridge, Frank Hahn of the University of Birmingham, Gideon Rosenbluth, Reinhard Loosch, K. S. Krishnaswamy, and G. S. Becker.

Mr. Leslie E. Carbert of the University of California read the manuscript and very kindly supplied a long list of suggestions and corrections which were most useful in revising it.

Unfortunately I have not been able to find a way to say what I should like to in phrases other than the standard preface platitudes. This mode of expression may suggest that my purpose is no more than compliance with the minimum requirements of academic etiquette. Nothing could, however, be further from my intent.

W. J. B.

Princeton, N.J.

Contents

Part IV
SINGLE EQUATION MODELS

Part VI
NEWER GROWTH MODELS

ECONOMIC DYNAMICS

AN INTRODUCTION

Chapter One

INTRODUCTION

It should not be expected that this introduction will attempt to lay down the law on the meaning and uses of economic dynamics. No neat and final definition can be given because here usage and convenience are the important factors, and these necessarily vary. Before suggesting our own definition, therefore, we may usefully review some of those which have been put forward in recent times to help give a general idea of the scope of the subject. No attempt is made at an exhaustive catalogue of definitions; we consider only those which are useful for our present purpose.

1. DEFINITIONS

Most authors, however much they disagree in other respects, have contrasted statics and dynamics,[1] all classing as dynamics that which does not fall under the head of statics. J. R. Hicks, for instance, suggests that we ". . . call Economic Statics those parts of economic theory where we do not trouble about dating; Economic Dynamics those parts where every quantity must be dated."[2]

This definition has been criticized on the grounds that it includes too much in dynamics. Hicks finds it convenient to class as static

[1] We shall only be categorical on definitions in insisting that "dynamic" should *not* be taken to mean "superior," and "static," "inferior."

[2] J. R. Hicks, *Value and Capital,* p. 115 (Oxford University Press, New York, 1939).

only the analysis of stationary situations, situations where nothing changes and where no attention need be paid to the past or to the future because the facts and analysis relating to the present will apply equally well at any other time. Once the system begins to change, then the analysis, according to Hicks, becomes dynamic, for at different dates things will be different. Whether or not we analyze the causes and effects of the change is, in the present context, irrelevant.

The main objection that has been made against this definition is that it includes in dynamics many problems where methods of static analysis suffice.

Mr. Harrod, in his *Towards A Dynamic Economics,* suggests that dynamics should be confined to the analysis of continuing changes as against once-and-for-all changes. (The analysis of the latter, comparing the system in equilibrium before and after a change, is termed *comparative statics.*) Frisch [3] has argued, however, that the essential of dynamics is the analysis of the *process* of change not the nonstationarity of the system analyzed, saying that a system is dynamic if values of variables at different points of time are involved in an essential way. As we shall see presently, the *statics involving time* of Hicks can, using identical methods, consider a system in motion (at a point in time) just as well as a stationary system where a once-and-for-all change occurs, since it is concerned with features of the system other than the process of change itself.

It seems an appropriate task for economic dynamics to enable us to answer questions such as "Here are the facts about yesterday; what will happen today as a result?" Its essence is thus prediction, not simply in the sense of forecasting stock-exchange prices, for example, but also in the general sense of relating an event to the events which preceded it. This brings us to our working definition: *Economic dynamics is the study of economic phenomena in relation to preceding and succeeding events.*

The important thing in this definition in common with that of Frisch is that it refers not to the nature of the thing studied but

[3] Ragnar Frisch, "On the Notion of Equilibrium and Disequilibrium," *Review of Economic Studies,* 1935–1936.

rather to the point of view from which it is considered. If the answer to the question "What is going to happen today?" is "Things will be unchanged," then we have *the stationary state* in which nothing ever "happens." Yet its study can, under our definition, be dynamic. This paradoxical aspect of the definition already arises in the classical dynamic analysis, one of whose essential points is that things are always tending toward a stationary state. Similarly the stagnation thesis, which maintains that the expansion of the American economy is (or is in danger of) slowing down because of the disappearance of investment opportunities is nothing if not dynamic. Perhaps it might even be convenient for some uses to distinguish between a "dynamic economy," i.e., one which is changing, and a "dynamic analysis," i.e., one which is concerned with the analysis of change (or its absence) in the economy.

The Hicksian approach, which we have preferred to call "statics involving time" rather than "dynamics," sheds a penetrating light on the essence of statics. Phenomena are not considered in their relation to preceding and succeeding events. If the process of change does not concern us, we can consider the situation at a given moment; we can, so to speak, study a photograph, a "still," of a system in motion considering the position of its various parts and the way they fit together. The "still" must be dated, but our analysis of it can be static. This, in fact, is the case in much of Hicks's work,[4] as we shall see in a later chapter.

The distinction can perhaps best be made clear by picturing the history of an economy on a multidimensional graph with time along one of the axes. This is illustrated in Fig. 1, which shows the demand for and supply of a particular commodity through time under conditions of perfect competition. The course of demand through time is given by the surface $D_1D_2D_3D_4$, which shows how much of the good will be demanded at different prices at each moment of time, and similarly the course of potential supply over time is given by the surface $S_1S_2S_3S_4$. The course of the equilibrium supply and demand

[4] *Op. cit.*, Parts III and IV. Of course, this description does not apply to his more recent analysis of the business cycle. Cf. J. R. Hicks, *The Trade Cycle* (Oxford University Press, New York, 1950).

situation, i.e., the time path of the price which continuously equates supply and demand (the moving equilibrium), is shown by EE'. Now if we take a cross section of the diagram perpendicular to the time axis at time OT, thus in effect considering a very thin slice of the diagram at that time, we have the ordinary static supply and demand curves at time OT, S_2S_3, and D_3D_2 respectively. Thus the

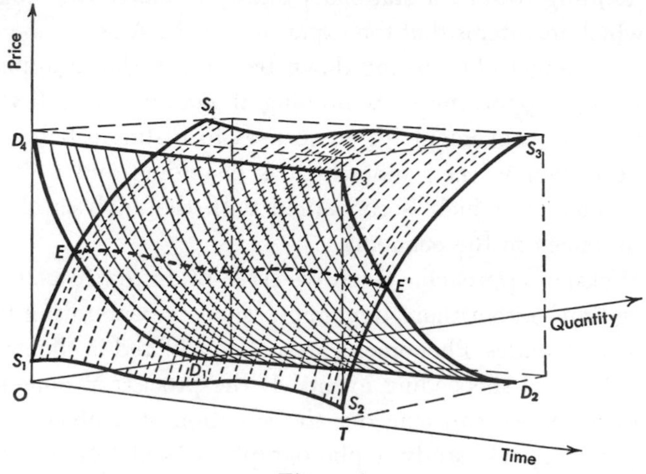

Figure 1

static method analyzes a "time slice," a cross section of the economy, thereby eliminating the *passage* of time from the problem, though, as we shall see, not necessarily eliminating the *influence* of time altogether. It is the study of such time slices which we call *statics*, whereas the study of economic problems where the time axis is not abstracted from we here call *dynamics*.

2. *THE CLASSIFICATION OF DYNAMIC SYSTEMS*

Samuelson [5] has proposed the following sixfold classification of dynamic systems:

a. Static and stationary

b. Static and historical

[5] P. A. Samuelson, *The Foundations of Economic Analysis*, pp. 315–317 (Harvard University Press, Cambridge, Mass., 1947).

c. Dynamical and causal (nonhistorical)
d. Dynamical and historical
e. Stochastical and nonhistorical
f. Stochastical and historical

The meaning of the first of these is fairly clear. It refers to the case where no change is taking place in the economy under consideration and where the method of analysis is such that the passage of time is not considered in any case. The second refers to the case where changes are taking place but solely as the result of exogenous or noneconomic causes. Thus if disturbances in the economy are taking place as a result of changes in the size of crops due to weather conditions, the economist is unable to formulate a dynamic analysis of the system unless he is prepared and able to include meteorological theory in his construction as well. Samuelson calls such a system "historical" because the description of such an economy will depend on whether we are considering the year 1857 or 1923, and any particular analysis will be valid only for a specified date.

By a "dynamical and causal" system, Samuelson means one where, given the initial facts, there is sufficient material to predict what will happen, say, ten years thereafter, this prediction being valid for 1870 if the facts apply to say 1860 and equally valid for 1933 if the facts apply to 1923. Thus in such a system what is important is the time that has elapsed since the initial information was valid, and the particular calendar date is quite irrelevant. This sort of system is characterized by all the relevant facts being economic, so that given the system, what happens depends only on the initial economic situation and can be predicted by economic analysis. Clearly, some systems can be either causal or historical, depending on whether or not we are willing to include the analysis of some elements (e.g., population changes) in our theoretical construction.

A "dynamical and historical" system is one where the course of economic events is only partly influenced by noneconomic factors. An example would be a system where business cycles occurred as a result of both changes in investment and variations in the weather. The word "stochastical" in the fifth and sixth items refers to the influence of random or chance happenings, which are of such a sort as to be amenable to analysis with the methods of probability theory. Thus both an internally complete (causal) system and one which depends on outside elements may be influenced by "chance" events.

Samuelson's classification is convenient for reference purposes, but here we have found it convenient to divide the subject into three somewhat broader categories to which the three parts of this book correspond.

Part one is devoted to what may be named "magnificent" dynamics, where this refers to the boldness, and is not meant to prejudge the quality, of the analysis. The method employed has usually involved simple deduction from fairly broad generalizations, often in the nature of alleged psychological or technological laws. The magnificent dynamics may also be distinguished by the ambitious subject considered—the development of the whole economy over long periods.

Part two will deal with the part of Hicksian analysis which we call *statics involving time*. We have already indicated its approach and subject matter.

Part three is concerned with "process" (or "sequence") analysis where the methods have tended to be mathematical in essence and often in form, with a bias toward the use of tautology, classification and definition. Here one usually treats of the pedestrian relationships between ordinary garden variety economic phenomena. As examples we may name the effects of the rate of change of the level of income on the rate of investment or the effects on next year's farm production of this year's price. Characteristic of this approach is that the span of time involved in the problems considered is rarely more than a few years.

It is true that the obvious difference between "process" analysis and "magnificent" dynamics is in the subjects considered. The difference which may interest us more is the difference in method which seems best indicated by illustration as we go along. Obviously, the choice of subject and of method of analysis cannot be made independently. It is thus that sweeping generalizations employed in the magnificent analysis seem best suited to the long-term problems considered, while the relatively painstaking techniques of sequence analysis appear to fit well with its subjects.

3. COMMENTS

Particularly in sequence analysis, the use of some mathematics in dynamics is often very convenient. We have therefore devoted considerable space to an excursion into some of the rudimentary mathematics of dynamics. It is hoped that we have done this in such a manner that any mathematical layman who knows only a little of the most elementary algebra will be able to follow, and even master, some of the technique.

Many of the arguments presented in this book are somewhat complicated and technical. This is not so much due to the use of mathematics (which until the last eight chapters is kept to a minimum) as to the complexity of the economics, and we have therefore tried to develop the discussion as simply as possible, subject to the requirement of precision, so that anyone with a training in elementary economic theory can follow. If, in some sections of the book, the reader considers the argument to be stated in too elementary a fashion, we beg his indulgence; tastes differ so that one product cannot satisfy everyone equally.

handled must in general be considerably more humdrum and
trian. This type of dynamics, which we call *process analysis*
cussed in Part III.

1. THE CLASSICAL APPROACH

By the classical economists we shall here mean those write
economic theory who worked largely in England during and
the time of Malthus and before the time of John Stuart Mill, an
the most famous of whom were Ricardo, James Mill, McCull
and Senior. These men did not, of course, hold identical view
that any restatement of *the* classical analysis must be a synthesi
synthesis is also to some extent forced on us because the analysis
these authors is not always complete in all details. Key points
often stated implicitly or only hinted at, while in some cases poi
are left vague by the writer either because he did not work t
matter through or because his exposition is obscure. In every ca
we shall here choose a more definite and unqualified statement
reference to one which is hazy and hedged in order to make
asier to construct a sharply defined model of the system. It shoul
e realized, however, that this method of selection tends to impart
the classical analysis a naïveté or lack of sophistication which can
metimes be unjust.

The basic theme in the dynamic analysis of the early English
nomists was the development of the economy from a progressive
e into a stationary state, the latter generally being considered
desirable than the former. This was considered to constitute an
line of the whole of economic history, although the ultimate
val at the stationary state at which wages would have reached a
imum acceptable level and net investment would have ceased
use of low profits, could be postponed indefinitely by a stream
ghly productive inventions.

e argument was based essentially on the theory of population
iated with Malthus, which predicted dire consequences as the
of excessive numbers of humans. The chain of causation,
we will presently examine in somewhat greater detail, was

Part I

THE MAGNIFICENT DYNAMICS

Chapter Two

THE CLASSICAL DYNAM

In this part of the book we shall begin by consi
earlier economic thought. This is not to show by contr
riority or inferiority of modern economics nor to searc
anticipations of present-day ideas. We consider these
systems simply because, although imperfect, they
approach of which there are few recent examples.
case may perhaps be attributed to the timidity of la
the approach is of a magnificent cast, ambitiousl
analyze the growth and development of entire
relatively long periods of time—decades or even c
The use of assumptions which were often dub
which involved marked but sometimes inspired
characterized classical dynamics. After the mar
the seventies, however, positivism came into vo
thought became less daring and imaginative
assumptions which seemed "obviously" justifi
that much theorizing amounted to little mo
classification. Emphasis was placed on such
theory of consumer behavior, and with the n
Schumpeter's work, very few significant con
were made.

Recently there has been a revival of in
(with several possible exceptions) as com
dynamics the approach is so much more c

this: The progressive state is characterized by a high level of investment (accumulation) which generally serves to increase total production but which also tends to keep up wages. This in turn leads to an increasing population. Because land is fixed in quantity there are diminishing average returns to additional labor in production. As population increases wages therefore tend to eat up the total product after rent payment and thereby reduce the profitability of investment until the inducement to invest disappears and the stationary state is attained. It is clear, then, that we must examine the classical theories of investment, profits, wages, and population in some detail in order to understand the system.

We may remark in passing that classical dynamics involved no recourse to the classification of economic systems into types such as feudalism and capitalism. It may perhaps be said that the classical economists saw all of history occurring in a rudimentary non-monopoly capitalist environment.

2. *THE ROLE OF INVESTMENT*

As has been said, one of the essential features of the progressive state in the classical analysis was a high level of accumulation.[1] By accumulation was meant the difference between production and consumption (saving), which was assumed to be undertaken for the purpose of investment in produced means of production, i.e., in capital. (In some wage discussions as we shall see, this term referred only to things like food and clothing, that is, to goods which can be used to make wage payments.) Thus, by adding to the productive resources available, accumulation permitted an increase in the output of the community, in effect increasing the productivity of labor and land.[2]

[1] E.g., McCulloch, *Principles of Political Economy*, 4th Edition, Part I, Chap. II (Adam and Charles Black, Edinburgh; and Longman, Brown, Green and Longmans, London, 1849).

[2] E.g., Nassau Senior, *An Outline of the Science of Political Economy*, p. 58 (Allen and Unwin, London, 1938). Senior refers to accumulation as abstinence, using this term in arguing that interest payments to capitalists were justified as a reward for the consumption they had denied themselves by using their capital in the productive process.

The rate of accumulation was taken to depend on the level of profit because high profits served as an inducement to accumulation.[3] It was not maintained that there was any fixed relationship between the level of profit and the rate of accumulation, but merely that they were positively correlated and that accumulation would always take place if (and only if) there were obtainable a rate of profit greater than some minimum level which was just barely acceptable to the savers.

3. *PROFITS*

Profits themselves were held to be the residue of production after wages and rent were paid out.[4] More specifically it was argued that on every unit of output produced in any industry the total rent and wage costs were closely related to the wage payments on a unit produced on the poorest land (natural resources) in use. The reason for this is that rent was so determined as just to eliminate any higher return to capital invested on better lands. If rents there were relatively low, entrepreneurs would all try to get hold of the better land for themselves driving the price up by their competition, whereas if the rent on the better land were too high it would pay entrepreneurs to use only the inferior land and the rent would be driven down for lack of tenants. Since the model assumed that there is no rent on marginal output, it follows that profit on this output will equal the value of the output minus its wage costs. Moreover, since the rate of return on capital must be everywhere the same, as we have just seen, the return on every unit of capital will be given by this same figure. Profit per unit of capital is thus equal to whatever is left over from the marginal unit after paying wages.

Total profits therefore depended on the total product of labor, on the level of wages, and on the quantity of labor necessary to produce the marginal unit, or if we prefer, on the marginal product of labor.

[3] Cf. McCulloch, *op. cit.*, p. 110. See also Ricardo, *Principles of Political Economy and Taxation*, Chap. VI, pp. 72–73 (Everyman Edition, E. P. Dutton and Co., New York, 1911).

[4] Ricardo, *ibid.*, Chap. VI.

4. THE PRODUCTIVITY OF LABOR

The productivity of labor was taken to depend upon the quantity of capital, as already mentioned, and the state of technique. More important, however, was its dependence upon the size of the laboring population. Since land was taken to be fixed in quantity and quality, it was argued that, as population and thus the labor force increased, recourse would be had to inferior and less productive land. (Land might from the economist's viewpoint vary in productivity for several reasons, for example, because of varying transport cost involved in bringing its product to market and not just because of varying physical productivity.) More and more labor would tend to be crowded into working on the better lands, and as a result here also the marginal product of labor would ultimately fall. This was the law of historically diminishing returns. Its action could be retarded by technical progress, but nevertheless, as population increased, the trend would ultimately always be toward a reduction in the average and marginal productivity of labor.[5]

5. THE THEORY OF WAGES AND POPULATION

The classical economists actually employed two theories of wages, both of which are important for our present discussion. These were the theory of "natural" or "subsistence" wages which tended to be approached in the long run and the theory of market wages which were the wages actually paid in practice.[6]

In the long run, it was held, wages tended toward a constant low standard of living which might be so low that laborers and their families could only just continue to exist on them. The familiar argument, based on the Malthusian population theory, was that whenever wages were above the conventional minimum the working population would reproduce itself at a more rapid rate. Since this would increase the labor force, the supply and demand situation

[5] Ricardo, *op. cit.*, Chap. II.
[6] Ricardo, *op. cit.*, Chap. V.

would turn against the laborers and drive their wages down. Ultimately it was more than the supply and demand situation which would do this since diminishing average productivity would advance to such a point that no more could be produced than would just serve to keep the working population at subsistence level. Wages too low for subsistence could not persist since population would then be reduced by starvation and malnutrition to a point where wages would rise at least to that level.

Sometimes population was taken to rise with wages because at a certain point people regarded themselves as financially able to have children, while in other cases it was held that people always attempted to marry and have children but that the death rate would only be low if wages were high. On the former interpretation, then, subsistence wages would necessarily vary with the level which people regarded as the minimum at which they could have children, and this level could rise with an increasing standard of living. This matter of interpretation is not, however, important for our present purposes.

The other rate of wages, the market rate, was taken to depend on the level of accumulation. When capital was being accumulated rapidly the competition of employers for labor would be great, thus raising the rate of wages. Indeed, a high level of accumulation could serve to keep wages above the subsistence level almost indefinitely. The classical writers varied in their explanation of the level of market wages. McCulloch went so far as to adopt a perfectly rigid wages fund theory which held that wages were given by the supply of capital divided by the number of workers, i.e., by the quantity of wage goods per laborer.[7]

6. THE SYNTHESIS

We may now readily see the workings of the classical system. These are conveniently explained with the aid of a diagram. It is

[7] *Op. cit.*, Part III, Chap. II, Sect. I. Cf. Senior, *op. cit.*, p. 154, for a contrary view.

assumed that we begin in an early stage of the classical economy, where population is small compared to natural resources and where consequently profits, the rate of accumulation, and thus wages are all relatively high. We shall at first assume that population adjusts itself relatively quickly to a change in the level of market wages.

In Fig. 2 we measure the size of the working population on the horizontal axis and the total product and the total wage payments to the entire working population on the vertical axis. Since the subsistence wage payment to 557 persons is 557 times the subsistence

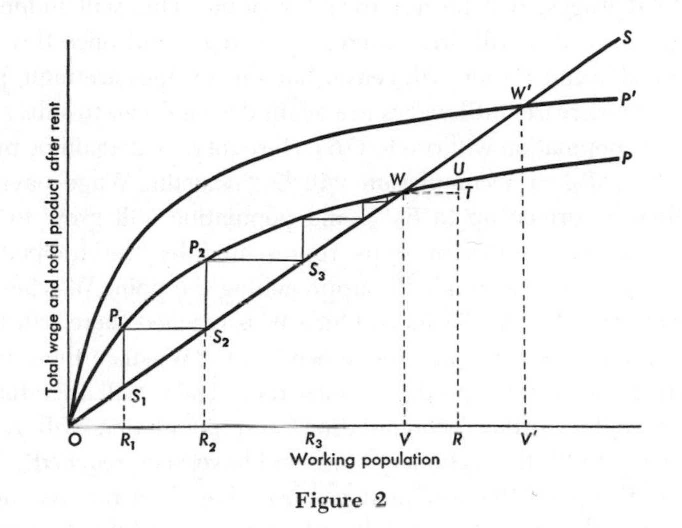

Figure 2

wage payment to one person and since the subsistence wage payment to a zero working population is zero, the total wage payments, if subsistence wages were always just paid, would be given by a straight line *OS* through the origin. The slope of *OS* (*VW* divided by *OV*) is thus total subsistence wage payments divided by the size of the working population, i.e., the wage necessary to keep one person at the minimum standard.

OP, on the other hand, is the curve giving the total product of the community after the deduction of rent payments. Because of the law of diminishing returns and because in the classical theory total rent payments grow with population,[8] this curve must be convex upward. This means, for example, that, when population increases from zero to OR_1, total product after rent payment increases by R_1P_1; when working population is higher an equal increase in population, this time from OV to OR, allows only a small increase in product TU.

Suppose now that we start out with population OR_1. If wages are initially at subsistence level, total wage payments will be R_1S_1 and an amount S_1P_1, the difference between total product minus rent and total wages, will be left over for profit. This will induce accumulation which will drive wages up to R_1P_1, and once this wage is reached accumulation will cease. But since wages are high, population will increase until wages are again driven down to subsistence level, i.e., population will rise to OR_2. Here there will again be profits, given by S_2P_2, so accumulation will begin again. Wage payments will then be driven up to R_2P_2, and population will grow to OR_3, and so on, in a series of steps represented by the stepped line $S_1P_1S_2P_2S_3 \cdots$, this gradually approaching the point W where the curve OP and the line OS meet. Once W is reached there will be no profits even with wages at subsistence level, VW, since these wages will then eat up total product minus rent. There will therefore be no motive for further accumulation, and population will remain stationary at OV; the stationary state will have been reached.

Up to this point the argument has been based on the assumption that population adjustments take place fairly rapidly. In practice this will clearly not be the case. As a result, once wages reach R_1P_1, population will only expand slowly. Long before it can reach OR_2, that is, long before wages again fall to subsistence level, some profit will again appear and further accumulation be induced. Wages will thus tend to be kept up, moving close to the total product curve OP.

[8] This is because once diminishing returns set in, each time an extra unit of output is produced more labor must be used in its production than was used on the last unit. Thus the wage cost of the marginal unit must rise, and so the rent payments on other (intramarginal) units must increase in order that rent plus wage payments on intramarginal units continue to make up for the now higher wage costs on marginal units.

Hence the actual course taken by the economy will not be indicated by $S_1P_1S_2P_2S_3 \cdots$ but will follow the total-product curve, *OP*, rather closely from below toward point *W*.

Of course, an increase in productivity brought about by inventions or discoveries can postpone the day of judgment. This can readily be indicated on the diagram; the increase in productivity would shift the total product curve upward from *OP* to *OP′* and hence move the point of stationary equilibrium to the right along *OS* from *W* to *W′*. Thus the upper limit to population would rise from *OV* to *OV′*.

7. METHODOLOGY

The reader may note how sweeping generalizations which were put forward as psychological or technological laws formed the basis of the entire argument. This is, of course, the main methodological characteristic of the magnificent dynamics mentioned in the introduction. The Malthusian population principle, the law of historically diminishing returns, the discussion of the inducement to accumulate, and the analysis of wages are all empirical hypotheses, some of which may only have been valid at the time and some of which may be questioned altogether. Some of them, such as the population analysis, are nowadays considered to treat of noneconomic variables and are hence usually brought in as data and not as an integral part of the analysis. In many respects the discussion represents a shrewd and courageous approach largely absent from present-day analysis. Moreover, the discussion of the paths in which the economy was moving may well have been sufficiently close to reality to provide valuable assistance in policy problems of the day.

Chapter Three

THE DYNAMICS OF MARX AND SCHUMPETER

The Marxian system is probably the most recent attempt to construct a comprehensive historical dynamic theory. It is unsatisfactory in many details even to those who are willing to accepts its broad features,[1] although this is sometimes ascribed to the fact that Marx died before completing *Capital*. Schumpeter, on the other hand, did analytic work on historical dynamics which is of great interest and importance but which forms only part of a system. Indeed, he himself said that he believed his analysis fitted in well with the Marxian dynamics.[2] For this reason it is convenient to consider their work at the same time.

The subject of this chapter is the motor mechanism which provides the impetus for growth. Central to the Marxian, the Schum-

[1] This point is agreed upon by many Marxists. Cf. Paul M. Sweezy, *The Theory of Capitalist Development*, Chap. VI, 3 and Chap. VII. (Oxford University Press, New York, 1949.) Cf. also Maurice Dobb's foreword to the English edition. On the reconstruction of the latter parts of *Capital* (Charles H. Kerr and Co., Chicago, Vol. I, 1906, Vol. II, 1907, and Vol. III, 1909) see the first part of Engels's preface to Vol. II.

[2] Cf. Joseph Schumpeter, *The Theory of Economic Development*, p. 60 n. (Harvard University Press, Cambridge, Mass., 1934). The present discussion of Schumpeter's ideas is based mainly on this book. In his *Capitalism, Socialism and Democracy* (Harper and Brothers, New York and London, 1942), Schumpeter did extend the scope of his discussion considerably, but he did this in a somewhat loose and conversational manner which makes it almost impossible to discern the details of the analytic framework.

peterian (and our own) view of the development process is the belief that the economy is set up in a way which precludes its standing still. The remarkable growth of our economy is not an historical accident. Rather it is a consequence of the nature of the capitalist process. The drive for increased wealth and the structure of its business institutions require the businessman to seek out every opportunity to expand his operations and improve his competitive position.

1. THE MARXIAN APPROACH

The basic element of the Marxian analysis is the "materialist interpretation of history." The fundamental proposition of this has been stated as follows: "In every historical epoch, the prevailing mode of economic production and exchange, and the social organization necessarily following from it, form the basis upon which is built up, and from which alone can be explained, the political and intellectual history of that epoch." [3]

This view is far more subtle than that of the "economic interpretation" school of historians who explain events in terms of the self-seeking behavior of the participants. Marxist theorists have little patience with this view. To them history is shaped *not* only by the greedy, calculating economic man—it can be affected profoundly by deeds which are heroic, altruistic or even irrational. Materialism maintains rather that behavior and personality in turn are largely conditioned by the natural and technological circumstances which together constitute the economic environment.[4]

Marx, therefore, unlike the classical economists, employed a historical approach. He maintained that capitalism is a transitory phenomenon which arose from the disintegration of the feudal economy and which will in its turn sooner or later be replaced. The seeds of capitalism, he said, were sown by the class struggle between serfs and feudal lords, and the merchant class was formed largely from

[3] Friedrick Engels, Preface to *The Communist Manifesto*.

[4] See G. Plekhanov, *The Materialist Conception of History* (Foreign Languages Publishing House, Moscow, 1946) and Lewis Feuer, "The Economic Factor in History," *Science and Society*, 1940, pp. 16–20.

among emancipated serfs. Because this class, unlike the feudal nobility and serfs, was subject in its work to the influence of competition and the incentive of economic advancement, it was better able to take advantage of the possibilities opened by the improvement of technique and discoveries and gradually came to dominate government and economic life. Since industry and commerce required a peaceful and orderly community, rising strong governments personified by absolute monarchs received capitalist support. The expropriation of the common lands served to create a stock of capital which supplemented mercantile wealth and at the same time gave rise to a class of free but propertyless individuals who had to sell their labor power to earn a living.[5]

2. *THE CAPITALIST PROCESS*

Marx, like the classical economists, placed accumulation in the forefront of his dynamic system. While, like them, he considered that accumulation was undertaken for its own sake, he also maintained that the capitalist accumulated in order to keep his profits high.[6] Thus in his system high profits were the prerequisite of accumulation, while at the same time accumulation was carried on in order to maintain high profits. In order to understand accumulation, therefore, we must examine the theory of profit, and here we turn to the work of Schumpeter.[7]

3. *WEALTH: THE PRESENT VALUE OF EXPECTED PROFITS*

The market value of a firm is a reflection of its expected future earnings, and it will be argued in Chapter Five that it may be the object of the owner of a firm to make this market value, called its *capitalized present value*, as large as possible.

[5] See *Capital*, Vol. I, Part VIII.

[6] *Capital*, Vol. III, Chap. XIII, esp. p. 257, and Vol. I, p. 647.

[7] Some passages in *Capital* indicate that Marx might well have agreed with what follows, e.g., Vol. I, Chap. XXV, Sec. 3.

Given the state of technique and of the market, the entrepreneur will then direct his firm to produce that output combination and make those investments which maximize this capitalized present value. From the point of view of the largely static analysis of Part II of this book, once the entrepreneur has made these investment and output decisions, his function is at an end.

However, there is more to the story than this, for by innovation he may increase the firm's profitability. Indeed, if we define an increase in the owner's wealth as an addition to the value of the firm which does not just represent a change in the form in which the businessman holds his assets (ordinary investment), then, excluding windfalls, he can increase his wealth only by innovating.

Before we go into the justification of this statement it would be well to explain what we mean by the term innovation. By an innovation we mean a change falling into one or more of the following five categories: [8]

a. The introduction of a new good or a new grade of a good already in use
b. The introduction of a new method of production (e.g., a new type of labor-saving machinery)
c. The opening of a new market (e.g., the commencement of sales of refrigerators to Eskimos)
d. The employment of a new source of supply of factors of production
e. The reorganization of an industry, several industries, or part of an industry (e.g., the monopolization of some industry)

What is crucial for any of these things in order for them to qualify as innovations in our sense is not their invention or discovery but their first commercial use. Thus some new product may be invented many years before it becomes an economic innovation, or a foreign source of raw materials may be discovered some time before entrepreneurs think it profitable to exploit it.

[8] Schumpeter, *The Theory of Economic Development,* p. 66.

Now, as has just been stated, profit, in the sense of an addition to the value of the firm, can only be obtained by innovation. In perfect competition this applies even to profits in the more ordinary sense (the difference between returns and costs). Here the argument is easiest to grasp, for in this case, in the absence of change long-run equilibrium involves zero profits after remuneration of management.[9]

But suppose, for example, that a process for producing some commodity at a cost lower than that now incurred in its manufacture comes to the attention of the entrepreneur. By being the first to employ this innovation he can still sell the goods at a price high enough to keep other firms in the field in business, and since his costs will be lower than theirs he will necessarily make a profit. Sooner or later, however, if other firms learn of and adopt the new process, the scent of profit will attract additional investment into the field, and the output of the commodity will tend to increase. This influx of capital will only cease when output has expanded so much as to lower the price of the good sufficiently to eliminate all further profits. It is clear that the earning of profit can then only take place again when some further innovation is introduced.[10]

This illustration, however, misses the essential point. Even where the return accruing to an entrepreneur is more or less permanent, as it may well be where the innovation consists of the successful establishment of a monopoly, wealth, in the sense we are here using it, will cease to grow after the introduction of the innovation. Once everyone recognizes that the new monopoly is likely to increase returns in a certain way, these additions will be taken account of in its market price which will rise by an amount equal to the capitalized present value of these expected additions to wealth. The gain in the value of the firm (wealth) resulting from the establishment of an innovation is thus of necessity in effect a once-and-for-all gain which *can* be collected (realized) in the market. A refusal by the entre-

[9] *Ibid.*, pp. 30–31.

[10] *Ibid.*, Chapter IV. We neglect the possibility of windfall profits arising from some outside event, e.g., a declaration of war.

preneur to realize such a gain at once by selling the firm once he has completed an innovation, i.e., the decision to collect it as returns accrue to the firm, does not change the conclusion that wealth growth, in our sense, ceases once the innovation is established. Such a refusal to sell merely expresses a predilection on the part of the entrepreneur for investment in that particular firm. In effect he has disposed of his gains by reinvesting them in the firm rather than, say, in fixed interest bearing securities. One reason why he may refuse to sell may, of course, be that he expects higher returns from the firm than does the market, so that he considers the market price too low.

We have thus obtained two separate results: The first result is that profits in the ordinary sense may usually be increased by the introduction of an innovation—by being there first with the change so the pressure of competition can be at least temporarily averted. The other is the result, true by definition, that the value of the firm will undergo a once-and-for-all enhancement as the result of the successful introduction of an innovation. In either case, the growth of asset value will cease once the innovation is firmly established.

From this we can draw two conclusions directly relevant to the dynamic system we are considering. The first is that the entrepreneur is always under pressure to innovate—to introduce changes and not let things stagnate. Here we can see some of the argument behind the statement that an essential feature of capitalism is change, or if one prefers the term, progress. It is this aspect of capitalism that Marx contrasted with feudal productive mediocrity. Certainly we can see that if the entrepreneur desires a continued increase in the value of his firm, he must innovate. It is true that he can add something by investing his own savings in the firm, but he cannot hope for unlimited investment by others since the capital an entrepreneur can raise depends largely on the prospective earnings of his firm which can only be enhanced by innovation.

The second conclusion is this: The very profitability of innovation supplies a motive for accumulation, for the establishment of an innovation requires capital. The recognition by an entrepreneur that some change, say in production technique, might be profitable is of little use to him if he does not have the capital with which to finance it.

The savings of the individual entrepreneur are, of course, by no means the only or indeed the most important source from which investment can be financed. Borrowing from the banks or selling stocks or shares in the market can also provide the necessary resources for introducing an innovation. But the amount which can be raised in these ways depends not only on the nature of the proposed innovation but also on "the credit" of the entrepreneur seeking to raise funds. In general he will probably be able to raise more money, other things being equal, the greater his own accumulated wealth.

4. THE SIZE OF THE FIRM AND THE RATE OF RETURN ON CAPITAL

We have now shown that the entrepreneur may be able to add to his wealth by increasing the capitalized present value of his firm through innovation. Obviously, he can also accumulate wealth more gradually by saving out of his returns (his profits).

It has sometimes been argued that competition will tend to make these returns proportional to the quantity of capital invested in a firm. If anywhere the return per unit of capital is higher than elsewhere, capital will be attracted out of low-profit enterprises and into high-profit enterprises. This will cause output and, possibly, costs to rise and prices to fall in the more profitable trades, and we will have the reverse effects in the less lucrative lines. The flow of capital will presumably continue until profit differences are no longer large enough to make up for the costs of capital movement. This argument does not, of course, apply to the case of monopolized industries where the entry of new capital is more or less effectively prevented so that the rate of return on capital is likely to be above that in competitive sectors of the economy.

However, it has recently been pointed out [11] that the return per unit of capital (the rate of return on capital) may, up to a point, be expected to increase with the amount of capital invested, i.e., with the size of the firm. The reason is that, while entrepreneurs with large quantities of capital at their disposal can compete with those having a smaller capital, the reverse is not generally possible. The large firm can, if it prefers, for example, operate a large chain of small cinemas in competition with small film exhibitors, but the latter cannot open a huge film theater of the magnificent proportions found in the centers of large cities. The result is that the profits of larger firms will tend to be at least as high as, and perhaps higher than, those of smaller ones, though this may sometimes partly be offset by diseconomies resulting from managerial difficulties in the larger firms.

This result, if it is accepted, serves to add strength to the argument that accumulation will tend to be undertaken for the sake of profit, for with a larger accumulated capital *and the resulting ability to borrow greater amounts* in the capital market, the entrepreneur may be able to increase his earnings more than proportionately to the increase in his capital.

5. THE LEVEL OF WAGES

Like the classical economists, Marx accepted different long-run and short-run theories of wages. His conclusions, but not the arguments on which he based them, were for the most part similar to those of his predecessors.

Thus he accepted the view that in the short run wages could be raised through the effects of rapid accumulation on the demand for labor. He also believed that in the long run wages tend to be driven down to subsistence level, but he did not arrive at this by recourse

[11] F. Hahn, "A note on Profit and Uncertainty," *Economica*, August 1947. See also J. Steindl, *Small and Big Business*, pp. 10 12 (Basil Blackwell, Oxford, 1945); Joan Robinson, *An Essay on Marxian Economics*, p. 58 (Macmillan & Co., Ltd., London, 1942); and W. J. Baumol, *Business Behavior, Value and Growth*, Chap. 5 (The Macmillan Company, New York, 1959).

to the Malthusian theory of population which he called "a libel on the human race." [12] He argued instead that an industrial reserve army of unemployed exists whose competition with employed labor acts to keep wages down. Even if accumulation should increase employment, Marx argued, the rise in wages would induce entrepreneurs to employ labor-saving machinery (indeed, this might be one of the main inducements for innovation in Marx's view), and this would generally increase the number of unemployed so forcing wages down again.[13] Where this did not occur the system would tend to break down; that is to say, a crisis would occur which would effectively replenish the army of unemployed.

6. MARX AND THE FUTURE OF CAPITALISM

Marx does not anywhere attempt to draw up a complete outline of his views as to the future of capitalism. While it is clear that in his opinion the eventual end of the system is certain, it is not clear how this end must come about.

One of the arguments employed is certainly fallacious. This is the argument about the tendency to a falling rate of profit [14] and the consequent increasing misery of the working classes. Marx maintains that if each worker spends, say, ten hours a day at work and the value of, say, six hours' product is required to pay him subsistence wages, then the profit per worker will be the value of four hours' labor. With a constant working population, total profits will then be fixed. But with the passage of time, more and more wealth will be accumulated and invested in fixed capital so that there will be the same amount of profit and more capital. Then the quantity of profit per unit of capital, i.e., the rate of profit, will necessarily fall. The main fallacy in the argument stems from the assumption that a fixed number of hours per day are required to provide subsistence, for as investment increases the product of one hour's labor will

[12] Cited in Sweezy, *op. cit.*, p. 86. See Karl Marx and Friederick Engels, *Correspondence: 1846–95* (Lawrence Wishard, London, 1934), p. 170.

[13] *Capital,* Vol. I, Chapter XXV, Section 3.

[14] *Capital,* Vol. III, Part III.

generally increase. This means, e.g., that only five rather than six of the ten hours worked may be required to provide subsistence wages and that the remaining time—the "exploitation" (surplus value)—will then increase from four to five hours per day's labor and total profits may even be able to increase as quickly as the capital stock.

From this "law" of the tendency to a falling rate of profit, Marx argued that in order to keep up profits entrepreneurs would be forced to increase the hours of labor and reduce wages, i.e., reduce the level of subsistence, so adding to the misery of the working classes. This would presumably have the effect of increasing class consciousness and thus hasten the end of capitalism. With the elimination of the law of the falling rate of profit and for other reasons such as the growing strength of the trade unions, this argument automatically falls to the ground.

Marx's view that there is a tendency for industry to become ever more monopolized and for wealth to fall into ever fewer hands is also relevant to his prediction of the eventual breakdown of capitalism. This idea is based on several grounds. First, entrepreneurs having larger capitals at their disposal can drive their lesser rivals out of the more lucrative fields. Second, the higher return on larger capitals will mean that they will grow relatively to the smaller capitals, and, finally, with the aid of credit which the capital market will readily grant to the wealthy, their relative power to earn and their control over the economy will greatly increase.

The implication of this is that the number of those who have a vested interest in the continuation of capitalism must gradually decrease as the smaller entrepreneurs are driven out. This, as has often been pointed out, neglects the growing importance of shareholders and of managerial and professional personnel who together form a new middle class.

It has also been suggested that Marx believed that crises would tend to grow in intensity until capitalism would finally collapse in a slump of great depth and duration.[15]

[15] Sweezy, *op. cit.*, Chap. XI.

Finally, some of Marx's followers have developed arguments which are somewhat akin to the stagnation thesis, i.e., the hypothesis that for various reasons investment opportunities may be drying up.[16] The essential point is based on the underconsumption argument. With maldistribution of wealth, capitalism will manifest a chronic tendency to underconsumption, so there will be a continuous search for new markets to get rid of surplus products. Backward territories serve as an ideal outlet for these products, according to this view, and also provide the basis for innovations taking advantage of sources of cheaper labor and raw materials. Competition then leads to demands for the exclusion of foreigners from the exploitation of these areas, and imperalist colonization begins.

However, these lands are not limitless, and as the pressure of underconsumption always leads to the search for still more markets, all the backward areas will sooner or later be colonized. There will then be a pressure toward further colonial expansion at the expense of other imperialist powers, so military preparation and wars of territorial redivision will begin.

At first, imperialist activity will benefit most of the people of the victorious country, for so long as all countries devote only a small portion of their resources to the cost of victory (which requires only that your preparation be a bit better than that of your opponent), it may be small enough to be offset by the resulting prosperity. But as armanent races become the rule, the military burden will have a depressing influence on living standards, and only the capitalists whose investment opportunities are expanded and protected by imperialist activity will stand to gain from it. In the defeated countries, of course, everyone loses, and the tendency to overproduction will only be offset by the direct destruction resulting from military operations.

In general, it is argued, this will increase the cleavage between the interests of the workers and those of the capitalists and intensify the class struggle, bringing the ultimate breakdown of capitalism nearer.

[16] Sweezy, *op. cit.*, Part Four.

7. SCHUMPETER AND THE FUTURE OF CAPITALISM[17]

Like Marx before him, Schumpeter predicted that the capitalist system will some day destroy itself, and he maintained that the process of decay was already well on its way. But Schumpeter's reasons for expecting the downfall of capitalism are really the very reverse of those of Marx and his followers. Schumpeter predicted that capitalism will die of a surfeit—that it will pass on as a result of the increasing prosperity rather than increasing misery of the bulk of the populace.

His arguments rest heavily on sociological and social psychological allegations which seek to describe the effects of economic developments under capitalism upon the political climate. He foresaw increasing popular hostility toward capitalism and increasing unwillingness to undertake an effective defense of the system on the part of those who might most be expected to do so.

The capitalist economy, said Schumpeter, is one which is not conducive to romanticism. It imparts rationalist attitudes and habits of mind to the people by emphasizing economic activity in which reliance on magic and superstition is most easily seen to be disappointing. Moreover, a money economy forces everyone to become familiar with the rules of arithmetic and hence with some elementary principles of logic. This provides the basis for working class discontent with its lot and for a utilitarian attitude which leads to demands for a welfare state—demands which are taken up and promoted by the intellectuals.

Rationalism, at the same time, reduces public awe of tradition and the hero symbols which in an earlier day represented the constituted authority. The romantic warrior king is replaced by the dull figure of the bourgeois who is indeed possessed of great power but little general respect.

[17] The material which follows is a summary of Chapters XI through XV of *Capitalism, Socialism and Democracy.*

This is the setting in which the Schumpeterian drama is played out. Developments now proceed from the very success of the capitalist economy. On the one hand, prosperity offers the worker the leisure in which he can nurse his discontent, while on the other, it tends to render the capitalist obsolete.

This elimination of the role of the capitalist occurs in several ways. The growth of the economy puts firms under pressure to compete for funds to finance their expansion. The growth of the corporations is, in part, a response to the need for credit; for it makes available to the firm the funds of the shareholders. But the corporate form transforms the manager of the firm into a hired employee whose identification with the interests of the company which he heads is decidedly limited. Nor do the stockholders, whose interests are often highly diversified and who are in any event at one remove from control of the firm, take up the role of the vanishing captain of industry.

Moreover, while this is happening, long experience and good bureaucratic big business practice have been reducing research and innovation to mere routine so that their occurrence becomes more regular and more dependable. With this the need for the Schumpeterian innovator-entrepreneur vanishes and the obsolescence of the capitalist-manager is well on its way.

Having entitled one of his chapters "Crumbling Walls" Schumpeter leaves the rest to the reader's imagination. The growing hostility of the public and gradual atrophy of the defenders of the system leave, in Schumpeter's view, no alternative. He simply goes on at this point to discuss the socialist economy which, he believes, is likely to follow.

8. METHODOLOGICAL COMMENTS

One of our primary purposes in presenting the materials of this chapter and, particularly, of the last two sections, lies in their methodological contrast with the content of the preceding chapter and those which are to follow. Neither Marx nor Schumpeter was a narrow specialist. Schumpeter has been described (by one who himself has grounds to claim the title) as "perhaps the last of the great polymaths"—of those giant intellects whose understanding and erudition permits them to roam widely among the many disciplines. History, sociology, political science, and other fields of knowledge all make their appearance in the works of both of these writers. As we have seen, their historical orientation led them to give to capitalism "a local habitation and a name"—to treat it as an historical event rather than as the archetype of economic activity from the birth of man to the day of his destruction. And in their attempt to look into the future they employed arguments which many would consider to be noneconomic in character.

But, perhaps to make room for this wealth of source materials, they had to pay a price. The dynamic systems of the Marxists and Schumpeter leave us with a sense of frustration because they are so vague and impressionistic. We are left feeling that their tale might just as easily have been given a different ending. Even if we were to accept their premises, we are under no obligation to go along with their conclusions!

The difficulty is that their premises do not form a logically complete system. For the same reason that the equation $2x = 7y$ does not permit us to discover the value of either variable, the assumption that entrepreneurs seek to innovate or capitalists to accumulate does not permit us to foresee their future with any degree of confidence. Too many parts of the system are missing and it does not form a deterministic model which grinds out history with an inexorability which permits us to predict it.

This feature of the Marxian-Schumpeterian approach to analysis of economic development contrasts strongly with the classical system which was described in the preceding chapter. There the premises about capitalists' and workers' motivations, the nature of wage and rent payment and the assumptions about population growth and diminishing returns preclude any alternative to the type of time path which is depicted in Figure 2. The prediction of a tendency toward a stationary state (which shifts in the production function may, of course, postpone indefinitely) is not a guess—it is a matter of straightforward deduction that can be confirmed by rigorous mathematical procedures. (Cf. Section 4 of Chapter Thirteen.)

Actually, the classical writings themselves represent a compromise between the two alternative approaches which have just been described—the rich, erudite impressionistic discussion which characterizes at least some of Schumpeter's writing, and the more rigorous analysis that is often the poorer in empirical content. The rest of this volume is devoted to the work of writers whose analysis is primarily of the latter variety. The approach has reached its culmination in the models of the mathematical economists described in the concluding chapters of this book.

9. *SUMMARY*

Unlike that of the classics, the Marxian and the Schumpeterian dynamic analyses made no attempt to chart a precise time path for the economy. They did, however, indicate how change must arise out of its operation and how that change must in turn affect the economy. In sum, Marx argued that a capitalist economy cannot function without progress, i.e., that continued technical advance almost necessarily follows from the existence of the system; in particular, the classical vision of a stationary capitalist state must, from a Marxist point of view, be an impossible monster. It must also be characterized by recurrent crises, chronic unemployment, low wages, and increasing monopolization and concentration of wealth via the accumulation process. Ultimately, capitalism must lead to imperialism and finally to its own destruction.

The Marxian method involved an analysis considerably less explicit in detail but more historical in viewpoint than that of the classics. This enabled him to discuss the rise and fall of entire economic systems without giving him an adequate foundation on which to commit himself on all the intermediate steps. It is for this reason that the exposition of this chapter is necessarily less tidy than the discussion of the classical system.

Chapter Four

MR. HARROD'S MODEL

As has already been mentioned, Mr. Harrod has constructed a dynamic system [1] which he says is to be taken as a first step toward a revival of magnificent dynamics. To a large extent it is one of several dynamic extensions of the Keynesian analysis, and therefore is preoccupied primarily with relatively short run problems.

1. THE SAVINGS ASSUMPTION

There are two basic assumptions in the model, one of which is later modified to increase its generality. Other assumptions, which are only implicit, will be brought in later in the discussion.

The first assumption is that the net saving of the community during any period of time, t, is a constant proportion, s, of the income received during that period, $Y(t)$. By *net* saving we mean total saving minus total dissaving. This refers not to the amount that people intend or plan to save but to the amount that they actually do save.[2] Actual saving may differ from intended saving if the

[1] "An Essay in Dynamic Theory," *Economic Journal,* March 1939. Harrod's lectures on the same subject, delivered at the London School of Economics in 1947 were published under the title *Towards a Dynamic Economics* (Macmillan & Co., Ltd., London, 1948). He there considers the topic in greater detail. Professor Domar has independently produced an analysis very similar to this. See below, Chapter Fourteen, Section 1, and Section 7. The present discussion is primarily based on Mr. Harrod's article of 1939.

[2] In a later chapter we shall use the conventional terms saving *ex ante* and *ex post* to indicate intended and actual saving respectively.

income of the period turns out to be greater or smaller than was expected. Thus if a man expects an income of $100 and plans to spend half of it, he intends to save $50. If, however, his actual income is only $90 and he spends as planned, his actual saving will be $40, so that his actual saving is $10 less than his intended saving.

Now the assumption that a constant proportion of income is saved normally relates to intended saving as a proportion of expected income, whereas Harrod's assumption relates to actual saving as a proportion of actual income. Thus, in order to make the assumption reasonable, we must assume that actual and intended saving are equal and that actual and expected income are equal.

The actual income of any period is, by definition, the production of that period minus that part which is set aside for the maintenance and replacement of capital equipment. Actual saving is income minus consumption, while actual (realized) investment is what is left over from income after consumption has taken place; it is the increase in the community's accumulated wealth. Thus, *by definition,* actual saving equals actual (realized) investment; they are the same thing.[3] On the other hand, there is no necessary reason to suppose that intended saving will equal intended (planned) investment. If one person intends to save an extra $100, there is no mechanism by which someone else will automatically be led to plan to invest an extra $100 in, say, machinery or stocks of finished goods.

If intended saving and investment differ from one another, the fact that realized saving and investment are necessarily equal means that saving intentions and investment plans cannot both be realized. Hence either intended savings must differ from realized savings or planned investment must differ from realized investment. A simple example of the latter is given by the case where a shopkeeper gets supplies of some good in the hope of selling them almost at once and his sales are disappointing. He then finds that he has unintentionally invested in stocks of that good.

But since Mr. Harrod assumes that saving intentions are always realized, he places the entire burden of any discrepancy between

[3] This is the same as saying that *ex post* saving equals *ex post* investment.

intended saving and intended investment on unintended investment; that is, he assumes that, if intended saving and investment differ, investment will not turn out as planned.

Having thus examined the implications of Mr. Harrod's first premise, we may restate it: Saving during period t, $S(t)$, will be a fixed proportion, s, of income during period t, $Y(t)$. This may be stated algebraically as

$$S(t) = sY(t).$$

Thus if 50 per cent of income is saved, so that $s = \frac{1}{2}$, then if national income during some stated period is \$60 billion, saving will be given by

$$S(t) = \frac{1}{2}(\$60{,}000{,}000{,}000)$$

i.e., savings will be \$30 billion.

2. *THE ASSUMPTION OF THE ACCELERATION PRINCIPLE*

Since realized and intended saving are both given by Mr. Harrod's first premise and since realized investment is equal by definition to realized saving, it follows that we now know realized and intended saving and realized investment. It remains only to state what determines planned investment. This is done in Mr. Harrod's second premise which supposes that the entrepreneur's desire to undertake investment depends on how quickly output is increasing. More explicitly, it is assumed as a first approximation that desired investment during period t will be a constant proportion, g, of the amount by which production (income) during period t exceeds that of the previous period $(t - 1)$, where a period is some fixed length of chronological time, e.g., a week, so that such an increase actually indicates that production has in fact been speeded up. The second premise is a variant of the *acceleration principle*, and the constant coefficient g is called the *relation*.

To see the reasoning behind the premise it must be realized that there is an important distinction between the *stock* of capital and the *flow* of investment. Investment is another name for an addition to the stock of capital, so that investment and added capital mean the same thing. Now in general when a large quantity of goods is being produced, a relatively large quantity of capital will be needed to help produce it. Thus if the stock of capital is adjusted to the level of production and if production begins to increase, new capital (investment) will be wanted. Further, the more quickly that output expands, the greater will be the new capital per period (investment per period) desired. Thus, while the demand for capital will vary more or less in proportion with production, the demand for investment will vary more or less in proportion to the speed with which production is growing. The magnitude of these proportions will to a large extent be determined by technological considerations; that is to say, the amount of new capital in money terms that will be needed if, say, shoe output doubles will depend partly on the type of machinery used in shoe production as well as on its price.

It is sometimes suggested that the use of the word "production" in this connection is misleading. Ultimately, so the argument runs, machines are made to produce consumer's goods, and so demand for investment should be related to the rate of increase of the production of consumer's goods and not to rate of increase of total production (consumer's goods plus producer's goods). However, the author of this book is inclined to disagree with this point of view. It takes machinery, raw material, etc., to make producer's goods, and hence an increase in the output of these can stimulate investment demand in much the same way as a rise in the output of consumption goods does. Machines are needed in the production of machines as well as in the production of shoes. Therefore an increase in production of either sort can legitimately be considered a stimulus to investment demand.

This, then, is the reasoning behind the acceleration principle which states that the quantity of investment demanded during a given period will depend on the rate of increase of production (income). If the income received during every period is, for example,

$5 billion above that of the preceding period, we say that income is increasing at an average rate of $5 billion per period, so that the difference between income in period t and income in the preceding period $(t-1)$ may be taken as the rate of increase of income at period t. We thus have Mr. Harrod's second premise: The desired investment, $[I(t)]$, of any period t will be a constant proportion, g, of the excess of income in that period, $[Y(t)]$, over the income of the preceding period, $[Y(t-1)]$; i.e., desired investment will be a constant proportion, g, of the difference $[Y(t) - Y(t-1)]$. This may be stated algebraically as

$$I(t) = g[Y(t) - Y(t-1)].$$

Suppose, for example, that entrepreneurs desire to have invested 25 per cent of any increase in output (income) that has taken place, i.e., $g = 1/4$, and that income during period t, $Y(t)$, is $300 billion and income during the previous period, $Y(t-1)$, was $220 billion. The increase in income $[Y(t) - Y(t-1)]$ is $80 billion. Then we have

$$I(t) = \frac{1}{4}(\$80{,}000{,}000{,}000)$$

so that entrepreneurs would have liked to have invested $20 billion during period t. Note that, if realized savings (realized investment) were $150 billion as in the example illustrating Mr. Harrod's first premise, entrepreneurs would have ended up investing a lot more in period t than they would have liked; i.e., they would end up with large quantities of unsold stocks of goods.

Mr. Harrod is, of course, well aware that his assumptions involve great oversimplifications. s and g no doubt vary in practice; thus people may perhaps tend to save a higher proportion out of their income as they grow richer so that s may tend to increase with income. Similarly, an increase in the rate of interest may discourage investment so that the quantity of investment entrepreneurs desire to make, and so g, may, other things being equal, fall when the rate of interest rises. Moreover, not all investment is desired because production has increased. Neither innovation investment nor the government's desire to invest in school buildings or military equipment may be affected by a small change in production. All these difficulties are, as has been said, recognized by Mr. Harrod, and as we shall see, he does take account of them at several points.

3. *DESIRED AND REALIZED INVESTMENT*

Our second assumption states that desired investment varies in proportion with the rate of increase of income. Our first assumption, however, states that realized investment (saving) is a fixed proportion of income, so it follows that, given income and hence investment, entrepreneurs will be satisfied with the quantity of investment if and only if income is increasing so quickly as to make them want to have invested as much as was actually invested. When income is growing at the rate required to make entrepreneurs desire to invest just the amount that is being invested, we say income is growing at the warranted rate, i.e., we call that rate the warranted or required rate of growth.

Now it is clear from our two assumptions that the higher the level of income the more will be invested, while the faster the rate of growth of income the more entrepreneurs will want to invest. Thus if income is relatively high so that investment is relatively high, the warranted rate of growth of income will also be high, and the higher the level of income the greater will be the warranted rate of growth.[4]

If income is positive, some saving (investment) will be taking place, and in order to induce entrepreneurs to desire this saving income must grow, although perhaps very slowly at first. However, growth of income means that income (and hence investment) will be higher in the next period, and in order to induce entrepreneurs to want this higher investment, income will have to grow even faster

[4] The term "warranted rate of growth" is here used somewhat differently from the way it is used by Mr. Harrod but to the same effect. Rate of growth here means the absolute increase and not the percentage increase per period. Clearly an income rising at a constant 2 *per cent* rate per year must rise faster and faster in absolute terms.

than before. This will lead to an even greater increase in income and investment in the following period, and so on. We thus reach the very startling conclusion that, in order for realized investment always to equal desired investment, income must increase at an ever-increasing rate in the manner shown by the curve YY' in Fig. 3.

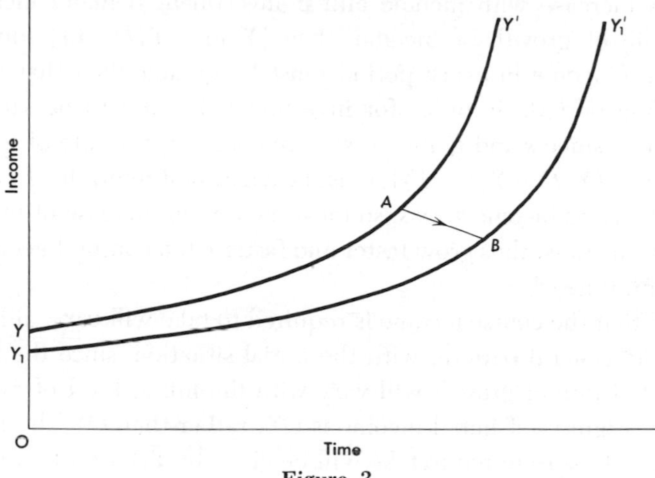

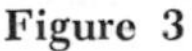

Figure 3

In other words, to keep investors happy the higher the income the faster income must grow, but the faster income grows the higher will tomorrow's income be. If we accept Mr. Harrod's two premises as even reasonable approximations, therefore, income must grow faster forever if investors are to be contented with the course of events.

This can be shown more rigorously by a simple algebraic argument. Since from our first assumption we have

$$\text{Realized investment (saving), } S(t) = sY(t)$$

and since our second assumption stated that

$$\text{Desired investment, } I(t) = g[Y(t) - Y(t-1)]$$

then investment desires will be realized if and only if

$$sY(t) = g[Y(t) - Y(t-1)].$$

Dividing both sides of this equation by g we obtain

$$\frac{s}{g}Y(t) = Y(t) - Y(t-1).$$

This means that if $Y(t)$, s, and g are all greater than zero, that is, if savings increase with income and if investment demand increases with rate of growth of income, then $[Y(t) - Y(t-1)]$ must be positive (income in every period must be greater than that in the preceding period) in order for investment demand to be satisfied. Moreover, since s and g and so s/g are constant, the rate of growth of income, $[Y(t) - Y(t-1)]$, must be a constant multiple of income $Y(t)$. Thus, as income grows, so must the rate of increase of income, and income must thus grow faster and faster (at a constant geometric rate with time).[5]

Note that the course income is required to take will vary, although not in its general pattern, with the initial situation, since the initial warranted rate of growth will vary with the initial level of income. Thus in Figure 3 if initial income is OY_1 rather than OY, the course income will be required to take will be given by $Y_1Y'_1$ rather than by YY'.

4. A MODIFIED ACCELERATION PRINCIPLE[6]

We shall now show that, with a somewhat milder form of the second assumption which attributes less influence to the acceleration principle on investment demand, the rather astonishing conclusion of the last section is not materially affected.

Let us assume that some investment demand such as government investment is independent both of the level of income and of its rate of increase, and let us designate this by L, where we take L to be a constant. Let us assume also that some investment demands are proportioned to income (production). A possible example of this

[5] But cf. the discussion in Sections 2 to 4 of Chapter Nine.

[6] Sections 4 and 6 of this chapter should generally be omitted on a first reading.

being negative, i.e., trade balance investment declining with income.)

So long as the amount saved (invested) is greater than non-acceleration investment demand ($sY(t)$ is greater than $KY(t)+L$) entrepreneurs must still, if desired investment is to equal saving be induced to take up some investment by a growth of income; i.e. there must be some acceleration investment demand. The required growth of income will clearly increase realized investment $sY(t)$, which will further increase the required rate of growth of income, and so on. Income must grow ever faster in order for investment demands always to be exactly satisfied just as before.[7]

5. DEPARTURES FROM THE WARRANTED RATE OF GROWTH

So far the conclusions of the argument, while they are no doubt surprising, may not strike the reader as being particularly important. What has been shown is that, subject to certain assumptions as to the behavior of the economy, if things are to be run in such a way as to keep investors at all times pleased with the world, the economy must behave very peculiarly indeed. Offhand it is not clear why we should be so concerned with the contentment of a rather limited economic class. We shall see, however, that, if things do not go on in the rather strange way required to produce investorial contentment, the results may be rather serious for the operation of the economy as a whole.

[7] It can be shown that in this case investment must grow at a greater than geometric rate. This is because the deduction from the influence of $Y(t)$ on $[Y(t) - Y(t-1)]$ represented by the subtraction of the constant L must grow relatively more and more insignificant as income and its rate of growth become large. We can see this if we divide our final equation through by $Y(t)$ in order to determine the proportion between the change in income and the level of income, i.e., in order to determine how large is the magnitude of the change relative to the level of income. This gives $(s-K)/g - L/[gY(t)] = [Y(t) - Y(t-1)]/[Y(t)]$. Since $L/[gY(t)]$ decreases when $Y(t)$ increases, this deduction from the left-hand side of the equation must fall as income increases, and the expression on the right-hand side of the equation, the ratio of the increase in income to the original level of income, must increase as the latter increases.

is provided by the community's trade balance which, sin
a net nonconsumption demand for the community's
for our purposes be considered a form of investmen
domestic demand for imports may be taken to rise w
can say that the balance of trade (net investment de
roughly in inverse proportion with income. For thi
ment demand we write $KY(t)$, where K is a consta
negative. We still have some investment deman
acceleration principle which we symbolize as be
$Y(t-1)]$. Total investment demand during perio

$$I(t) = g[Y(t) - Y(t-1)] + KY(t$$

and in order that this be equal to realized invest

$$S(t) = sY(t)$$

i.e., in order that investment desires be satisfie

$$sY(t) = g[Y(t) - Y(t-1)] + K$$

Subtracting $KY(t) + L$ gives

$$sY(t) - KY(t) - L = g[Y(t) -$$

and dividing by g we get

$$\frac{sY(t) - KY(t) - L}{g} = Y(t)$$

If we compare this with our previous
acceleration principle, namely,

$$\frac{sY(t)}{g} = Y(t) - Y$$

we see that in general the rate of grow
required for any given level of inco
than before, inasmuch as there is s
subtraction of $KY(t)$ and L. (This

The argument is fairly simple. Suppose income does not rise as quickly as is required to induce people to desire the existing level of investment. Mr. Harrod argues that this will lead to a situation involving general overproduction (an inability to sell all that has been produced) and that this overproduction will get cumulatively worse. If, on the other hand, production (income) rises so rapidly that entrepreneurial investment desires are not satisfied by available saving, an ever-growing underproduction (production falling short of demand) will result.

This conclusion, which we have not yet attempted to justify, is on the face of it every bit as peculiar as our earlier result. In effect it is the paradoxical statement that if we increase our production too rapidly we will have produced too little, whereas if we do not increase it rapidly enough we will have produced too much! If we pursue our desires too rapidly we will lose ground to them!

The explanation lies in the effect which we have assumed an increase in output to have on demand. While an increase in output which is more rapid than warranted will increase the quantity to be sold, it will, as we are about see, increase demand even more and so the result will be underproduction. But why should demand be expected to increase even more rapidly than output when output increases more rapidly than warranted?

Whether income is high or low and whether it is increasing slowly or rapidly are two independent questions whose answers have nothing to do with one another at any given period. Now we have assumed that actual investment, that is to say, the supply of output left over after consumption, is determined by the level of income and is thus given once the level of income is given. But the demand for these investment goods depends partly on how quickly output rises, and the demand for investment will be higher the more rapidly output expands

If income in January is $20 billion and investment is $5 billion and if income by increasing at 10 per cent per month results in exactly $5 billion being demanded for investment, then if output increases more rapidly than this, more than $5 billion in investment will be demanded by entrepreneurs. With only $5 billion of investment actually supplied it will turn out that not enough was produced to fill investment demands. Similarly, if output increases by less than 10 per cent a month, there will be overproduction in January.

So far the argument can all be deduced from our two premises. At this point, however, Mr. Harrod tacitly introduces a third assumption concerning entrepreneurial behavior. He goes on to argue that when entrepreneurs have been unable to sell all they have produced they will become pessimistic to such an extent that they will keep the rate of increase of output below the warranted rate. This will then again bring about a situation involving overproduction which in turn will add further fuel to their pessimism making them keep their rate of increase of output still further below the warranted rate, and so on. He also argues that a departure from the warranted rate of growth in the upward direction will be self-sustaining for similar reasons. Thus in his view once the economy goes off the rails it may well be extraordinarily difficult to get it back again. It may even be that the economy can easily shoot almost straight downward or upward when the warranted rate is departed from. If entrepreneurs are in fact actually inclined to reduce output every time they find they have overproduced, then a continuing state of overproduction such as Mr. Harrod predicts for the case where the rate of increase of output falls below the warranted rate must result in a cumulative fall in production.

We shall later have a few comments to make on this last part of the argument about the inability of the economy to get back on the rails once it has left them. One point may, however, profitably be made now. Once the warranted rate of growth has been departed from, the rate of growth that will be warranted after the departure will generally be different from what would have been warranted if the departure had not taken place. For example, if the rate of growth falls below the warranted rate so that after a time income is less than it would have been if the fall had not occurred, then with the lower income less investment will take place. This will mean that a smaller rate of growth of income will be required in order that entrepreneurs will desire this smaller quantity of investment. Hence income will not have to rise as rapidly as it would otherwise have had to in order to induce entrepreneurs to desire the actual quantity of investment. In general, therefore, when the rate of growth of income falls below the warranted rate, the warranted rate itself tends to fall.

In Fig. 3, YY' shows the warranted course of income if income were initially OY, and $Y_1Y'_1$ shows the warranted course of income if income were initially OY_1. If income were in fact initially OY and followed its warranted course up to point A and then instead of going on rising along AY' fell to B, then in order for investors' demands to be satisfied thenceforward, the course of income does not have to return to YY'. Instead income must follow the warranted path corresponding to point B, namely BY'_1. Thus the requirement that the economy return to the rails after it has left them is not that it climb all the way back to its original path but the simpler requirement that it follow the new set of rails from the point at which it now finds itself. A similar argument holds for a departure from the warranted rate of growth in the upward direction.

6. VARIATION IN s AND g [8]

So far we have argued on the assumption that the proportion saved out of a given income, s, and the amount entrepreneurs desire to invest expressed as a proportion of a given rise in income, g, are constant. On this basis we obtained the paradoxical conclusion that too rapid an expansion of output will lead to underproduction and too slow an expansion to overproduction.

As pointed out earlier, we know that s and g do in fact vary, and the question arises whether they are apt to do so in such a way as to upset our conclusion. Mr. Harrod considers it likely that this possibility will make no essential difference. He maintains that, while accidental variations of s and g may sometimes weaken our results,

[8] This section should generally be omitted on a first reading.

such changes as are usually brought about by the processes we are considering are not likely to upset them completely.

Consider first what happens to g as income departs from the warranted rate of growth. In a depression situation there will generally be unused plant and equipment so that a rise in output can be taken care of at least partly with the aid of existing capital. This means that when there is a depression a given rise in output will occasion little demand for new investment, so that g will be small. When, however, things are going well, excess plant capacity will be small or nonexistent, so there will be a relatively large demand for more equipment when output rises, and g will be relatively large. Thus when output increases at a rate less than warranted, g will tend to fall because overproduced investment goods pile up, and the reverse may be expected when output rises more quickly than warranted.

This makes it more difficult to stop the overproduction in the one case and the underproduction (excess demand) in the other. Taking the case of overproduction, for example, since there will be some accumulated equipment the demand for new capital will rise relatively little when consumer demands go up. In general, therefore, changes in g appear to sharpen Harrod's conclusions in every case.[9]

What about the effect of variations in s? Here the argument is more complicated, for variations in s may well be such as to act to weaken the conclusions. Harrod maintains, however, that it is most unlikely that variations in s will be sufficient in magnitude to upset them completely.

That s may vary so as partly to offset overproduction or underproduction may be seen in this way. It is possible that as income rises, people save a larger proportion of their income so that s rises. Hence if income increases above the warranted rate, s will tend to rise and more will be invested (saved) than would otherwise have been the

[9] Several readers have complained that these paragraphs are not sufficiently critical. Certainly autonomous investment (investment independent of the rate of change of income) *can* misbehave sufficiently to upset Harrod's conclusions

case. This added investment will take care of some of the investment demand that would not otherwise have been satisfied. The rise in s will thus help offset the underproduction resulting from the rise in output above the warranted output. The same sort of possibility arises in a movement in the downward direction.

Let us now see whether a change in s with a change in income sufficient to eliminate completely over- or underproduction seems plausible. To investigate this suppose that the rise in the output of period t over that of the previous period, $Y(t) - Y(t-1)$, is greater than the warranted rise, w, and exceeds it by

$$x = [Y(t) - Y(t-1)] - w.$$

The excess investment demand resulting from this excess rise in income, x, will be gx, and so an extra amount, $H = gx$, will have to be saved to offset the extra investment demand due to the rise of output above the warranted rate.

How high is g likely to be? To answer this we must inquire into the meaning of g a bit more carefully. By definition, it is the proportion that the extra investment demanded *during period t* will be to the rise in income of period t over that of the previous period. In other words, since $I(t) = g[Y(t) - Y(t-1)]$,

$$g = \frac{I(t)}{Y(t) - Y(t-1)}.$$

We have not yet specified what sort of period we are using, and the length of the period is decidedly relevant, for if output has increased by $10 billion in a month, much more additional equipment will be needed than if the period in which output has increased by $10 billion is a year. Thus the smaller the period in which a given increase takes place, the greater will be the relative demand for capital occasioned by that increase, i.e., the greater will be g.

If the period is chosen of such a length that entrepreneurs reexamine their equipment needs just once during it, each entrepreneur will bring his equipment demands up to date in the light of the change in output from the preceding period. g, the ratio to this change of the extra capital demanded, will then presumably be the same as the ratio between output per period and the capital required for that output.

It seems reasonable to assume that in a modern industrial economy firms will examine their equipment needs at least once a year and that the value of capital equipment required is apparently more than two times annual output.[10] This means that, if decisions are in fact made once a year, g will be well over unity and if decisions are made more frequently so that our period is less than a year, g will be greater than that.

Having arrived this far by means of a rather tedious argument, we may now go back to the problem of the increase in saving needed to offset over- or underproduction caused by departure from the warranted rate of growth. We saw that the added investment (saving), H, that must take place to offset the underproduction of investment goods which would otherwise be associated with an x unit rise in income above the warranted rise is

$$H = gx$$

where g is greater than one. This means that the rise in saving required to upset Harrod's result must exceed the magnitude of the rise in income which brings it about; e.g., people must save well over $10 more every time their incomes rise by $10, which is hardly likely.

7. LIMITS TO THE EXPANSION OF INCOME

Mr. Harrod points out that in general there is, at any given time, an upper limit to national output which is determined by the size of the labor force, the nation's natural resources and capital equipment, and the state of technical knowledge. This maximum

[10] For a useful bibliography of the empirical data see D. Hamburg, *Economic Growth and Instability* (W. W. Norton, New York, 1956) pp. 36, 45 footnotes. Part of the argument of this section does not appear in Harrod's work and the present author must accept complete responsibility.

output is presumably that which would be produced if there were full employment, with resources and labor being used as efficiently as possible.[11]

The upper limit may, of course, change with time, and it has in fact been rising more or less steadily in relatively recent times if we except the war period. With population growth, the development of inventions and the accumulation of production equipment, this is generally to be expected. But while the amount that can be produced is subject to growth, sometimes to phenomenal growth, it may not be able to shoot up precipitously and without limit as income is required to do if it is to grow at the warranted rate, as does *YY′* in Fig. 3. This means that, even if income does grow at the warranted rate for a while and if nothing else causes it to stop, capacity national income (output) will eventually be reached. When that happens income cannot continue to grow at the warranted rate, and so by the argument we have ben considering, overproduction will tend to arise, and this, according to Mr. Harrod, will lead to a cumulative income fall.[12]

The existence of this upper limit to the rate at which national output can in fact grow, which Mr. Harrod calls the natural rate of growth, means, so he maintains, that crises and depressions may occur even if nothing else exists to bring them about, for the natural rate of growth may well prevent the economy from growing indefinitely at the rate (the warranted rate) which is necessary for the avoidance of booms and slumps.

[11] The way in which we put this proposition begs the index-number problem of the definition of the size of the national output. We cannot generally say, for example, whether, other things being the same, an output involving the production of 5 million pairs of shoes and 3 million hats of a given specification is greater or smaller than one involving the production of 2 million pairs of shoes and 7 million hats. This question has really been begged whenever we spoke of the course of the community's income. But in any case it seems unlikely that the gist of the statement about an upper limit to the community's output can seriously be questioned.

[12] Hicks later incorporated this idea in his trade cycle model. Cf. J. R. Hicks, *A Contribution to the Theory of the Trade Cycle* (Oxford University Press, New York, 1950). See esp. Chapter VIII, p. 99. For a description of Hicks' trade cycle model see Chapter Thirteen, below.

8. *COMMENTS*

We have now gone over the main points of the Harrodian dynamic system. Two major conclusions are offered us. First, in order for a free-enterprise economy of the sort considered to proceed without running into difficulties of general overproduction (excess supply of goods) or underproduction (excess demand for goods), income must increase at an ever increasing rate, and this may be prevented by the physical limitations to expansion if by nothing else. Second, we are offered an even more serious conclusion: The slightest deviation from this warranted rate of growth is likely to be self-sustaining and possibly self-aggravating. This second conclusion implies that we must almost continually be in serious trouble since it is so easy to go off the rails and so difficult to get back on once we have left them.

The first conclusion follows directly from the three major assumptions that investment demand is determined at least partly by the acceleration principle, that saving depends more or less directly on the level of income, and that realized and desired savings are always the same. The oversimplification involved in these premises may cast doubt on the details of the construction. Nevertheless the analysis at the very least suggests some ways in which long run problems of overproduction and unemployment can be affected by the rate of growth of the economy.

The second conclusion, that deviations from the warranted rate and their results are likely to be self-sustaining, requires recourse to an additional assumption about which a few remarks may be made. This is the assumption that expectations are so strongly affected by overproduction that entrepreneurs are led to contract their output plans to a point where the rate of growth is once again below the warranted rate. We leave the simple modification of the argument to the case of underproduction to the reader.

But if income has been rising at the warranted rate for some time before the difficulty in question arises, entrepreneurs may refuse to be moved to pessimism by a single unhappy experience. It is even possible that entrepreneurs will generally believe in the "normalcy" of the economy and so will regard any case of overproduction as a temporary phenomenon soon likely to disappear.

If any such possibility applies, it no longer necessarily follows that a situation involving overproduction must result in such a contraction of output plans that the warranted rate of growth will fail to be reattained.

It should be emphasized that in this chapter we have abstracted entirely from changes in price and the rate of interest, and in so doing we may well have left out some of the most important parts of the problem. This is characteristic of acceleration principle models which usually assume that the desired capital output ratio is unaffected by prices and interest rates and treat both capital and outputs as though they were homogeneous items whose composition is irrelevent to the analysis. Such premises must rule out the possibility of stabilizing price and interest rate movements. E.g., in times of "overproduction," reduced interest rates can make capital intensive processes and heavily capital using outputs more profitable and lead to an increased demand for capital, thereby reducing the excess supplies of commodities.

Note finally that Mr. Harrod has inherited from earlier dynamic method little more in the way of specific aims and premises than an emphasis on the problem of accumulation (investment saving).[13] Neither the broad generalizations nor the ambitious predictions are to be found. Yet the emphasis of longer-term economic problems and the author's acknowledged debt to the classic approach make this a convenient bridge between the earlier magnificent dynamics and the process analysis which will be considered in Part III. First, however, it is convenient to turn to a consideration of what we have called statics involving time.

[13] Even here the analysis differs considerably from the classics' in its preoccupation with shorter-run Keynesian problems where saving is viewed primarily as a deduction from demand and hence as a deterrent to production rather than as a means for providing the real resources to increase capital equipment and hence long run productive capacity.

Part II

STATICS INVOLVING TIME

Chapter Five

THE EQUILIBRIUM OF THE FIRM

In analyzing the state of the economy at a particular moment, that is, the details of any particular "time slice," we can neither ignore the influence of the past nor deny the relevance of the future. The state of economic affairs at any point of time depends upon the past in a multitude of ways—the nature and quantity of capital equipment, existing techniques, the established institutional framework, and so on. What is past, however, is history and cannot be altered, so we accept it as given.

The future, however, affects the present in an entirely different manner. It affects it through the minds of men in that they think of tomorrow as well as of today and arrange their activity with reference to what they expect and want in the future as well as in the present. A decision to invest in machinery is an example of a present activity undertaken with an eye to the future, for it is usually in the future that the greater part of the services of a durable machine can be obtained. Thus if we wish to find out how much will be invested today we must first find out what investors expect for the future. Note that we are not asking at present about the effect of the investment on what *actually* happens in the future, for in our present static analysis we are not at all interested in what actually will happen. We are only interested in what people *think* is going to happen in so far as this affects their present activity.

1. EXPECTATIONS

We may reasonably assume that people's expectations about the future are pretty vague; they may feel that "things are getting better" or that "the price of wheat is due for a fall," but they will not say to themselves "I expect that on May 26 the price of the wheat I am growing will be $1.97 a bushel." Since, however, vague assumptions about the future and their effects are very difficult to analyze or even to describe, we have to assume that anticipations are perfectly precise but not in the sense that they always, usually, or indeed ever turn out to be correct. Rather we mean by precise expectations only that there are perfectly definite ideas about the future.

In this chapter we shall largely follow the exposition in the third and fourth part of J. R. Hicks' *Value and Capital.* Professor Hicks, while assuming that expectations are precise, recognizes that they will not be held with full certainty, i.e., that people realize that their expectations may be disappointed and so may not be prepared to consider anticipated future prices on a par with present prices. He suggests that we avoid this difficulty to some extent by making an allowance for risk. To take an example, the anticipated $1.97 for each bushel of the farmer's wheat mentioned above, since it is only a bird in the bush, might be worth the same to him as the certainty of $1.80 at the same date. In this case we shall consider the $1.80 and not the $1.97 as the price expected by the farmer.

Hicks' analysis is based on the further assumption that there is perfect competition, so that any buyer can buy and any seller can sell as much as he desires at the current market price. If we assumed imperfect competition, the sellers' expectations would have to relate to a whole demand schedule rather than to a single price. By assuming perfect competition, we can base our analysis of the effect of the future on the current behavior of the firm entirely on the entrepreneur's anticipations of the state of technology and prices which together tell him how much any given output will cost him to produce. The technological data enable him to determine how to produce that output most economically, given the expected prices of factors of production. His product price expectations indicate the revenue he anticipates from the sale of that output; thus he forms an estimate of the profit to be obtained from its production. In this way, he will judge the profitability of every alternative output in the future and in the present on the basis of this information and so decide where to concentrate his efforts.

2. INPUTS AND OUTPUTS

Hicks defines an input as "something which is bought for the enterprise" and an output as "something which is sold by it." The concept of a firm's inputs is thus very like that of its factors of production, a term which we avoid largely because of some of its past associations.

If we consider only the present, it is clear that a firm can usually increase its output of some good by increasing one or more of its inputs, e.g., by employing more labor and raw material. Similarly, a firm may increase some output at the expense of another, for example, by transferring labor and materials from one use to another. Finally, a firm may substitute one input for another, e.g., by installing labor-saving machinery. Notice that as far as its production decisions are concerned, a firm cannot make any change which does not fall in one of these three categories—substitution of one input for another, substitution of one output for another, or a simultaneous change in both inputs and outputs so long as the firm does not buy anything it does not use nor produce anything it does not sell. If less is produced of some output, a smaller input will be required for that output and either the purchase of inputs must be reduced or more of them must be employed in producing other outputs.

It will be observed that we are considering the general case where the firm produces or considers producing several commodities at the same time. We may readily extend the argument to the firm's inputs and outputs over time. We may increase next year's shoe output at the expense of current automobile output by transferring labor from current automobile production to the production of labor-saving shoemaking machines, and conversely the current output of automobiles can be increased at the expense of next year's hat output by reducing the current output of hat machinery. As a special case of this we can substitute current for future outputs of the same commodity and vice versa. Indeed, it may be convenient to regard the future output of, say, automobiles as a different commodity from automobiles sold today and to adopt a similar convention about inputs. In this case the discussion of present inputs and outputs applies without change to production over time.

Specifically, besides the substitution of one output for another (or for the same output at a different date) which has just been considered, we may have the substitution of one input for another including substitution over time, as, for example, when we produce more machinery now and hire less labor later. Finally, we have the increase or decrease of both inputs and outputs where these need not occur at the same date, as where we purchase more machinery now to increase hat output later, or increase hat output now by using machinery more intensively and so increase replacement costs later.

All this is leading us toward our discussion of the equilibrium of the firm. It must first be pointed out by way of definition that the firm is said to be in equilibrium when there is no motive for the entrepreneur to modify his activities in any way. Since we have just argued that the firm may generally make only three basic types of changes in plans, or any combination of these, then we must describe the conditions under which no substitution of any output for another, no substitution of any input for another, and no change of both inputs and outputs will be to the firm's advantage. When these conditions are satisfied, and only then, will the firm be in equilibrium. Before we can formulate these conditions, however, there are several other matters which must be considered. We adopt the usual assumption that the entrepreneur seeks to maximize the profits of the firm, so that our requirement for equilibrium is that no possible change in production plans would increase the profits of the firm. We must now examine the production plan as well as the method whereby the firm's profit calculations include consideration of expected future profits.

3. THE PERIOD AND THE PRODUCTION PLAN

Usually inputs are obtained and outputs are produced, not once-and-for-all but more or less continuously over time. That is, the level of output must be described as so much *per week* or *per month.* We say that inputs and outputs are *flows* rather than *stocks.* Other examples of flows are income, investment, and births, while gold reserves, bank notes in circulation, a firm's capital resources, and a nation's capital are stocks. As flows have a time dimension we can measure them only by using a time unit such as a week.

We define a new period to begin every time any price changes are expected, so that for every period expected prices will remain unchanged. In reality, of course, some price is being changed somewhere at almost every moment during business hours, so that this period must be exceedingly short. In practice, however, firms cannot keep up with all these changes and re-examine their plans with an eye to revision every time some such price change occurs, though that is just what the nonexistent perfect entrepreneur would have to do to wring the last drop of profit out of the situation. But since our analysis is static, and we are dealing not with actual changes but with expected changes, a new period must be said to begin every time the entrepreneur whose plan we are analyzing expects some price to change.[1] This excludes the prices of goods in which he is not interested.

We can now define the production plan. It is merely a list of

[1] Hicks defines the period as the length of time during which changes in price can be neglected and assumes that significant price changes do not occur very often [*Value and Capital,* p. 122 (Oxford University Press, New York, 1939)].

the inputs and outputs planned for future periods. Written down, it will be of the following form:

Period	0	1	2	3	...	*N*
Inputs:						
Coal, anthracite (tons)	50	1,000	799	157,300	...	809
Cloth, herringbone twill, olive drab (square yards)	10	570,000	0	3,000	...	900
Etc.	...	...	...	...	...	...
Outputs:						
Hats, men's, felt, size 7¼	1,000	50,000	300	0	...	9,999
Electric heaters, model 73a	4,000	4,000	4,000	4,500	...	7,000
Etc.	...	...	...	...	...	...

The period, *N*, after which the plan ends, is called the "economic horizon." It is not implied that the firm plans to go out of operation after *N* periods but rather that it is so far ahead that the entrepreneur considers it to be useless or even impossible to plan further into the future. We shall see presently that very distant outputs and inputs can generally be taken to be relatively unimportant in the plan. It is theoretically possible to deal with a plan which does not end, but the approach adopted seems more realistic.

The entrepreneur cannot enter any figures he would like into the plan. Once he has decided on his outputs, for example, he must be sure that his inputs are sufficient for his planned outputs. At most he can arbitrarily decide the amount and dating of all his outputs and all but one input. The quantity of the last input will then be the minimum amount required to produce the outputs he has decided upon with the aid of the other inputs whose quantities and dating he has already decided. Alternatively he can decide at most all but one output and all his inputs, the magnitude and dating of the remaining output being determined by the amounts and dating of the inputs he will have left over after producing the other outputs he has decided upon. Often he will not have even this much freedom of choice—to produce hats at all he must have both labor and raw materials, and there is no process known whereby wool can be produced without producing mutton.

4. THE DISCOUNT FACTOR AND THE CAPITALIZED VALUE OF THE PLAN

The sum of the money values of his outputs during a period is the entrepreneur's total revenue for that period, and the sum of the money values of the inputs is the total cost incurred during that period. The difference constitutes his total surplus for that period. Now if a dollar of surplus were equally important whatever period it was earned in, we could add up the surpluses of all N periods and say that the entrepreneur will choose that plan for which this total is greatest. In fact, however, present profits and future profits are not directly comparable, even after we have made allowance for the greater uncertainty of anticipations concerning the more distant future. This point is simply that money held now can earn its owner some interest so that a dollar today is more valuable than a future dollar.

In order to find out the value of a profit of, say, \$100 in the current period plus an expected profit of \$750 one period in the future, we must find out how much \$750 of money one period in the future is worth now. The answer is a quantity of money, x, which, together with one period of interest earnings, is equal to \$750. If the relevant rate of interest is i, say 5 per cent per period, then by definition principal plus interest at the end of the period will be

$$x(1+i)$$

that is, x plus 5 per cent of x. We require that this quantity be equal to \$750 or, in general, to any quantity of money P obtainable after one period, whose present value we are seeking to determine. This gives

$$x(1+i) = P$$

that is,

$$1.05x = \$750.$$

Multiplying by $1/(1+i)$, that is, by $1/1.05$), we get

$$x = \frac{1}{1+i} P$$

that is,

$$x = \frac{1}{1.05} \$750.$$

In other words, to obtain the present value of any quantity of money, P (\$750), receivable one period hence, we must multiply P by the quantity $D = 1/(1+i)(=1/1.05)$ which we call the discount factor, or the discount ratio.

Suppose now that P_2 is receivable after two periods and the relevant rate of interest remains at i. Then let P_1 be the value at the end of the current period of P_2 and let $x = P_0$ be the present value of P_2. Then obviously $P_1 = DP_2$, since the interest lost by waiting one period for one's money is (on the hypothesis that i remains unchanged) the same whether that period is the present or the succeeding period. Moreover the present value P_0 of P_2 is the same as the present value of P_1, since by definition the interest loss of a two-year postponement in money receipts is the sum of the one year's loss and the (compounded) second year's loss. Thus we have $P_0 = DP_1 = D(DP_2) = D^2P_2$. Similarly we may show that the present value of a sum of money, P_n, receivable after n years is D^nP_n.[2]

We are now ready to evaluate the stream of expected surpluses, that is, to find the capitalized value of the production plan. Suppose that our production plan is such as to lead us to anticipate a net surplus (or deficit) of P_0 during this period, P_1 during the next period, and so on, ending with a surplus of P_N during the Nth period. We know that the present value of the surplus of any period, say

[2] This result can be shown directly by the compound-interest formula for accumulated interest plus principal after n years, which is

$$P_n = P_0(1+i)^n$$

where P_0 is the principal and i the rate of interest; then

$$P_0 = \frac{1}{(1+i)^n} P_n = D^nP_n.$$

the *t*th, is D^tP_t. The total present value of all these surpluses, R, which is, of course, the present value of the plan, is therefore

$$R = P_0 + DP_1 + D^2P_2 + \cdots + D^NP_N.$$

This quantity, R, is called the capitalized value of the plan, and if there are several R's each corresponding to one of the plans considered by the entrepreneur, he will presumably adopt that plan (or one of those plans) which yields the largest value of R.

This greatest R is called the capitalized value of the firm and is the amount of money the entrepreneur could get by selling the firm (provided that the buyer's expectations are the same as his and that there is a perfect capital market). The reason why this is the price for which the firm can be sold is that R has been so defined that, if an investor bought R dollars worth of securities with an interest yield of i per period and kept these for N periods, he would then end up with as much money as he could get by collecting the firm's surpluses and getting interest on them for N periods. Since we have assumed perfect competition, this implies that no one would be prepared to buy the firm if its price were more than R, for investors would then do better to buy securities. Similarly, if the firm were offered for sale at a price below R, the rush of potential buyers who were prepared to get rid of securities and buy the firm with the proceeds would drive the price of the firm up to R.

We can now, incidentally, justify the statement made in the last section that very distant outputs and inputs are apt to be relatively unimportant in computing the value of the plan. This is simply because their money value must be heavily discounted in computing their present value.[3]

Before leaving the question of the computation of the present value of the plan we should note that this computation does not depend on any subjective elements such as time preference if the market rate of interest is given. Subjective elements do, of course,

[3] If the rate of interest, i, is greater than zero, then $1/(1 + i) = D$ is less than unity, and it is an elementary analytic result that for such a D, D^n can be made as small as we like by choosing n sufficiently large.

enter when we adjust for risk since first the entrepreneur's (subjective) expectations must be determined and then an adequate allowance for risk deducted, the latter quantity being dependent not only on how risky the entrepreneur thinks the thing but also on how averse he is to gambling, i.e., on how much he requires as compensation for undertaking the given risk.

5. MARGINAL AND SECOND-ORDER EQUILIBRIUM CONDITIONS: A DIGRESSION

We are now almost ready to state our equilibrium conditions. Before we do so, however, we must see exactly what we require such conditions to include. In this section we shall therefore examine a simple equilibrium problem, that of a firm buying its inputs in a perfect market and producing only one product with them.

It is well known that one of the equilibrium conditions in this case is that marginal cost must be equal to marginal revenue. The argument is that, if marginal cost were less than marginal revenue, a small expansion of output would add more to revenue than to cost and hence increase the firm's surplus. If marginal cost exceeded marginal revenue, a small contraction of output would prove advantageous. This argument only shows that equilibrium cannot occur where marginal cost and revenue are unequal, i.e., that if we are at equilibrium, marginal cost must equal marginal revenue. It does not follow that where marginal cost equals marginal revenue the firm must be in equilibrium. To argue thus would be the same as maintaining that if all bearded humans are men, all men are bearded humans.

This may perhaps be elucidated with the aid of a diagram. In Fig. 4 the lower diagrams show several types of marginal cost (dotted lines) and revenue curves (solid lines), and the upper diagrams show what happens in each case to the firm's total profits as output is varied. Note that every time marginal cost is less than marginal revenue, total surplus is going uphill to the right so to speak; i.e., it is increasing with output. Where, and only where, marginal cost exceeds marginal revenue, surplus is moving downhill

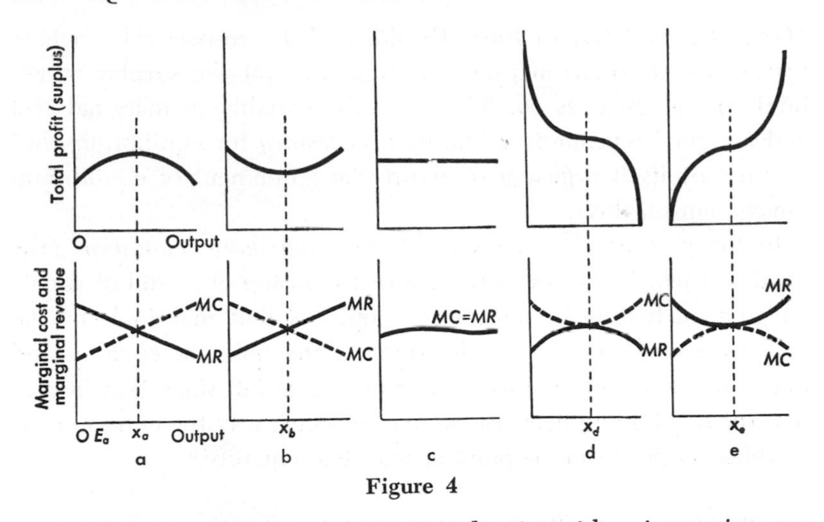

Figure 4

to the right. Finally, every time surplus is neither increasing nor decreasing, whether this occurs at the peak of a hill, the trough of a valley, on a plateau, or on a level plane, marginal cost equals marginal revenue. The reasons for this follow directly from the definition of marginal cost and revenue and have already been given in the argument showing that the equality of marginal cost and marginal revenue is an equilibrium condition.

From the diagrams it is clear that, where surplus is really at a maximum (output Ox_a in Fig. 4a and any output in Fig. 4c), marginal cost is equal to marginal revenue.[4] But there are outputs

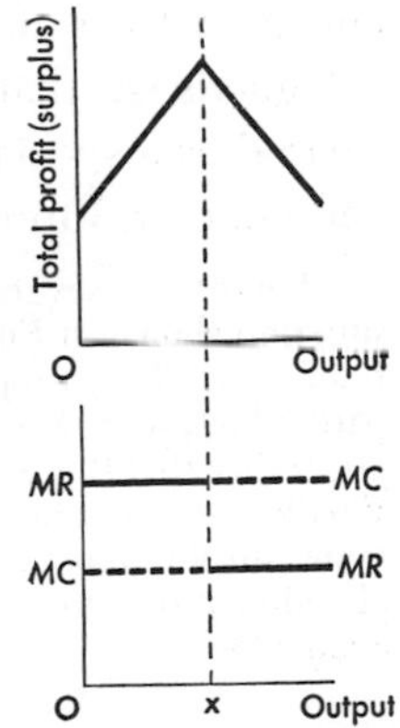

[4] This argument holds strictly only where there are no kinks or discontinuities in the total-surplus curve. In the figure at the right, maximum surplus is at Ox, but marginal cost and revenue are not even defined there. The argument also requires that the maximum value does not occur where $x = 0$. Thus in Figure 4d the maximum profit point is on the y axis where marginal cost exceeds marginal revenue.

Note also that in the upper part of Figure 4 we assume some fixed positive initial revenue as in a theater where ticket holders buy permanent places at its opening. This permits the surplus curves to lie above the x axis throughout their length.

(Ox_b, Ox_d, and Ox_e in Figs. 4b, 4d, and 4e, respectively) where marginal cost equals marginal revenue and yet the surplus is certainly not as great as possible. Thus the equality of marginal cost and marginal revenue is a condition *necessary* for equilibrium, but it is not by itself *sufficient* to assure the attainment of equilibrium (maximum surplus).

In the present case the *second-order maximum condition* (the condition which assures us we are really on top of a "hill of profit" and not on bottom or on a level slope) is that marginal cost be above marginal revenue to the right of the point of equality and below marginal revenue to the left of that point, since that insures that the surplus will decrease no matter which way the entrepreneur modifies output from the point of marginal equality.[5]

6. THE MARGINAL CONDITIONS OF EQUILIBRIUM

We are now ready to begin our statement of the conditions of equilibrium. We begin with the marginal conditions, and since we have decided that there are three general types of alternative open to the entrepreneur in changing from one plan to another, namely, substitution of one output for another, of one input for another, or increase or decrease of inputs and outputs together, we shall expect three sets of marginal conditions, each stating in effect that no small change of the sorts under consideration will prove profitable. We treat an output of a commodity at some period, t, and the output of the same good at another period, p, as constituting different goods, so that the choice between producing now and later is treated as a special case of the choice between producing one good and another. Inputs are similarly treated.

[5] There are several complications which might be mentioned. First, the situation shown in Fig. 4c has no points either of true equilibrium or disequilibrium, since the entrepreneur has no motive either to stay at or depart from any particular point. Second, it should be noted that we have not discussed the possibility that there may be more than one peak of the same or varying heights. Finally, we have not yet mentioned the equilibrium condition that total maximum surplus must be positive, for otherwise it will pay the entrepreneur to abandon production altogether. This last condition will be mentioned again in Section 9.

Finally, when we speak of prices we shall speak of discounted expected prices minus the risk premium, that is to say, the *present value* of prices, since it is the present (capitalized) value of the plan which the entrepreneur seeks to maximize. We have still to define appropriate terms which serve the same purpose in the analysis of the three types of decision which we are discussing as did the concepts of marginal cost and marginal revenue for the single output decision process described in the previous section.

a. *Marginal condition of equilibrium with respect to the substitution of one output for another.* We first define the *marginal rate of substitution of output x for output y* as the decrease in y (the total money value of all inputs and of all other outputs remaining constant) needed to permit an increase in the output of x by one unit. This quantity is given by the technical nature of the processes in which the firm is engaged and by the resources of the firm, and it will generally vary with the size of the outputs of x and y. This can be seen by means of a concrete example. We can, we are told, produce sheep, by selective breeding, which are exceedingly woolly but which have poorer and less meat, and similarly we can also produce particularly meaty but not very woolly sheep. Now it is conceivable that, in substituting more and more wool for meat, diminishing marginal returns will in due course set in. This will mean that more and more meat value will have to be given up for every additional ounce of wool as the quantity of wool per sheep increases. This is obviously the same as saying that the marginal rate of substitution of wool for meat increases, i.e., more meat must be given up for each extra unit of wool as the quantity of wool per sheep increases.

We can now state our first equilibrium condition, namely, that the outputs of x and y must be such that marginal rate of substitution of output x for output y, Sxy, must equal the ratio between the price of x, Px, and the price of y, Py; in other words we must have

$$Sxy = \frac{Px}{Py}$$

for any outputs x and y of the firm. An additional unit of x is worth Px, and this must be accompanied by a loss of Sxy units of y, each valued at Py, i.e., by a pecuniary loss of $SxyPy$. Now we require that this change involve neither gain nor loss, for otherwise it will pay either to effect the change or a change in the opposite direction, that is, to increase or decrease the output of x at the expense of y. But there is neither gain nor loss from the change if and only if the money gain from the extra unit of x, Px, equals $SxyPy$, the money loss from y. By dividing through by Py we obtain our first equilibrium condition.

b. *Marginal condition of equilibrium with respect to the substitution of one input for another.* We now define the *marginal rate of substitution of input a for input b, Rab,* as the quantity of b which can be dispensed with when one additional unit of a is obtained, the total money value of all outputs and all other inputs remaining the same. Again the information on the basis of which Rab is computed is primarily technical. The magnitude of Rab varies with the magnitude of the quantities of a and b employed by the firm. The reasoning is exactly the same as in the case of Sxy, and the reader can easily reformulate the mutton and wool example in terms of labor and machinery.

Our second equilibrium condition is that the inputs of a and b must be such that the marginal rate of substitution of input a for input b equals the ratio between the price of a, Pa, and the price of b, Pb, i.e.,

$$Rab = \frac{Pa}{Pb}$$

for all inputs a and b employed by the firm. This is again because we require that neither profit nor loss be caused by a small shift from a to b. The extra cost of the additional unit of a is Pa, and the saving on each of the Rab units of b dispensed with is Pb, making a total saving on b of $RabPb$, so that no profit from the change means $Pa = RabPb$, which, on dividing through by Pb, gives our second equilibrium condition.

c. Marginal condition of equilibrium for the simultaneous increase or decrease in one input and one output. Let us now define the *marginal rate of transformation of input a into output x, Tax,* as the increase in the output of x made possible by the employment of an additional unit of a, the total money value of all other outputs and inputs remaining unchanged. Again this is largely a technical factor, and the magnitude of Tax varies with the quantities of x and a. A diminishing marginal rate of transformation with increasing use of a is simply a case of ordinary diminishing marginal returns to input a in producing x.

Our last marginal equilibrium condition is that the output of x and the input of a be of such magnitudes that the marginal technical rate of transformation of a into x be equal to the ratio between the price of a, Pa, and the price of x, Px, i.e., that

$$Tax = \frac{Pa}{Px}$$

for all inputs, a, and outputs, x, of the firm. This is required in order that no change of the sort considered shall be profitable, which means that the cost of the extra unit of input is $Pa = TaxPx$, the value of the extra output resulting, and dividing this by Px we have our last marginal equilibrium condition.

7. THE SECOND-ORDER CONDITIONS OF EQUILIBRIUM

We have now determined the marginal conditions of equilibrium which, if satisfied, assure us that we are, so to speak, going neither uphill nor downhill on the graph representing the firm's surplus. This is, however, not all we want to know, for there is a variety of situations in which we are not going up or down, e.g., on top of a hill as in Fig. 4a, at the bottom of a valley as in 4b, or on a level plane as in 4c. We want to be certain that we are really on top of a hill, i.e., that the firm has chosen the most profitable plan. The second-order conditions and the first-order conditions together assure us of this. The second-order conditions as usually given and as we shall give them below require that there be only a hill and no valleys, plateaus, or level planes on the surplus graph. Clearly, when this is the case, if the firm is not going uphill or downhill on the graph, it must be on top, since we exclude all other possibilities. The reader may note that this requirement is more strict than is absolutely necessary. It can, however, very easily be modified to make it completely general as follows: If some point is a point of equilibrium it is on top of a hill, and so there must be an area of the graph around that point (called a neighborhood of the point) in which there is only a hill and no plateaus, valleys, or level stretches. Thus even if the conditions we are about to list were satisfied only in the neighborhood of the point in question but not necessarily throughout the entire graph, the point would still be on top of a hill.

There is an essential difference between the natures of the second-order and the marginal equilibrium conditions: The second-order conditions for the most part assure us that there is a hill in the graph, and whether there is or is not such a hill is, from the point of view of the firm, a matter of accident. If there is no hill (no maximum surplus position) there is nothing the entrepreneur can do about it. As we shall see, whether there is or is not a hill is largely a technical question. It is then meaningful to ask, as we shall ask, whether it is likely that the second-order conditions will be satisfied in practice, that is, whether there are or are not likely to be hills on the surplus graph.

The first-order (marginal) conditions of equilibrium, on the other hand, assure us for the most part that if there is a hill, then the firm will have climbed it, that is, the entrepreneur will have maximized his surplus. More accurately these conditions assure us that the firm has moved to a point where it will be neither climbing nor descending if it moves forward slightly. Clearly, whether or not such a point is reached is up to the entrepreneur, assuming that he has accurate information about the terrain, i.e., about the profitability of the various alternative courses of action open to him.

Again we have three second-order conditions, one for each of the three types of change in plan open to the entrepreneur:

a. The first is that the marginal rate of substitution of output x for output y must increase as the quantity of x increases and decrease as the quantity of x decreases. This assures us that once the corresponding marginal condition is satisfied, no substitution of x for y will be profitable. The marginal condition assured us that the amount of y the firm had to give up to produce an extra unit of x was so great as to eliminate any surplus from the change. An increasing marginal rate of substitution of x for y as x increases means that, for any further additions to the output of x, even more units of y than before will have to be given up for every extra unit of x. With prices remaining the same (perfect competition) any such change must certainly be unprofitable if the initial and less disadvantageous change was unprofitable. The argument is the same for an increase in the output of y at the expense of x, so that when this first second-order condition is satisfied in addition to the marginal condition, the firm must be producing the most profitable combination of x and y.

b. Our next second-order condition of equilibrium is that the marginal rate of substitution of input a for input b must decrease as the quantity of a increases, and vice versa. The argument is similar to that of the preceding condition. The second *marginal* condition assured us that by adding another unit of a the firm would be enabled to dispense with so little of input b that the change would add nothing to its surplus. Our present second-order condition assures us that still further additions of a will permit the release of even smaller quantities of b per unit of a, so that such additions must certainly be unprofitable. Thus when the second marginal and second-order conditions are satisfied the firm must be employing the most profitable proportions of a and b.

c. The last second-order condition of equilibrium is that the marginal rate of transformation of input a into output x diminishes as x increases, i.e., that we have diminishing marginal returns to a. Again the argument is that, since using more of a to produce more of x yields no surplus when the third *marginal* condition is satisfied, the use of still further quantities in this way must certainly be unprofitable, inasmuch as the firm will obtain still smaller (diminishing) returns from the use of further units of a.

8. DIAGRAMMATIC INTERPRETATION OF THE EQUILIBRIUM CONDITIONS[6]

A diagrammatic interpretation of the first- and second-order maximum conditions may conceivably help clarify their significance. We shall consider only the conditions determining the relative magnitudes of the various outputs, i.e., the conditions which assure us that the proportion between any two of the firm's outputs is consistent with maximum profits. However, the diagrammatic analyses of the proportions between any two inputs and between any input and any output are so similar to the problem we shall consider that the reader should be able to extend the analysis to cover these other cases if he so desires.

In Figs. 5a and 5b, the quantity of one of the firm's outputs, say, mutton, is indicated on the horizontal axis and the quantity of another of its outputs (e.g., wool) on the vertical axis. Suppose now that the quantities of all the firm's inputs and all its other outputs are given. We can then draw a curve TT', indicating the various combinations of wool and mutton the firm can produce in these circumstances, under the assumption that the firm will use all its inputs and produce any output combination as efficiently as it can. Thus, for example, if the firm produces quantity OX of mutton it will be able, according to Fig. 5a, to produce just OY of wool with the given facilities and inputs. This curve is called a production possibility or transformation curve since it indicates how the firm's facilities can be transformed into wool production from mutton production, and vice versa.

[6] The reader who finds the discussion of the two preceding sections perfectly clear, or who finds geometric arguments confusing, may prefer to omit this section.

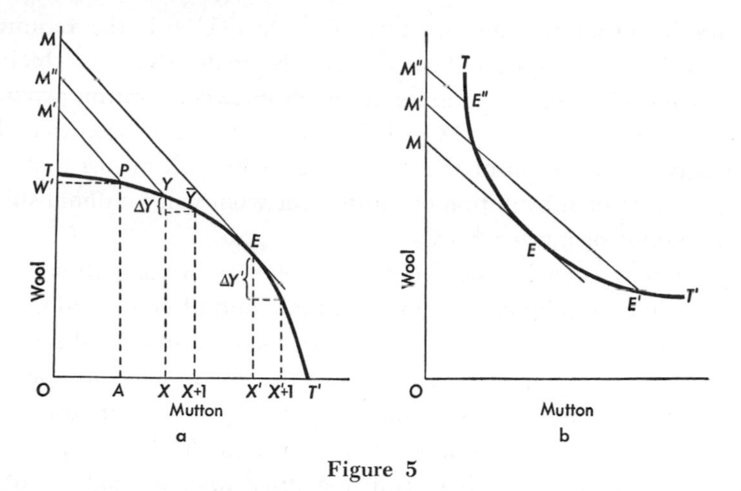

Figure 5

Suppose now that the firm desires to increase its output of mutton by one unit from OX to $OX+1$. In order to do this it must reduce its output of wool from OY to $O\overline{Y}$, i.e., by ΔY. But this is the marginal rate of substitution of mutton for wool as we have defined it; i.e., it is the quantity by which the output of wool must be reduced in order to permit a unit increase in the output of mutton. It will be noted that this quantity (when adjusted for sign) is the slope of a straight-line connecting point Y with $\overline{Y}$, since the slope of that line is $\Delta Y/(X+1-X) = \Delta Y/1 = \Delta Y$, which, as we have seen, can be defined as the marginal rate of substitution of mutton for wool. More precisely it is customary to define the marginal rate of substitution of mutton for wool at output OX of wool as the absolute value [7] of the slope of the transformation curve TT' at point Y.

The concavity to the origin of the TT' curve means that there is an increasing marginal rate of substitution of mutton for wool as the quantity of mutton produced increases. This can be seen at once by noting that the TT' curve gets steeper as we move to the right and that hence the marginal rate of substitution which we have defined as that steepness must be increasing. To see this more directly, consider a mutton output OX' which is greater than OX. If we increase

[7] For a definition of the term "absolute value" see Chapter Nine, footnote 8.

the firm's output by one unit from OX' to $OX'+1$, the required decrease in wool output will be $\Delta Y'$. This is greater than ΔY which is the amount of wool which must be given up when mutton production goes up from OX to $OX+1$. Similarly, it can be seen that the convexity to the origin of the TT' curve in Fig. 5b means that the marginal rate of substitution of mutton for wool will be diminishing as the output of mutton rises.

Let us now consider the profitability of the various outputs as a first step in determining the most profitable output combination and also in order to examine the relevance of the first-order and second-order conditions. Suppose the firm decides to produce the output combination represented by point P; i.e., $OA = W'P$ mutton and AP wool. Let Pm be the price of mutton and Pw be the price of wool, and let $M'P$ be a line, call it a *price line,* through point P whose slope is $-Pm/Pw$, i.e., a line whose steepness is given by the price of mutton in terms of wool. But the slope of price line $M'P$ is, as we know, defined to be $-W'M'/W'P$, so that we must have $W'M'/W'P = Pm/Pw$, i.e., $Pw \cdot W'M' = Pm \cdot W'P$. This means that the money value of $W'M'$ wool is exactly the same as the money value of $W'P$ mutton.

We may now evaluate the product of the firm represented by point P in terms of wool, for we see that this product consists of OW' wool plus $W'P$ mutton which is worth $W'M'$ wool, so that the entire product is worth OM' wool.

It can be seen at once that, as we move to the right along TT' from P to, say, Y, the revenue of the firm will increase, other things being equal. For, under perfect competition this modification of our firm's output will not affect prices. Thus a price line $M''Y$ through Y (whose slope is by definition given by the ratio of mutton price to wool price) will have the same slope as $M'P$ and hence will be parallel to it. The revenue from the sale of the outputs represented by point Y will then be OM'', which is greater than OM', the revenue corresponding to point P.

Revenue will increase as we move to the right along TT' until we reach point E, the point where the price line ME is tangent to the transformation curve, TT'. Here the firm's revenue from mutton and wool sales will be OM, and it is clear that any movement along TT' either to the right or to the left will reduce that revenue. E is thus the point of equilibrium (the point of maximum revenue) between the output of wool and mutton.

We can see that the first-order maximum condition is satisfied at that point. There the slope of the price line is the same as the slope of the transformation curve. But we have defined the slope of the price line to be (the absolute value of) the ratio of mutton price to wool price and (the absolute value of) the slope of the transformation curve to be the marginal rate of substitution of mutton for wool. It follows then that at point E, the point of equilibrium (and at no other point in the diagram), the marginal rate of substitution of mutton for wool will be equal to the ratio of the price of mutton to the price of wool. This is, of course, our first-order maximum condition.

We have already noted that our second-order maximum condition is satisfied in Fig. 5a, i.e., there is an increasing marginal rate of substitution of mutton for wool, but that this condition is not satisfied in Fig. 5b. We have just seen also that there is a position E, in the situation in Fig. 5a which gives a true revenue maximum. It is easily seen now that there is no such position in Fig. 5b, although there is a minimum revenue position.[8] This is point E in Fig. 5b, which, with price line EM, yields revenue OM. It should be clear that revenue will be increased by moving either to the right, say, to point E' or to the left, say, to point E''. In these circumstances it would pay the firm to expand the output of wool or of mutton indefinitely at the expense of the other. The point is simply that the

[8] The reader is reminded that the other two second-order conditions, i.e., the second condition, pertaining to the determination of the proportion between inputs, and the third condition relevant to the determination of the level of inputs and outputs together, call in effect for *diminishing* marginal rates of substitution, so that it will be found in the diagrammatic examination of these conditions that true equilibrium will be attained in a situation whose diagram looks like Fig. 5b and not one which looks like Fig. 5a. The reason roughly is that the first second-order condition deals with revenue maximization, whereas the other two conditions involve cost-minimization problems.

way we have drawn the TT' curve in Fig. 5b, the firm becomes in effect more and more efficient in transforming say, wool into mutton as mutton output increases, so that however much it specializes in mutton output it pays the firm to increase its specialization even further if it can.

9. PLAUSIBILITY OF THE SECOND-ORDER CONDITIONS

We may now inquire briefly whether there is any reason to believe that our second-order conditions are likely to be satisfied in practice. There are two types of argument that have been applied. The first is based on the fact that all of these conditions are forms of diminishing returns, as has already been indicated. The usual arguments for expecting diminishing returns may then be employed. Roughly we may say that since factors of production are to some extent specialized we cannot expect to shift resources from one use to another without getting diminishing returns, i.e., without diminishing the marginal rate of substitution of one output for another, nor can we expect to substitute one factor for another without diminishing returns, i.e., without a diminishing marginal rate of substitution of the one input for the other. Finally, we cannot expect to increase the quantity of just one of the factors employed in producing some commodity without diminishing returns.

This specialization of inputs argument is insufficient, for it may be possible for the firm to expand by increasing all inputs and outputs without encountering diminishing returns. So while this argument assures us that by doing any *one* of the things considered the firm does not seem likely to benefit, it is still possible for it not to be in equilibrium with respect to all possible changes. If, however, there is some factor available to the firm whose quantity is fixed much as the quantity of "land" is fixed in the classical argument, then diminishing returns should still set in for the reason that the firm cannot make all the adjustments it would like in making the changes in question.

In the short run the established firm usually has some fixed equipment such as its land, its buildings and machinery, and its stocks of raw materials and goods in process which are not readily adaptable to a changed production plan, and these may be taken to serve as factors fixed in quantity which make for the existence of diminishing returns of the sort required by the second-order conditions. In the long run or for new firms, however, this obstacle does not arise, so diminishing returns, if they are present, must be attributed to the increasing difficulty of management as the firm increases in size. Hicks suggests that "Another obstacle, also present generally, but particularly present with new firms, is the element of risk. As the planned size of firm increases, the possible losses become steadily greater . . . ,"[9] and this, in effect, amounts to diminishing returns for expansion of the firm.

An alternative argument intended to indicate the likelihood that the second-order conditions will in fact be satisfied runs as follows: If we had perfect competition and firms did try to maximize their profits, then if the second-order conditions were not satisfied for any range of input-output combinations there would be no hill in the surplus graph. In that case it would pay firms not to produce at all, as in Fig. 4d, or it would pay them to attempt to increase their output (or undertake whatever change happens to be in question) beyond any limit, as in Figs. 4b and 4e, or they would end up, as in Fig. 4c wandering aimlessly about in the position of Buridan's ass faced with the choice between the two identical bales of hay. Since firms do not behave in these queer ways we can conclude either that the second-order equilibrium conditions are in fact satisfied where a firm is operating under conditions fairly close to perfect competition or that some motive other than the profit motive is significant in its decisions.

Before leaving the question of equilibrium of the firm we must add one equilibrium condition, the "total" condition that the plan as a whole must be sufficiently profitable to induce the entrepreneur to undertake it at all. This implies that the plan must be such that the

[9] *Op. cit.*, p. 200.

capitalized value at every future date of all that remains to be carried out must be greater than zero. This means that the firm must expect to make a net surplus in all the periods after the present period taken together, in all the periods after the next period taken together, and so on. If this were not the case—if, for example, the entrepreneur did not expect to make a net surplus on all the periods taken together after the fifth—it would clearly pay him to go out of business after the fifth period.

This statement should not be taken to imply that the entrepreneur must expect a profit in each and every period after the fifth. He might, for example, be willing to take a loss during, say, the seventh and yet stay in business, provided he expected to make such great profits in some periods after the seventh as to make up for the loss. This condition will, by definition, be satisfied if the capitalized value of the plan after the fifth period (and every other period) is positive.

10. EXPECTED PRICES, THE RATE OF INTEREST, AND THE PRODUCTION PLAN

Up till now we have examined what we may call the equilibrium production plan on the assumption that all expected prices and the rate of interest were given. We may now say a few words about how the equilibrium plan, that is to say, the most profitable plan, may be expected to change when some expected price or the relevant rate of interest changes.

Consider first a change in some expected price. If the marginal equilibrium conditions were originally satisfied, a rise in the price of an output, other prices remaining equal, will generally lead the firm to attempt to increase its output of that item both at the expense of other outputs and by increasing its inputs. The marginal conditions required that at the old price small changes of this sort involved neither loss nor gain, so with the new, more favorable price for this output these changes must now be profitable.

Similarly, a rise in the price of an input, other prices remaining equal, will generally lead the firm to diminish its use of the item, partly at the expense of output and partly by substituting some other inputs for it. A decrease in some price, other prices remaining unchanged, may generally be expected to lead to the opposite results.

We can say a bit more about the matter. Suppose the expected price of shoes five periods hence rises with no change of any sort in other prices expected in any other period. It may then be advantageous not only to produce more shoes at the expense of, say, hats, but it may also pay to produce (sell) more shoes in the fifth period at the expense of shoe sales in other periods. This may be done by increasing stocks of shoes in earlier periods, by devoting some of the funds which might have been used for shoe production in earlier periods to the production of shoe machinery which will help increase the output of shoes during the fifth period, by using shoe machinery more intensively during period five to the detriment of future outputs, or by any combination of these. This means that not only will shoe outputs in period five be affected by the change in the price of shoes expected then but also that shoe outputs in other periods will be affected. We cannot even be certain that shoe outputs during all or most other periods will be decreased. If, for example, much additional machinery is brought in to help expand shoe output during period five, outputs in many of the succeeding periods will be increased too.

Suppose now that all expected shoe prices and present price as well are increased. This too will generally result in an increase in shoe output. But again there are difficulties of adjustment, and it may be that output will rise gradually over that originally planned as plant and equipment are gradually adapted to higher planned levels of output. It is even conceivable that shoe outputs may at first be reduced below the old planned levels despite the increased price. This might occur, for example, if the price rise made it profitable to install new equipment which required the temporary closing down of plant and cessation of production.

The foregoing remarks may readily be adapted by the reader to cover the cases of decreased output prices and of changes in input prices.

Now consider a rise in the relevant rate of interest. This will not affect current prices, but since the future prices which concern us are discounted future prices and since the discount ratio depends on the rate of interest, it is clear that future prices will in effect be changed. The reason we discount future prices at all is because of the interest lost in not getting money now, and when the rate of interest rises the interest loss in getting money next period rather than now is greater than before. This means that the present value of a sum of money receivable next period is less than before so that a rise in the rate of interest is tantamount to a fall in next period's price. Moreover, because interest is compounded, the interest loss which results from the rise in interest rate on money receivable n periods from now is more than n times the loss on money receivable one period from now. More rigorously, since the discount ratio is $D = 1/(1+i)$, D decreases when the rate of interest, i, increases. It can be shown mathematically that the discount ratio for n periods from now, D^n, will, when D is less than unity, fall more than in proportion to D.[10] Thus prices in the distant future will in effect fall more than prices in the near future when the rate of interest rises. This means that the *ratio* of more distant to less distant future prices will be decreased which, as we have seen, is the important thing in determining the equilibrium position. A rise in the rate of interest will therefore induce producers to concentrate their outputs toward the present, for in essence the interest cost of postponing receipts has become more expensive. Similarly there will be an incentive to increase future inputs at the expense of present inputs, for example, to postpone replacement of machinery so that the money that would be tied up in that machinery can be kept earning the now higher interest.

[10] The ratio between the proportionate fall in D^n and that in D is given by $\frac{d(D^n)/D^n}{d(D)/D}$, where $d(x)$ is the differential of x, and this is equal to $\frac{d(D^n)/d(D)}{D^n/D}$ $= n$.

11. CURRENT AND EXPECTED PRICES

Besides depending on information about phenomena such as the state of the weather, the political situation, the state of consumer tastes, crop prospects, and the like, which must for our present purposes be considered fortuitous, expected prices no doubt depend on the trend and level of current prices. The dependence of expected future prices on present prices can be conveniently measured by the *elasticity of expectations*. This is defined as the ratio between a proportionate (percentage) change in current price and the resulting proportionate change in every expected price of some item. If current prices change and expected future prices change more than in proportion, we say that expectations are elastic or that the elasticity of expectations is greater than unity. *This does not mean that we expect future price to rise above current price* but merely that future expected price, though it may originally have been and may still be below current price (as are xR and xR' in Fig. 6a), has risen above its old level more than has current price (that is, the percentage rise from xR to xR' is greater than that from OP to OP'). In Fig. 6a a set of initially expected prices (the solid line) and the set of revised expectations (dotted line) when current price rises from OP to OP' are shown. In this figure the expectations are elastic. This is because the rest of the line has risen more than in proportion to the rise in the end of the line on the y axis, the latter rise representing the

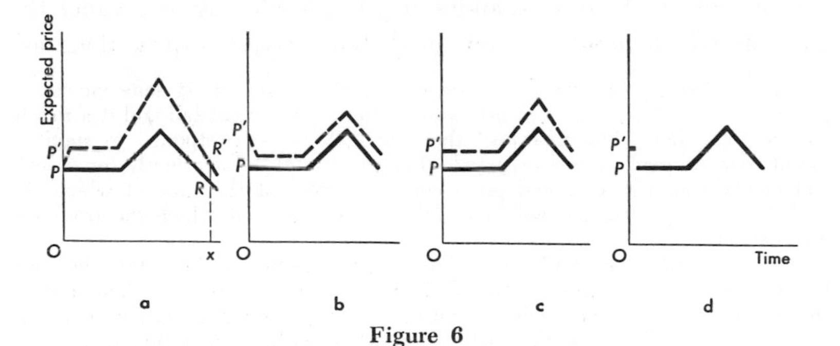

Figure 6

change in current price. Similarly, in Fig. 6b the case of inelastic expectations (elasticity of expectations less than unity) is illustrated: Expected prices rise less than in proportion to current prices. Figure 6c shows a case of unit elasticity of expectations where expected prices rise exactly in proportion to current prices, and finally, Fig. 6d shows expectations of zero elasticity, that is to say, a case where expectations do not respond at all to a change in current prices.

It should be noted that the measure requires that when current price changes *all* future prices change simultaneously in an equal, greater, or smaller proportion than the change in current prices. This means that if, for example, the price expected next period rises more than in proportion while that expected in the subsequent period rises less than in proportion to a rise in current price, the measure cannot be used. However, since, as pointed out earlier, expectations are apt to be pretty vague, a rise in current price is likely to affect the whole vague bundle of expectations in very much the same way, so that it does not do too much violence to reality to assume that expected prices generally move together roughly in the way required by the measure.[11]

We may now very briefly examine what the effect of a change in current price will be on the production the firm will find it most profitable to adopt. If current price rises and expectations are elastic, expected future prices will rise relatively to current price; i.e., the ratio of future price to current price will be greater than before,[12] so that it will pay to postpone outputs if the price in question is an output price. If the price is an input price, it will pay to advance the dates at which inputs are obtained. Similarly, if expectations are

[11] Exceptions to this generalization can easily be found. If someone is expecting a cyclical movement in prices involving an imminent fall and if a rise in current price leads him to expect the price fall to be postponed to such an extent that the peak is now expected when the trough was formerly forecasted, and vice versa, then expected price will have risen at the time at which the peak is now expected and will have fallen at the date at which the trough is now expected.

[12] We are concerned with *proportionate* price changes, since it is the ratio between present and expected prices which is relevant for the marginal equilibrium conditions. This ratio will, of course, rise, fall, or remain constant as future prices rise more than, less than, or in proportion with, current prices.

inelastic and a current output price rises, it will pay to speed up outputs, since expected future prices will have risen less than in proportion. If an input price rises in these circumstances it will pay to postpone inputs to a greater extent than before. Finally, if expectations are of unit elasticity, a rise in current price should induce no substitution between current and future inputs or between current and future outputs since the ratio between current and expected future prices will remain unchanged. The reader may analyze the case of a fall in current prices for himself.

In the next chapter we shall again use the elasticity of expectations, this time for a considerably more important purpose.

12. COMMENTS

It may be noted by the reader that very little we have said in this chapter has told us much about the world in which we live. For the most part we have merely provided a system of classification in terms of which we may conveniently analyze the behavior of the firm.

It is formally possible to subject the behavior of the consumer to this sort of treatment, but as Hicks points out, such a view of the matter is excessively mechanistic and is not likely to help us much in analyzing consumer behavior. The assumption that the consumer performs elaborate calculations is certainly neither realistic nor, as Professor Samuelson has shown,[13] is it necessary for the construction of the theory. We shall therefore jump from the consideration of the theory of the firm at a moment of time to an examination of the operation of the economy as a whole.

[13] P. A. Samuelson, *Foundations of Economic Analysis*, pp. 107–117 (Harvard University Press, Cambridge, Mass., 1947).

Appendix to Chapter Five

UNCERTAINTY AND THE EQUILIBRIUM OF THE FIRM

1. THE VALUATION OF CAPITAL ASSETS

Following Professor Knight,[14] it has become customary to distinguish between risk and uncertainty. Examples of risk are the possibility of a low crop yield or of fire, and it is distinguishable from uncertainty in that empirical evidence from a large number of cases in the past enables the calculation of the probability of each of the various possible outcomes. Thus on the basis of vital statistics the probability that an average person will live to the age of, say, sixty can be calculated actuarially. It follows, at least conceptually, that risk can be insured against, as is in fact the case with fire and life insurance.

Uncertainty, on the other hand, is said to exist when we cannot even form any objective estimate at all on the basis of past experience. The mean probability of an investment yielding a certain profit cannot be calculated, for the "law of large numbers" cannot be applied where there are no statistics of the profitability of a large number of exactly similar investments. Where there is uncertainty, therefore, expectations can only be founded on a mixture of experience, intuition, and guesswork.

[14] F. H. Knight, *Risk, Uncertainty and Profit* (Houghton Mifflin Co., Boston and New York, 1921, reprinted by The London School of Economics, London, 1933).

By the nature of the problem it is impossible for the economist to give any precise analysis of situations involving uncertainty, since expectations are largely subjective. We can, however, go some way in separating out the different elements in such situations. As an example of this we may take the simple case of the valuation of a capital asset.

In discussing this matter (Section 4 of this chapter), we said simply that the present value of an asset equals the sum of the discounted values of the expected net return in each future period, where a risk premium [15] is subtracted corresponding to the degree of uncertainty before discounting.

The question is, how is this risk premium to be determined, or, more precisely, how does one determine the amount of money expected with certainty (called the certainty equivalent of the prospect) which the entrepreneur considers equivalent in value to the uncertain prospect?

It has been suggested that the entrepreneur does in his mind what amounts to the construction of a probability (likelihood) distribution [16] of the prospective earnings. Thus he can feel that there is a 10 per cent likelihood that his earnings will fall between $10 and $15, a 10 per cent likelihood that it will fall between $150 and $200, etc. Here likelihood does *not* mean probability and represents only a subjective feeling about the matter which is based in some vague way on a combination of experience, analysis, and hunch. The result of these deliberations may be represented by a graph where we indicate the different amounts which the entrepreneur thinks he may earn along the horizontal axis and the likelihood with which each of these is regarded along the vertical axis. It is then suggested that the certainty equivalent of this prospect (the amount of money expected with certainty at which the entrepreneur values the prospect) depends upon the standard properties of this distribution. These include the mean (the weighted average of prospective earn-

[15] This is the customary term, but "uncertainty premium" might be better.

[16] For a definition and description of probability (frequency) distributions and their properties see almost any book on statistical method or statistical theory.

ings using the likelihoods as the weights), the dispersion (a measure of how widely the fairly likely possibilities are scattered), and the skewness (a measure of the symmetry of the distribution).

A more explicit determination of the certainty equivalent has been suggested roughly as follows: Suppose the entrepreneur feels that he will certainly lose no more than $30 on the deal. Suppose he considers it 97 per cent likely that he will do $10 better than that, 83 per cent likely that he will get still another $10 from the prospect, etc. The rest of the relevant figures are given in the table and can theoretically be determined from the entrepreneur's likelihood distribution. The likelihood figure, L, say, 0.57, may be so defined that, to the entrepreneur, X, e.g., $10, expected with likelihood L is worth $XL = 0.57 \times 10 = \$5.70$ expected with certainty. Then the value (certainty equivalent) of each of the relevant possible increments above −$30 is given in the last column, and their sum indicates the amount by which the value of the prospect on this view exceeds −$30. This figure, minus $30, which comes out to $22.90 in the example of the table, is the certainty equivalent of the entire prospect.

Amount	*Likelihood*	*Certainty Equivalent*
1st $10 above −$30	0.97	$ 9.70
2nd $10 above −$30	0.83	8.30
3rd $10 above −$30	0.79	7.90
4th $10 above −$30	0.70	7.00
5th $10 above −$30	0.62	6.20
6th $10 above −$30	0.51	5.10
7th $10 above −$30	0.40	4.00
8th $10 above −$30	0.32	3.20
9th $10 above −$30	0.15	1.50
10th $10 above −$30	0.0	0
Value of the prospect above − $30 (total)		$52.90
Value of the prospect (subtract $30 from total)		$22.90

If some sort of probability figure is attached to a given, but in practice noninsurable, outcome, e.g., if a bet has been made on a single throw of a die and will win only if a 3 turns up so that there is a 1/6 chance of winning, it has been suggested that a certainty equivalent may be obtained with the aid of the entrepreneur's indifference map (Fig. 7). On the horizontal axis, amounts of money (positive or negative) are represented, and on the vertical axis (running from 0 to 1), the probability with which these amounts may be expected are measured.

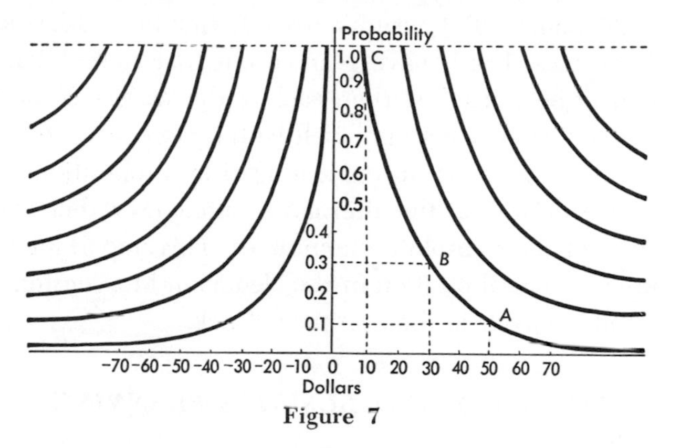

Figure 7

Since points *A* ($50 with probability 0.1), *B* ($30 with probability 0.3), and *C* (the certainty of $10) are on the same indifference curve, we know that the entrepreneur is indifferent among $50 with probability 0.1, $30 with probability 0.3, and the certainty of $10, so that $10 is the certainty equivalent of the other two.

The above remarks contain elements based on the work of Marschak, Makower, Hart, Tintner, Svennilson, and others.[17] Dr. G. Shackle has put forward a considerably different approach.[18] It assumes that the individual is less of a calculating machine, and following from that it assumes that what is relevant to a decision is less the profit or loss itself than the *present* joy (or anguish) of anticipating future profit (or loss). Moreover it supposes that the

[17] For some references see the reading list. See also e.g., G. Tintner, "The Theory of Choice Under Subjective Risk and Uncertainty" and "The Pure Theory of Production Under Technological Risk and Uncertainty," both in *Econometrica,* 1941. Also Ingvar Svennilson, *Ekonomisk Planering,* Chap. 5 (Almqvist and Wiksells Boktryckeri, Uppsala, 1938).

[18] *Expectation in Economics* (Cambridge University Press, Cambridge, 1949).

entrepreneur focuses his attention exclusively upon one particular gain and on one particular loss as epitomizing the possibilities of gain and loss respectively.

Some of this discussion seems to suggest that it is good policy to choose that prospect which offers the highest expected money value, e.g., that a 0.2 probability of 90 dollars is better than a 0.8 probability of 20 dollars. But writers from Bernoulli to Marshall and many others since then [19] have pointed out that each dollar of the 80 dollars may be worth less than each of the scarcer 20 dollars, so that the second proposition may well be the more advantageous. In other words, it is sensible, in evaluating risky propositions, to take account of the *utilities* of the alternative outcomes rather than their dollar values or their absolute magnitudes. This important observation occupies a central position in the Neumann-Morgenstern theory of utility and behavior in the presence of risk.

2. UNCERTAINTY AND BUSINESS PLANNING

Professor A. G. Hart has shown [20] that an analysis of business planning in terms of the certainty equivalents of the entrepreneur's expectations concerning prices, productivity, etc., passes over one particularly important feature of business planning, namely, the preservation of flexibility.

Suppose that an entrepreneur is planning now with respect to sales a year hence. Very likely, he will expect that during the course of the year he will acquire more information which will reduce the amount of uncertainty in his expectations. The result of this will, therefore, be that in beginning production now he will plan it in such a manner that it will be easy to alter the planned output during the course of the year without too big a rise in unit cost should his

[19] See e.g., Jacob Marschak, "Why 'Should' Statisticians and Businessmen Maximize Moral Expectations?" *Proceedings of the Second Berkeley Symposium on Mathematical Statistics and Probability* (University of California Press, 1951).

[20] *Anticipations, Uncertainty and Dynamic Planning, Journal of Business,* October 1940, and *Studies in Business Administration,* Vol. 11, No. 1 (The University of Chicago Press, Chicago, 1940).

expectations of demand be modified. Thus the existence of uncertainty will lead to the use of equipment whose scale of operation is flexible—uncertainty will affect the quality of investment as well as the quantity.

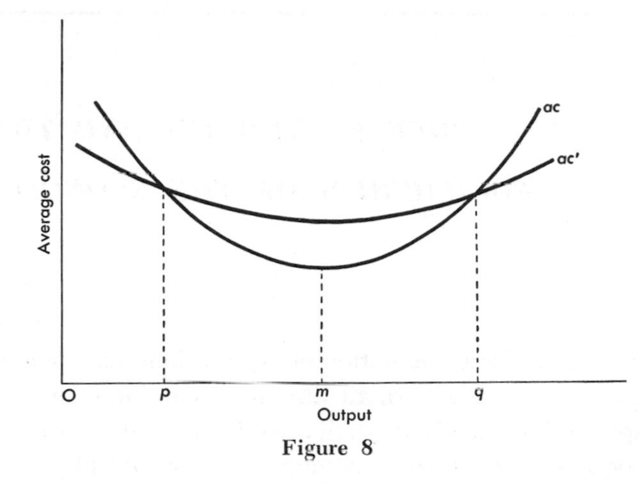

Figure 8

We can express this in another way with the aid of Fig. 8. Suppose at the beginning of the year, the entrepreneur in setting up his plant considers that the most profitable output will be *Om* and he does not anticipate any reduction in uncertainty enabling him to revise his expectations. He will then try to minimize his costs and work according to an average-cost curve such as *ac*. But if he does anticipate a clarification of expectations so that he may come to consider an output other than *Om* to be most profitable, then he may work according to an average-cost curve such *ac′*. While this means higher costs if his original output plan is unaffected by the acquisition of further information, it will mean lower costs if this information causes him to raise planned output above *Oq* or lower it below *Op*. Thus if, at the beginning of the year, he considers it quite likely that as time passes he will obtain a very different picture of the market situation, he may choose a flexible plant (i.e., a plant with an average-cost curve *ac′* rather than *ac*) because it will offer a better profit prospect.

Chapter Six

PRICE FLEXIBILITY AND THE EQUILIBRIUM OF THE ECONOMY

Having considered the notion of equilibrium and some related problems, we shall now turn to disequilibrium situations and see what happens. Specifically we shall consider a situation where everyone is not able to sell or buy as much as he would like at current prices which, therefore, tend to change. Much of the analysis of this chapter falls under the head of comparative statics since the idea is to compare the situations before and after a given change without paying much attention to the process whereby the change comes about.

For the most part the analysis will assume that when sellers are unable to sell as much as they would like at current prices, their offer price, and consequently the market price of the commodity, will fall and that, when buyers cannot buy all they would like at current price, demand price, and consequently market price, will rise. This property of an economy is referred to as *price flexibility.* Of course not all commodities do in fact have flexible prices—some prices, because of custom or institutional arrangements (e.g., certain types of oligopoly) are not affected by the appearance of small quantities of unsalable supplies or of unfilled demands. Such prices we call *rigid.* In most of this chapter we shall assume that there are no rigid prices. We shall also assume, as in the last chapter, perfect competition, though Lange[1] has shown that the argument may be modified so as to apply when this assumption is dropped.

We shall call the difference between the demand and supply of a commodity at each price (using this word to include inputs) the *excess demand* for that commodity and the difference between the supply and the demand for that commodity at each price the *excess supply*. Thus excess demand equals (is identical with) "minus" excess supply. A rise in the former is the same as a fall in the latter. If at a certain price demand equals supply, then at that price excess demand and excess supply are both zero.

If all present prices fall and all expected future prices fall in exactly the same proportion (unit elasticity of expectations), then the present, i.e., discounted values, D^nP, of future prices, P, will only fall in the same proportion if the rate of interest remains constant since the discount ratio, D, varies with the rate of interest (cf. Section 4, Chapter Five). Therefore, when we speak of all prices falling in proportion it is to be understood that the rate of interest is taken to be unchanged.

We then say that the real quantity of a stock of cash is unchanged if the stock of cash falls in exactly the same proportion as prices, for example, if the quantity of cash falls by 10 per cent when prices all fall by 10 per cent. We say this because the purchasing power of the total stock of cash is not changed by the fall in prices. If the quantity of cash falls by a greater percentage than prices, we say that its real quantity has fallen, and if it does not fall by so much as prices we say, since its purchasing power has increased, that its real quantity has risen. Similarly, if all prices rise in the same proportion we say that the real quantity of any stocks of cash (say, the cash in my pocket) is unchanged, increased, or decreased as its quantity rises proportionately, more than proportionately, or less than proportionately with prices. For simplicity we speak of the real quantity of cash being increased, decreased, or unchanged.

[1] *Price Flexibility and Employment*, Chap. VII (The Principia Press, Bloomington, Indiana, 1944). The present chapter is largely based on Chaps. III to V of this work, together with the last part of Hicks' *Value and Capital*, (Oxford University Press, New York, 1939).

1. WALRAS' LAW AND SAY'S LAW

Our analysis will be based to a large extent on a tautological proposition which Lange calls "Walras' law." This states that, the supply of all commodities taken together, including the supply of securities and money offered, is identically equal with the total demand for all of them. This is so because people only offer to sell commodities (including their labor) in return for the pecuniary equivalent of these commodities either in other commodities or in money. This means that every offer of a good for sale automatically involves a demand for its equivalent either in money, securities, or other goods. The statement is a tautology because it follows from the definition of a sale or a proposed sale. It follows from Walras' law that, where some commodity is in excess supply, there must be an excess demand for some other commodity or for money, since otherwise the total of all demands and of all supplies could not be equal.

Walras' law seems rather similar to the standard version of Say's law. "Supply (of goods and services) creates its own demand." [2] There is, in fact, only one important difference between them. This form of Say's law implies that there is always zero excess demand for (and supply of) money. For since by Walras' law demand for goods (including securities) plus demand for money equals supply of goods plus supply of money, then if, in accord with Say's law, demand for goods equals supply of goods, it follows by direct subtraction that demand for money must equal its supply. This will be so whether prices are high or low or whether the quantity of money is large or small.

Say's law in this form is completely incompatible with the quantity theory of money or for that matter with any other explanation of the general price level. The quantity theory requires that a rise in

[2] But cf. G. S. Becker and W. J. Baumol, "The Classical Monetary Theory: the Outcome of the Discussion," *Economica*, Nov. 1952, esp. pp. 371–375, for other variants of "Say's Law."

the price level can produce an increase in demand (and hence with supply fixed, an excess demand) for money, contrary to the Say's law requirement. More generally the proposition implies that nothing will change in the system when all prices rise or fall in proportion, even though the quantity of money remains unchanged. People will only care how many hats they can get for a pair of shoes and will not be at all concerned with the number of money counters which change hands in the process. In this case any price level will be equally possible with any other. The general price level will be completely indeterminate.

Say's law has been used in various guises to show that general unemployment, i.e., excess supply of labor, is impossible. It follows from Walras' law that if there is overproduction (excess supply) of any commodity (including factors and money) there must be excess demand for some other. Now Say's law requires that the demand for money equal its supply. If this is true, the item in excess demand cannot be money and must be a *bona fide* commodity.[3] This implies that supply must be misdirected rather than generally excessive; that is, if hats are the item in excess supply and shoes the item in excess demand, all that is required is a shift of labor and resources from hat to shoe production. Then since (it is argued) the excess supply of hats will cause a fall in hat prices and the excess demand for shoes will bring about a rise in shoe prices, the necessary adjustment will be brought about by entreprencurial self-interest, so that overproduction and unemployment will automatically be eliminated. In effect Say's law implies that the economy operates like a barter system where people always demand commodities for commodities so that general overproduction can never occur.

Where Say's law does not hold, and there is an excess demand for money, it is not ordinarily possible to eliminate much unemployment by just shifting men and resources from the production of the

[3] I have ignored the case where securities are the item in excess demand. But if securities *are issued only* to finance the creation of real assets they cause no difficulty since an excess demand for securities must be reflected in an excess demand for real assets.

items in excess supply to the production of the item in excess demand, money, because of the nature of the money supply process.[4]

2. *THE METHOD OF APPROACH*

Suppose that as the result of a fall in the price of a commodity in excess supply (e.g., a fall in the wages of labor when there is unemployment) all other prices, including expected future prices,[5] fall in the same proportion. It is then convenient, as a matter of pure classification, to divide the possibilities into three cases, which Lange calls the case where the monetary effect is absent, the case where the monetary effect is positive, and the case where the monetary effect is negative:

a. *The case where the monetary effect is absent:* This case is characterized by the absence of change in the economy's excess demand for cash in real terms, i.e., by a lack of response of this sort to the general price fall. Then since, by definition, the public desires to get rid of no more and no less money in real terms (purchasing power) than before, nothing will happen to the total excess supply of all commodities. Since, in this case, the allocation of expenditures among different commodities and the proportion in which they are supplied both depend only on relative prices [6] which are assumed unchanged, the excess supply of each and every commodity will be the same as before. In other words, since the same amount of purchasing power will be spent as before and since it will be divided up among the various commodities as before, the same quantities of goods being produced as before, nothing will really have changed

[4] There may be an exception to this if gold serves as money and its production can be expanded sufficiently to take up all the labor which is in excess supply. (This condition hardly seems realistic.) This exception seems to be the main burden of Rueff's criticism of the Keynesian theory. See "The Fallacies of Lord Keynes' 'General Theory,'" *Quarterly Journal of Economics,* May 1947.

[5] But, as we assumed above, the rate of interest remains unchanged.

[6] They depend only on *relative* prices, since, where the monetary effect is absent a change in absolute prices (the price level) is by definition shorn of its usual effect—its influence on the excess supply of commodities (the excess demand for cash).

but the price level; the good initially in excess supply will remain in excess supply.

b. *The case where the monetary effect is positive:* This is the case where, when all prices fall in the same proportion, the real excess demand for cash decreases so that people want to get rid of more of their cash than before in terms of purchasing power. Then any combination of the following may happen:

(a) They may use this cash to buy more of the good than before, thereby helping to eliminate the excess supply.

(b) They may buy more of other goods, thereby forcing up the price of those goods relative to the price of the good in excess supply and thus in turn tending to induce an increase in demand for that good.

(c) They may attempt to invest their added excess cash in securities rather than using it to buy goods (including in this category producer's goods) which will tend to drive up the prices of securities. This is the same as driving down the rate of interest payment on securities, as may be seen from the example of an increase from, say, $100 to $200 in the price of a security entitling the bearer to $3 per year (in perpetuity). This may be viewed either as a doubling in the price of the security or as a fall in the interest payment from 3 per cent to 1½ per cent per annum.

The fall in interest rates will, because of the reduction in the cost of financing it, induce entrepreneurs to increase investment which, directly or indirectly [as in (b) above], will raise the demand for the commodity in excess supply. This effect will be strengthened by the multiplier effect of the increase in investment.[7]

[7] It may be observed that point (c) above contains the essence of the Keynesian analysis as to how a fall in wages or an increase in the quantity of money may increase employment. In general, Keynes does not consider possibilities (a) and (b) which involve a direct increase in demand for labor or for goods requiring labor in their manufacture. See *The General Theory of Employment, Interest and Money*, esp. pp. 260–269 (Macmillan and Company Ltd., London, 1936).

c. *The case where the monetary effect is negative:* This is the remaining case where, with a general proportionate fall in prices, the real excess demand for cash rises. In this case people want more cash in real terms than before and so reduce the amount of cash in terms of real purchasing power which they offer for goods or securities. Thus we have the rather astonishing conclusion that the excess supply of the commodity we are considering will have been aggravated by the fall in its price. This will occur because the decline in the real quantity of cash people attempt to get rid of (a) induces them to spend less on the commodity, (b) induces them to spend less on other goods, thereby lowering their prices relatively to that of the commodity in excess supply and causing substitution of these other goods for the overabundant good, or (c) induces them to demand less securities so that interest rates will tend to rise and investment to fall.

3. THE PROPORTIONAL FALL OF PRICES

We have now listed the three alternative possibilities that are relevant when the price of a commodity in excess supply falls and all other prices fall in the same proportion. We can now conceptually separate the reactions to the fall in the price of the commodity in excess supply into two stages. First, all other prices fall in the same proportion. Second, something may happen to offset or continue this fall. This something can only be a change in the real excess demand for cash, for, as we have seen, if that remains constant the price reduction will result in nothing but the price level being changed. Our conclusion is thus that whether or not price flexibility will remove an excess supply of (or excess demand) for a commodity depends upon the effect of a general price fall (rise) upon the real excess demand for money.

The complicated nature of the argument arises from the fact that we are not prepared to assume that "other things are equal" but examine all the repercussions throughout the economy. Failure to do this can sometimes lead to serious mistakes. Thus the simple argument that wage cuts are certain to increase employment because they make it cheaper to hire workers is a standard example of such a fallacy. It neglects the repercussions on demand of the fall in workers' incomes, and this factor can clearly work in the opposite direction; i.e., while it is true that a fall in wages will reduce money costs of production, workers' purchasing power may well fall and reduce demand so much that it will be no more profitable (or even less profitable) to hire workers than before the general wage cut took effect.

Before we can continue our analysis we must overcome a difficulty which the reader may have noticed. We began by assuming that at first *all* prices fall in the same proportion with the appearance of a single overabundant commodity (given the excess demand for money) and that if as a result the excess demand for cash changes, only then can the proportions between changes in price differ. We must then explain why, if the excess demand for cash does not change initially, an attempt to reduce the price of the item in excess supply (which is really what we must expect in the first instance) can make *all* other prices fall in proportion.[8]

If, now, the real excess demand for cash is constant and the price of a commodity which is initially in excess supply falls, this reduces its excess supply but it cannot lead to general equilibrium. Excess supplies of other commodities must appear; for there has merely been a transfer of part of the fixed amount of purchasing power toward the purchase of the originally overabundant commodity, and this must mean that less is spent elsewhere. If the goods now in excess supply had also fallen in price, since the real excess supply of cash is by assumption unchanged, excess supplies of still other goods must appear. Thus there can be no equilibrium so long as

[8] It is difficult to define an unchanged *real* excess demand for cash when (initially) only one price falls. This is, of course, an index-number problem, as we must determine what happens to the real value (purchasing power) of a dollar, and as such it has no perfect answer. We are therefore forced into the somewhat unsatisfactory course of assuming that we do in fact have a perfect index number by which we deflate the nominal amount of cash demanded (the actual number of dollar bills) to obtain the real amount.

prices do not fall throughout the economy to a point where relative prices are the same as they were initially. This is true because so long as the prices of some goods have not fallen fully in proportion, some of these goods will tend to be in excess supply and will hence (with price flexibility) fall in price. This is the comparative statics [9] argument which maintains that the excess supply of one commodity cannot lead to a disproportionate equilibrium fall in all other prices.

4. THE REAL SUPPLY OF CASH

We have shown that whether or not price flexibility will remove the excess supply (demand) of a commodity depends upon whether the monetary effect is positive, negative, or absent, i.e., on the effect of a general price change on the real excess demand for cash. Since this is defined as the difference between the real demand for and the real supply of cash, we must examine what happens to each. In this section we consider the real supply.

The real supply of cash is constant if the nominal supply (the number of dollar bills) changes in the same proportion as prices; if it falls less than prices the real supply rises; and if it falls more the real supply decreases. Now since the nominal supply of cash is determined by the banking system and by government monetary policy, we cannot easily generalize about the effect of a general fall in prices upon the nominal supply.[10]

Let us temporarily assume that when prices fall the real demand for cash remains constant. Whether or not there will be a positive monetary effect then depends on the effect on the real supply. Suppose prices fall and the money system is not so "responsive" that the nominal supply falls enough to prevent a rise in the real supply of cash; i.e., the rise in the purchasing power of cash resulting from

[9] Note the nature of the argument which proceeds by ruling out various possibilities as incompatible with equilibrium. It never discusses the sequence of events.

[10] Professor Pigou has, however, attempted an analysis of some of the important types of banking (monetary) policy which goes considerably further than we do here. Cf. *Employment and Equilibrium,* pp. 60–63 (Macmillan and Company Ltd., London, 1941).

lower prices is not completely offset by a fall in the quantity of cash. Then with real demand constant and real supply rising, the real excess demand for cash will fall; i.e., there will be a positive monetary effect. The excess supply of the commodity in question will thus decrease through one or all of the mechanisms described in Section 2.[11] In particular this will happen if, with the real demand for cash constant, the nominal quantity of cash remains unchanged when prices fall, for then with all prices lower the purchasing power of the unchanged quantity of cash must clearly rise.

It should be noted that our argument applies only to cash money and not to credit money such as bills of exchange which involve both a creditor and a debtor. In the case of credit money a fall in prices will in effect increase the purchasing power of the creditor, but this must be exactly offset by the debtor's loss resulting from the increased purchasing power of his debt.

Generally, it is asserted that the analysis therefore does not apply to checking accounts (demand deposits) which are so important a part of our money supply. This is because they are a debt of the banks. But the theory is taken to apply to Federal Reserve notes and to government bonds because unlike a private debtor, the government does not usually change its spending when the real value of its debts is changed.[12]

5. THE REAL DEMAND FOR CASH

The effect of a general fall in prices on the real demand for cash depends upon the elasticity of expectations (defined in Section 11 of the preceding chapter). We may consider three cases:

a. *Elasticity of expectations greater than unity (elastic expectations):* This means that a fall in present prices changes expected

[11] It has been argued that this is precisely the case "classical economists" had in mind when arguing that a fall in wages may be expected to decrease unemployment. The fall in wages increases the purchasing power of cash and so can produce a positive monetary effect. Cf. A. C. Pigou, "The Classical Stationary State," *Economic Journal,* December 1943.

[12] Cf. Don Patinkin, *Money, Interest and Prices* (Row Peterson, New York, 1956) pp. 202–204.

future prices more than proportionately, in other words that present prices *rise* relatively to expected future prices. Buyers will thus postpone some of their planned purchases; i.e., increase present demand for money, and sellers will endeavor to speed up sales (increasing their demand for money) so that the total real demand for cash rises. This will make prices fall further if the real supply of cash is kept constant. In this case, therefore, price flexibility will increase the excess supply of the commodity in question; i.e., there is a "negative" monetary effect. We can explain this in a rough way by saying that a fall in prices, by creating expectation of more appreciation of the currency in the future than previously expected (or less depreciation), leads people to "go into money," reducing prices further; or in other words people expect that the current price fall is only the beginning and heralds an even greater (relative) fall in the future, so that it will pay to postpone expenditures. Thus the price fall will tend to *reduce* current sales!

b. *Elasticity of expectations less than unity* (*inelastic exceptions*): If current prices fall, expected future prices fall less than proportionately, which means that they rise relatively. This will induce postponement of sales to await the relative expected price rise and a speeding up of purchases to take advantage of the, so to speak, temporary relative fall in current price. Thus with expectations inelastic, a fall in current price will lead to a postponement of demands for cash, a speeding up of attempts to get rid of cash, and so to an increased current real demand for goods. On the assumption that the real supply of cash is constant, this is a positive monetary effect: The fall in prices will decrease the excess supply of the commodity in question.

c. *Unit elasticity of expectations:* A fall in current prices in this case leaves the ratio between current and expected future prices unchanged so that there will be neither speeding up nor postponement of purchases or sales. Thus the real demand for cash will be unaltered, and, if the real supply is constant, the real excess demand for cash and the excess supply of the commodity will be the same. This is a neutral monetary effect.

There is one complication which should be mentioned here. It arises when some price expectations are elastic, some are inelastic, and some are of unit elasticity. In this case generalization is difficult, but we may remark that the relative elasticity of expectations for different commodities may be such as to upset some of the preceding conclusions. If, for example, the elasticity of expectations for x, the commodity in excess supply, is very great, then a positive monetary effect may be insufficient to bring about a reduction of the excess supply of x when its price falls. For the current price of x will then rise sharply relative to its future value. People may then postpone their expenditures on x (and increase their current supplies of x) even though they are increasing expenditure generally. It should be clear from this argument that, other things being equal, the smaller the elasticity of expectations of the price of x, the more effective will a fall in its price tend to be in reducing the excess supply of x.

6. STOCKS AND FLOWS OF CASH

It should be observed that throughout the discussion we have been dealing with the quantity of cash taken as a *stock*, that is, as the sum total of all bank notes, coins, etc., in existence at a given moment. The amount of cash *spent* is, of course, a *flow* and has no direct connection with the stock of cash, for the same cash can be used over and over again and the rate of flow of cash expenditures can change through changes in the velocity of circulation as well as through changes in the quantity of cash. It is the stock of cash and not the flow over which the banks and the monetary authorities have direct control.

Now when, for example, there is an increase in the excess supply of cash, in other words when the public has more cash than it wants, the sale of goods and securities is affected by the rate of flow of cash. People will try to get rid of the new excess by buying more. This, however, can never reduce the total stock of cash as far as the public as a whole is concerned. What one man has got rid of, some other man has gained, for cash does not get used up by being exchanged as do most commodities. Spending only passes unwanted cash on to someone else who, in turn, will try to spend it. In this way increased money stocks will increase money flows and the demand for goods.

In all our discussion we must be very careful to distinguish between stocks and flows of cash, since the two are quite different and to some extent independent. The stock of money may, for example, fall, and yet because of a large increase in the velocity of circulation the rate of flow of cash may increase. The only connection between the stock and the flow that has been employed in the argument, and it is a connection we can be sure of almost by definition, is that, when there is an increase in the *excess* supply (not just the supply) of cash (the stock), there will be a tendency for the excess supply of cash outflows to increase.

7. COMMENTS

If excess supplies of commodities occur and if there is general price flexibility, a continued general fall of the price level will occur unless there is a positive monetary effect. It seems to be the possibility of a zero or negative monetary effect that Keynes had in mind when he argued in his *General Theory* that if unemployed workers reduced money wages they might drive prices down to zero without decreasing unemployment.

We have so far considered only goods in excess supply, but the analysis is equally applicable to excess demands. Here *an increase* in the real excess demand for cash balances will improve the situation. Thus an unchanged supply of cash will help, since the rise in prices resulting from the existence of a commodity in short supply will reduce the purchasing power of the economy and hence help reduce excess demands. That is one reason why a fixed money supply may eventually stop an inflation.[13] Inelastic expectations will also be

[13] This suggests, paradoxically, that rising prices can help decrease inflationary pressures by reducing the real money supply. But their effects on expectations are of course apt to be inflationary.

helpful, since this means people will believe that future prices will not rise in the same proportion as present prices and it will therefore pay to postpone purchases, hence reducing current excess demands. Similarly, elastic expectations will only tend to aggravate the initial excess demand. Thus all our conclusions are symmetrical with those of the excess supply (overproduction) case considered above.

It appears relatively "easy" for the situation to be such that the price level will rise or fall without limit, for this will clearly be the case where the monetary effect is negative or absent, so that, for example, a price fall will never tend to reduce the excess supply causing it. It is therefore appropriate to consider whether there are any offsetting (stabilizing) factors present. Three such elements seem to be of particular importance:

a. A relatively fixed nominal supply of cash which acts to increase the real supply of cash (purchasing power) when prices fall and to decrease it when prices rise. The effects of this have already been discussed in considering the real supply of money.

b. A psychology of "normalcy" by which we mean a widespread belief that very high or very low prices are unlikely to persist. This view tends to keep expectations inelastic since a large change in current price will not then be followed by a correspondingly large change in expected future prices. As we have already seen that inelastic expectations tend to reduce the excess demand for cash when prices fall and that for similar reasons they tend to increase it when prices rise, a belief in a return to "normal" is clearly stabilizing.

c. Rigid prices, which we have so far assumed not to exist, tend to have a stabilizing effect since they help increase the demand for commodities in excess supply at the expense of commodities whose prices are rigid, for the prices of the latter undergo a relative rise when flexible prices fall. (The same sort of argument applies to a movement in the upward direction.) It can thus be argued that, while the refusal of unions to accept wage cuts may conceivably increase unemployment, their refusal will help prevent the price level from falling very far. Actually in this case, as in the general case where the rigid price is that of a factor of production, it would largely work indirectly by keeping up the prices of the products whose production involves a relatively large use of labor. The result would tend to be a reduction in the sales of these products and, at their expense, an increase in the demand for other goods which would help keep their prices up as well.

Our analysis, even considered merely as a classification of the possibilities, is not perfectly complete. We have not considered the possibility that the adjustments following the fall in the price of a commodity in excess supply may include some change in the distribution of income, with well-known effects on the propensity to consume. Moreover the analysis is static, and the influence of speeds of reaction has therefore not come into the picture at all. Thus, for example, a wage fall may serve to increase employment, though it would otherwise result in a negative monetary effect, if enough employers are at once led by the anticipated decrease in costs to increase their investments in producers' goods, thereby offsetting any adverse effects on demand which might later have resulted from the fall in workers' purchasing power. The important thing here is that employers' investment demands must react more quickly to the wage change than do workers' consumption demands, so that the course of events through time is the essence of the matter.

This, then, is a more dynamic sort of problem (in the sense in which we use the term here) than those which we have considered in this and the preceding chapter. We shall deal with speed-of-reaction problems in somewhat greater detail in the next chapter.

Chapter Seven

DYNAMICS, COMPARATIVE STATICS, AND THE STABILITY OF STATIC EQUILIBRIUM

It is difficult to decide whether this chapter belongs in Part II or in Part III of this book. In method there is little doubt that it falls under the head of process analysis, as the reader may convince himself by rereading it after going through Part III. However, the subject is ultimately the dynamic implications and requirements of the statics involving time, and for that reason it has been placed here.

Until recently it was customary to refer to an equilibrium situation as *stable* if, following any small departure from that situation, there were forces tending to move things back toward that situation. We can illustrate this in terms of the upper diagrams of Fig. 4, Chapter Five, which show the relationship bteween the output and profits of a firm. The customary definition indicates that in Fig. 4a output is in *stable* equilibrium at Ox_a, for with a higher or lower output the entrepreneur would have an incentive to decrease or increase output respectively. It is tacitly assumed that the incentive to decrease or increase output toward Ox_a will ensure that output actually becomes OX_a.

On the other hand, the customary definition declares the output Ox_b in Fig. 4b to be a position of *unstable* equilibrium and any output in Fig. 4c to be in *neutral* equilibrium. The reason is that, given any output in Fig. 4c, if for some reason there is any departure from it, the entrepreneur has no motive either to return to the old output or to refrain from doing so, since no matter which he does his profits will be unaffected. For output Ox_b in Fig. 4b there is no motive to return to it once it is departed from, since such a return must always mean a reduction in surplus.

These definitions may be criticized on several grounds. The objection may be raised that output Ox_b is not an equilibrium output at all. There is simply no motive for the entrepreneur to produce Ox_b.

Much more important, even if upon a departure from equilibrium there are forces which tend to produce a return movement, it is not sure that the equilibrium will be regained. In terms of Fig. 4a if output falls from Ox_a to OE_a, can we be certain that it will actually return to Ox_a? For a movement back toward the equilibrium point can easily overshoot the mark, and then, when it is returning toward equilibrium again (this time moving in the other direction), it can overshoot once more and so on. In other words the system may end up oscillating about the equilibrium point, possibly in a manner which is unstable in the sense that the amplitude of the swings keep growing larger and larger.

The engineer's experience indicates that this is a very real danger. Perhaps his biggest problem in designing automatic control systems has been to avoid this sort of unstable oscillation. It is, for example, easy to design an automatic ship steering mechanism which is stable in the sense of Fig. 4a in that it turns the wheel to the right whenever the ship has swung off its path toward the left, etc. But if the wheel only returns to the straight ahead position just at the moment the ship hits its course once again inertia will make the ship swing off its course in the other direction. The first time it will overshoot toward the left then toward the right, etc., and these oscillations are very likely to be unstable. Ultimately the stability of static equilibrium can only be analyzed by dynamic methods as is shown very clearly in the problem we now proceed to discuss.

1. THE COBWEB THEOREM

Static analysis tells us that under perfect competition the price and quantity of a good is indicated by the intersection of the supply and demand curves. In terms of Fig. 9, where *DD′* is the demand curve and *SS′* the supply curve, the equilibrium price will be *OP* and the equilibrium quantity *OQ*. On the older definition, this equilibrium is stable, for if price falls to *OP′*, the amount demanded will rise to *OV*, while only *OR* will be supplied. There will thus be an excess demand of *RV* inducing sellers to raise the price and buyers to accept the increase.

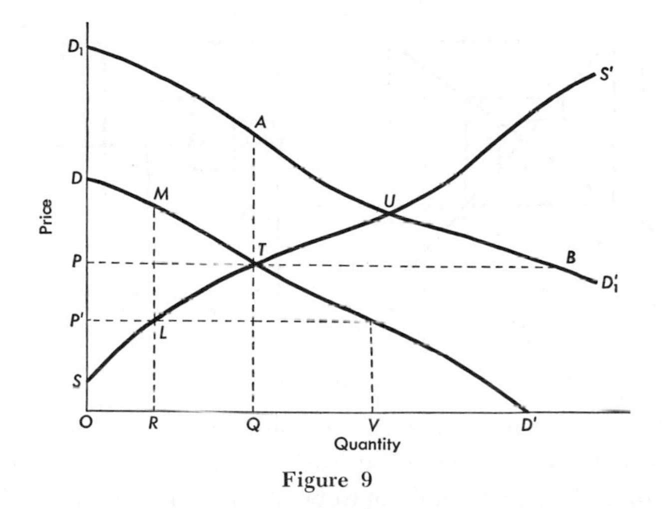

Figure 9

But let us suppose our commodity is produced in an annual crop as is wheat. Once the crop is planted the supply may be taken as more or less fixed for the year, if we neglect the effects of the weather and the possibility of "ploughing under," i.e., deliberate failure to harvest the grain and bring it to market. A change in price will therefore have no effect on the magnitude of this year's total supply. It will, however, affect next year's supply since a low price may induce farmers to plant less for next year. Let us represent the effect of price on next year's supply by the curve SS' in Fig. 10a. Then with a price of OP_1 in the first year, OQ_2 of wheat will be supplied in the second year. Let DD' be the ordinary demand curve for wheat which we assume not to change over the years considered. Then with OQ_2 supplied in the second year the crop will be sold at price OP_2. At this lower price less wheat will be planted, and so the third year's crop will be given by OQ_3. With this quantity, price will rise to OP_3, and so on. The path of the annual price-quantity positions is traced by the thick cobweblike line connecting them, which is drawn in the diagram only for the first five years.

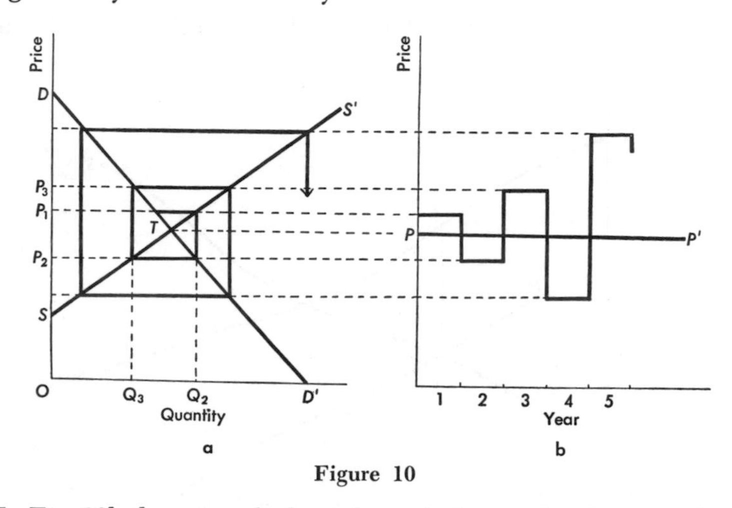

Figure 10

In Fig. 10b the price of wheat through time under these conditions is shown. A similar diagram can easily be drawn to show the quantities sold. The important thing to be observed is that in Fig. 10a the cobweb line keeps moving further and further away from the point of equilibrium, T. In other words, each year the price and quantity sold move further away from the equilibrium price-quantity combination. This can be seen clearly in Fig. 10b, where the equilibrium price is shown by the height of the line PP' above the x axis. *Each year prices start by moving in the equilibrium direction but overshoot it in ever increasing amounts.* It follows that the equilibrium at T in this case is unstable.

We can show that this is because the demand curve is steeper than the supply curve throughout and that in the reverse case the equilibrium will be stable. This alternative case is illustrated in Fig. 11 where, beginning at point *R*, price and quantity move ever

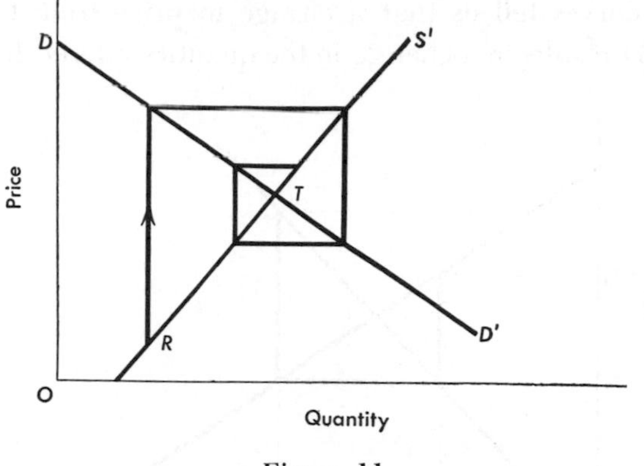

Figure 11

closer to point *T*, the point of equilibrium. Finally, Fig. 12 shows that if the supply and demand curves are both straight lines and if they are both equally steep, a departure from equilibrium to any point like *P* will set things waltzing around the point of equilibrium, *T*, indefinitely, along the path *PWRQ*.

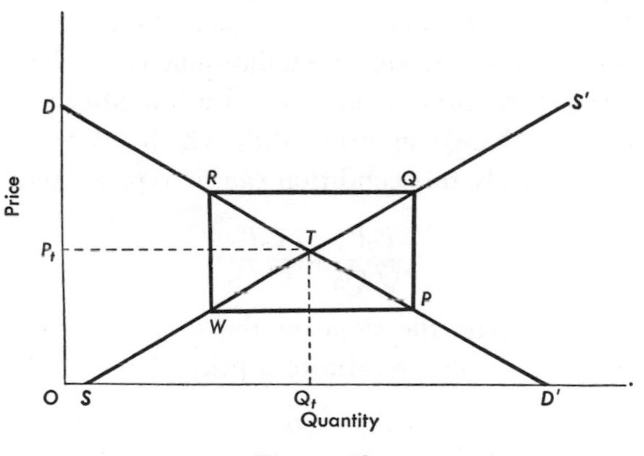

Figure 12

Let us examine the relationship between the slope of the curves and the stability of equilibrium. The DD' curve in our diagrams is really a price-reaction curve, for given a quantity it indicates what price will be. Similarly, the SS' curve is a quantity-reaction curve, showing for any price what quantity will be in the following year. These two curves tell us that a change in price from OP_1 to OP_2 (see Fig. 13) results in a change in the quantity offered from OQ_2 in

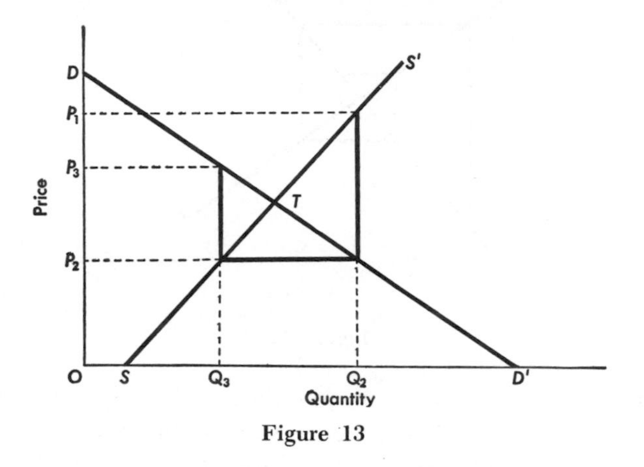

Figure 13

year 2 to OQ_3 in year 3 so that price changes from OP_2 in year 2 to OP_3 in year 3. A stable movement toward equilibrium requires that the second price change be smaller than the first, so that there are successively smaller and smaller price fluctuations until, when they die out altogether, a position of equilibrium is reached. Thus the price change P_2P_3 resulting from the fall in quantity Q_2Q_3 must be smaller than the change in price P_1P_2 which caused that fall in quantity. Symbolically this condition can be represented as

$$\frac{P_2P_3}{Q_2Q_3} < \frac{P_1P_2}{Q_2Q_3}.$$

P_1P_2/Q_2Q_3 is, however, the slope of the supply curve,[1] as can be seen from Fig. 13, being the ratio of a price change to the quantity

[1] We can neglect the sign of this expression since we are really concerned only with the steepness of the curve.

change it causes. Similarly, P_2P_3/Q_2Q_3 is the slope of the demand curve, being the ratio between a price change and the quantity change causing it. The stability condition is thus that the average slope of the demand curve must be less than that of the supply curve.

For our purposes the main conclusion to be drawn from this discussion of the cobweb theorem is that the stability of a static equilibrium situation may very well depend on dynamic considerations. In this case a one-year lag in wheat supply in conjunction with the shape of the supply and demand curves makes all the difference. For the reader to see why we refer to point T in the diagrams as a position of equilibrium he need only consider what would happen if point T were somehow attained. With a price OP_t (Fig. 12) it would pay to produce OQ_t the next year, so that price would then again be OP_t, and supply the year after would continue at OQ_t. This applies in all the cases shown in the diagrams of this section and has no direct connection with the problem of whether or not T is a stable position.

2. *THE SPEED OF ADJUSTMENT AND STABILITY* [2]

We have already seen that the speed of reaction of relevant factors may be very important to the stability of an equilibrium situation. A once-and-for-all general fall in wage rates may increase employment and so act to stabilize prices if employers react to the fall in costs quickly, hiring extra workers and increasing the demand for capital equipment before the wage fall can effectively reduce demand through a fall in workers' purchasing power.

In general terms we can consider the dynamic problem of the stability of equilibrium by analyzing the speed with which the various elements in the situation react. We now define equilibrium

[2] The present section is largely based on Professor Reder's exposition in *Studies in the Theory of Welfare Economics,* Part II (Columbia University Press, New York, 1947). Ultimately like most of this chapter it is based on Samuelson's work.

to be stable if at least fairly small departures from it will automatically be eliminated or become negligible in the calculable future.

The possibility of analyzing stability of equilibrium exclusively in terms of the speed and nature of the reaction of the relevant factors can be clearly shown by a completely trivial example. Suppose we somehow know that the equilibrium price of wheat is $1.90 a bushel, that if the price falls below $1.90 it will rise at the rate of 5 cents per week until it reaches the equilibrium price and then stop, and, finally, that if the price of wheat rises above $1.90 it will fall at the rate of 1 cent per week until equilibrium is reached. We can then say that, if for some reason the price were to fall to $1.65 per bushel, it would be back at its equilibrium value in five weeks and that the price equilibrium is stable.

We can readily see that the equilibrium will be unstable if any of the following conditions exist:

a. The price reacts by moving in the wrong direction, e.g., it falls when it is below its equilibrium level.
b. The price fails to move if it is above or below its equilibrium level.
c. The price moves in the right direction but does not move quite far enough to get back to equilibrium.
d. Price moves in the right direction but it does not stop at the equilibrium point, and its overshooting produces unstable oscillations.

In general, the price movement cannot be expected to take place at a constant rate such as five units per week. Instead we may expect a pattern of movement something like that shown by the curve *PP′* in Fig. 14. The price will perhaps change more rapidly the further away it is from its equilibrium level, so that the speed of adjustment slows down as the equilibrium level is approached. This might occur because a large excess demand causes a rapid rise in price (sellers react strongly to the favorable market and buyers become panicky at the thought of not being able to get the good) and a

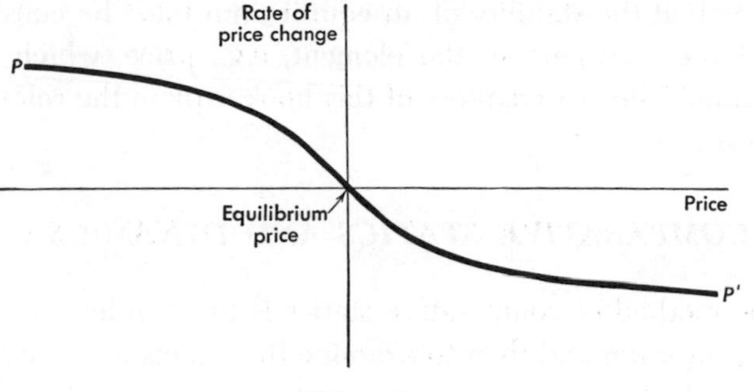

Figure 14

smaller excess demand causes a less rapid rise. This would mean roughly that, if the equilibrium price were *OP* (Fig. 15) and for some reason price fell to *OR*, then the path of adjustment would have the form *RR′*, so that price would approach its equilibrium level, though never quite reaching it. Whether one prefers to call

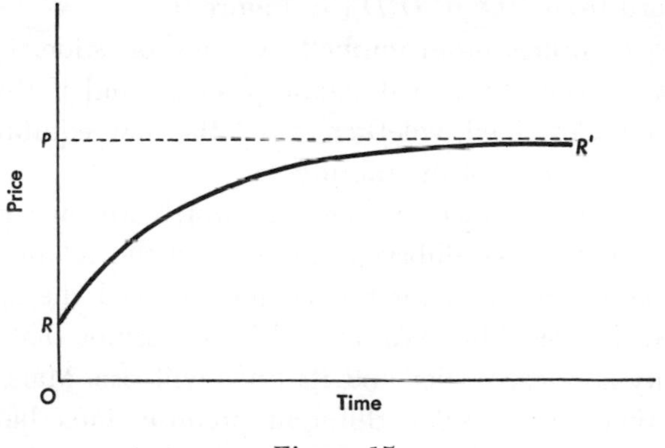

Figure 15

this equilibrium stable or not is a matter of taste. We might in this case prefer to speak of an equilibrium price *neighborhood* and say that all prices close to *OP* are in equilibrium, rather than referring to a unique equilibrium price. Usually, however, this is called a stable case and we shall adhere to this usage.

We see that the stability of an equilibrium must be considered in terms of the time path of the element, e.g., price, which is out of equilibrium. The last chapters of this book explain the relevant tools of analysis.

3. *COMPARATIVE STATICS AND DYNAMICS*

The method of comparative statics is to consider a situation of static equilibrium and then to examine the effects of a once-and-for-all change in one or more of the conditions determining that equilibrium. Thus the analysis of the preceding chapter—of the effects of the appearance of an excess supply of some commodity—involves such a problem. Again, if we take a situation of supply and demand equilibrium under conditions of perfect competition, typical questions of comparative statics are what will happen to the equilibrium if a permanent tax is levied on the commodity, or what will happen if a new use is discovered for the good so that the demand curve shifts upward from DD' to $D_1D'_1$ in Figure 9.

This at once brings in an implicit dynamic question. For, as we have just seen, stability is a dynamic problem and if the demand curve shifts as described, whether or not the new equilibrium will be attained is a matter of its stability.

Now, as we have shown, one way in which we may investigate the stability of these equilibria is to examine the relationships between the excess demand for the commodity and the speed with which price changes. Thus Walras and Hicks assume that whenever a commodity is in excess demand its price will rise. Marshall, however, sometimes employed a different premise, interchanging the role of price and quantity in the Walras-Hicks assumption. We can state it as follows: Let OR (Fig. 9) be any *non*equilibrium quantity of a good. Then the price RL at which sellers are willing to supply that quantity must be different from the price, RM, which buyers are willing to pay for it. We may call the difference between the buyer's price, RM, and the seller's price, RL, the "excess (demand) price." Marshall assumes that whenever there is an excess (demand) price, supplies of the good will increase, the argument being that at the higher price offered by buyers it will pay the sellers to offer more for sale.

All this means that, if (Fig. 9) the demand curve shifts upward from DD' to $D_1D'_1$, so that T becomes a position of both excess demand, TB, and of excess (demand) price, TA, Walras and Hicks assume that then price will rise, while Marshall assumes that quantity will increase. In a situation such as that shown in the diagram this makes no difference because the new equilibrium position, U, involves increases in both price and quantity, and if the Walrasian or the Marshallian assumptions are stretched to imply that (as in Figs. 14 and 15) price and quantity neither stop short of nor overshoot their equilibrium values, the new equilibrium situation may be expected to turn out to be stable on either premise. In this case a comparison of the equilibrium situations T and U is all that is wanted for a static analysis, since both the price and the quantity will move from position T to position U.

There are, however, some cases in which the two assumptions do not give the same results, that is, situations which on Walras' assumption would lead to different consequences from those which would result if we took Marshall's assumption.

Thus let us suppose that the supply curve SS' (Fig. 16) is downward sloping and that the demand curve DD' slopes downward more steeply, so that they intersect at T. Let us assume that the demand curve now shifts to $D_1D'_1$, so that the new point of intersection is U. Now following the shift in the demand curve, there is both excess demand (TB) and excess (demand) price (TA). But the new point of intersection involves a larger quantity and a *lower* price than does point T. Thus in a Marshallian world U might well be a point of stable equilibrium, since when output is at OQ so that there is excess (demand) price, output will increase and thus move toward point U. In a Walrasian world, on the other hand, since at price OP there is an excess demand, price will rise further so that the price-quantity situation will move away from, and not toward, point U. In such a world U will not be a point of stable equilibrium. In a

Walrasian economy, therefore, the ordinary approach of comparative statics, a comparison of the point of intersection before and after the shift in demand would not tell us what is in fact likely to happen. The method would, however, continue to give us satisfactory results in a society in which the Marshallian premise was valid. Which of the two assumptions is in fact valid can of course only be determined by an empirical examination of the particular problem in question.

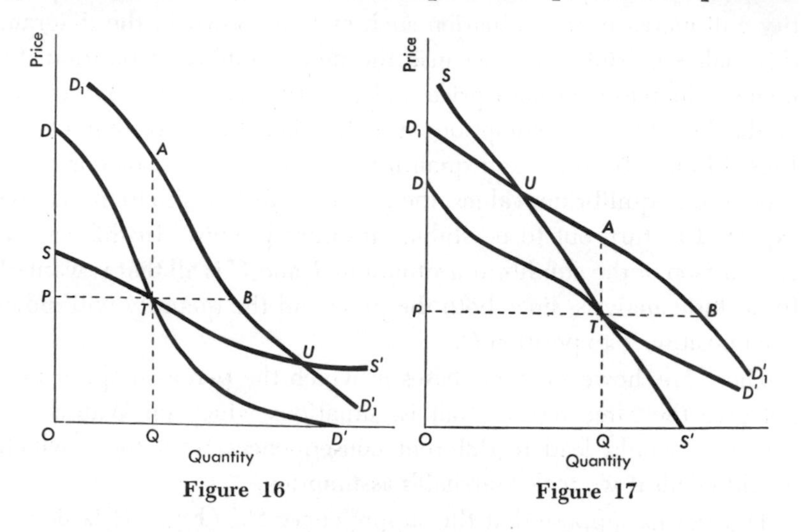

Figure 16

Figure 17

In Figure 17 a supply and demand situation is illustrated where the comparative statics analysis of the effects of a shift in the demand curve from DD' to $D_1D'_1$ may give stable results in a Walrasian world but not in a Marshallian world. The reader may easily verify this for himself.

The economic interpretation of the Walrasian and the Marshallian stability conditions and their relation to the situations in Figures 16 and 17 merits some clarification. Since a positively sloping supply curve makes for stability in both cases one might expect that the greatest departure from this slope, i.e., the most negatively sloping supply curve relative to the demand curve (Fig. 17) will always be the more unstable. Though we have seen this surmise to be incorrect we shall find that it has nevertheless an element of validity.

First we must distinguish between two types of negatively sloping supply curve, which Professor Viner has labeled backward rising and forward falling:

i. *A backward rising supply curve* slopes negatively because a rise in the price of the commodity supplied makes the supplier wealthier (income effect) and so permits him to keep more of his commodity for himself. The standard illustration is the decreasing supply of labor which often accompanies rising wages presumably because workers can then better afford leisure. This negative slope then represents a response of the quantity supplied to a change in price, and so when the supply curve is of this variety any movement toward equilibrium must involve a mechanism which pushes price in the right direction.

ii. *A forward falling supply curve* has a negative slope because there are in the industry economies of large scale production. Here in the short run a *rise* in price may be needed to induce firms to expand their outputs (positively sloping short run supply curve). But when enterprises do all expand, businessmen will find that their costs have fallen and so (perfect) competition will force upon them a corresponding reduction in their selling price. Thus a forward falling supply curve represents a *long run* response of price to an expansion of output. Here then, any equilibrating mechanism must be able to move quantity in the right direction.

Now a Walrasian world is one in which *price* adjusts in response to disequilibrium. In other words the Walrasian dynamic mechanism can produce a movement along a backward rising supply curve. Similarly, the Marshallian premise that quantity adjusts when there is disequilibrium applies to a forward falling supply curve. We saw earlier that Figure 16 represents a stable Marshallian situation or an unstable Walrasian situation. It follows that it is a stable situation if the supply curve is forward falling (so that the Marshallian mechanism applies) or it is an unstable situation if the supply curve is backward rising. The reverse holds for Figure 17.

Note now that in a backward rising supply situation price and not quantity is the independent variable so that, by convention, the curves should in this case be redrawn with the axes reversed—price on the horizontal axis and quantity on the vertical axis. By replotting the figures in this way the reader can easily see that in the revised Figure 16 the slope of the supply curve will be greater than that of the demand curve—the replotting will have reversed the relative slopes of the two curves. The same phenomenon occurs in replotting Figure 17. The reason is simple—if the slope of quantity on price in the original Figure 16, PS/PT, is small, its reciprocal, the slope of price on quantity in the redrawn diagram, PT/PS, will be large. We conclude that when the supply curve has a negative slope because it is forward falling (Marshallian case) so that the diagrams do not require redrawing, the stable situation is represented by Figure 1 in which the supply curve has the relatively small negative slope. On the other hand when the negatively sloping supply curve is backward rising (Walrasian) the diagrams must be redrawn so that now it is in Figure 17 (the backward rising stable case) that the supply curve will have the relatively small negative slope. We can see now the element of validity in the idea that even with a backward rising supply curve in its Walrasian world stability requires that the supply curve depart relatively little from a stable positive slope.

4. THE CORRESPONDENCE PRINCIPLE

We see that before we can be confident that the use of the method of comparative statics is valid for the examination of any particular problem, this problem must first be subjected to at least some sort of dynamic analysis.

Professor Samuelson has carried the argument further and has shown that where our knowledge of the relevant curves and functions is inadequate to enable us to describe the equilibrium position directly, we can, on the dynamic hypothesis that the situation is stable, derive meaningful results in comparative statics. Thus often ". . . we find ourselves confronted with this paradox: in order for the comparative statics analysis to yield fruitful results, we must first develop a theory of dynamics." [3]

Samuelson has called this correspondence between meaningful results in comparative statics and the dynamic assumption and analysis of stability the *correspondence principle.*

A fairly trivial example of the results which can be obtained in this way is the statement that in a *stable* Walrasian world price must rise when demand rises, and the demand curve will *not* have a steeper negative slope than does the supply curve. We know this is so from our dynamic analysis, for if, as in Figure 16, demand did have the steeper slope, we have just seen that the Walras dynamic assumption implies that equilibrium will be unstable. In sum, the correspondence principle together with the dynamic stability assumption and the Walrasian assumption that price will rise when and only when there is an excess demand, permit us to deduce that the supply-demand situation will either be as depicted in Figure 9 or as in Figure 17. Similarly, in a Marshallian world the correspondence principle precludes the situation in Figure 17 but not the one in Figure 16.

[3] Samuelson, *Foundations of Economic Analysis,* pp. 262–263 (Harvard University Press, Cambridge, Mass., 1947). See also Chapter Sixteen, Section 6 below.

Part III

PROCESS ANALYSIS

Chapter Eight

PERIOD ANALYSIS

1. WHY PERIOD ANALYSIS?

Fundamentally the economist is concerned with quantities and their prices. These quantities may be either *flows* through time, e.g., the time rate of labor input of a firm, or *stocks* at a moment of time [1] such as the amount of capital existing at any given date. Correspondingly the prices may be the price of a flow, for example, the sales price of a commodity which is in continuous production, or the price of a stock at a given moment such as the value of land.

Since many prices and flows may be changing continuously, it would seem that economic analysis should be in terms of time rates of flow at each and every moment of time, treating the economic process as continuous through time. This conclusion, however, is not inevitable, and for many purposes it is preferable to assume that the variables considered change discontinuously, so that instead of talking of a rate of flow at a point of time we talk of the *amount* (used, produced, sold, etc.) during a *period* of time. If we do this, then we have the great advantage of being able to construct a step-by-step analysis of economic changes through time.

To illustrate this, consider a firm which produces, say, radios. We choose a period such that no changes in output are made during its length. Then for any such unit of time the number of radios produced depends on the decision as to output at the beginning of the

[1] See the discussion of stocks and flows in Chapter Five, Section 3.

period. At the end of the period, the firm considers the results of the period and decides how many radios to produce next period. Thus we can investigate the determination of the output of the firm by considering the plans which are made at the beginning of each period on the basis of the results of the last period and the expectations of the future they give rise to and by considering the putting into effect of the plans during the period. What is done during the period depends on the output plans made at the beginning, and these in turn depend on the results of previous periods.

In this way a step-by-step analysis is possible. This is known as period analysis. We may define it crudely as the splitting of time into periods such that, apart from exogenous changes, the events of any period can be explained with reference to the events of previous periods.

Professor Lindahl has concisely stated the procedure of period analysis as follows: [2]

> Starting from the plans and the external conditions valid at the initial point of time, we have first to deduce the development that will be the result of these data for a certain period forward during which no relevant changes in the plans are assumed to occur. Next we have to investigate how far the development during this first period—involving as it must various surprises for the economic subjects—will force them to revise their plans of action for the future, the principles for such a revision being assumed to be included in the data of the problem. And since on this basis the development during the second period is determined in the same manner as before, fresh deductions must be made concerning the plans for the third period, and so on.

The concepts of *ex ante* and *ex post*, which we owe to Professor Myrdal, are fundamental for period analysis. They can best be explained by giving some examples. *Ex ante* sales are the sales expected for a period by sellers, while *ex post* sales are the actual sales of that period. *Ex ante* output is the output planned for a period, while

[2] Erik Lindahl, *Studies in the Theory of Money and Capital*, pp. 38–39. Copyright 1939, by George Allen and Unwin, Ltd., London. Reproduced by permission of George Allen and Unwin, Ltd., London, and Rinehart and Co., New York.

ex post output is the realized output of that period. *Ex ante* saving for a period is the saving intended, and *ex post* saving is the saving actually achieved. Thus *ex ante* can mean "expected," "intended," or "planned," while *ex post* means "actual" or "realized." Professor Marschak has used the terms "prospective" and "retrospective" with the same meaning.

The question now arises whether the concept of *ex ante* is realistic. When it refers to what is *expected* its usefulness is self-evident. Sellers and purchasers cannot decide upon their actions without considering what may happen in the future. This is not to say that a seller or a purchaser necessarily has unique, single-valued expectations, so that, for example, our radio manufacturer expects to sell 500 radios in the next period no more and no less, but we may be able to say that he acts *as if* he considers the sale of 500 units the most probable. This "as if" clause is of great importance in economic theory. We do not suppose that a producer consciously endeavors to equate marginal revenue and marginal cost; clearly, he may never have heard of them. We only postulate that he acts *as if* he did in that he seeks to find that price which will maximize his profit.[3]

When *ex ante* refers to what is *planned* or *intended*, the meaningfulness of the idea that what happens during a period is merely the carrying out of certain plans formed at the beginning of the period has been explained by Professor Lindahl: [4]

> In some important cases the planning is quite obvious. The state and other public bodies furnish us in their budgets with examples of definite plans. Private enterprises usually outline similar plans for their activity though they are generally not divulged; first there is a general plan for a comparatively long period of time and then there are more detailed plans for the immediate future. Even individual consumers do not infrequently draw up some plans for their economic behaviour during a longer or shorter period. In certain other cases our assumption that economic actions are the result of planning activity may seem more difficult to apply. It can hardly be pretended that every individual has a clear con-

[3] See Lindahl, "Professor Ohlin om Dynamisk Teori," *Ekonomisk Tidskrift,* p. 243, 1941.

[4] Lindahl, *Studies, op. cit.*, pp. 36–37.

ception of the economic actions that he is going to perform in a future period. Nevertheless, in the greater number of cases it will certainly be found that underlying such actions there are habits and persistent tendencies which have a definite and calculable character comparable to the explicit plans already mentioned. We may accordingly without danger proceed to generalize our notion of "plans," so that they will include such actions. Plans are thus the explicit expression of the economic motives of man, as they become evident in his economic actions.

Having shown that the use of periods to which the *ex ante* values relate is not only permissible but also has a positive advantage in that it is a reasonable approximation to reality, we may add another point. The statistics [5] we have of flows in the economy do not relate to time rates but to amounts during a period. We do not know the *ex post* rate of exports at three o'clock on February 3, but we do know the *ex post* exports of the whole of February. Our knowledge of much of the economic system is discontinuous, so that an analysis which is discontinuous with regard to time is obviously well suited for application.

2. *THE DISEQUILIBRIUM AND THE EQUILIBRIUM METHOD*

In the use of period analysis there are two possibilities open to us regarding the treatment of prices. We can either assume that prices are fixed by sellers at the beginning of the period or we can assume that they are determined during the period by the interaction of supply and demand.

The first alternative has been called the *disequilibrium method*.[6] In the interval between two periods, sellers, on the basis of *ex post* results of previous periods, decide what price they will charge and announce it. Knowing prices, buyers then decide how much they

[5] All statistics of trade, production, income, employment, prices, etc., are of course *ex post* since they tell us what has actually happened, not what was planned or expected. We could obtain *ex ante* figures only by asking people what they *intend* to produce, sell, etc., during the next week or month.

[6] Lindahl, *op. cit.*, p. 60.

wish to buy. During the period the plans of buyers, producers, and sellers are, as far as is possible, carried out.[7] At the end of the period, sellers find out the *ex post* results (which may turn out to involve excess supplies or demands, hence disequilibrium) and make their plans for the next period, and so on.

The second alternative is called the *equilibrium method.* (The term refers to Marshall's market equilibrium [8] and does not mean that there is complete equilibrium in the sense of self-perpetuation of the situation.) At the beginning of a period, producers decide on their output on the basis of the demand they expect. In the period, production takes place and prices are reached which equate supply and demand. There is no necessity for us to regard supply as identical with the amount produced so that the supply schedule is totally inelastic, since a variation of inventories is possible. At the end of the period producers compare the *ex post* results of the period with the *ex ante* values and make their plans for the next period, and so on.

In order to make the relationship between these two methods clearer we shall use a diagram showing conditions in one market.[9] We assume, in order to get a determinate demand curve, that prices in all other commodity markets are constant. Then for the period we are considering we can draw a demand curve *DD′*. Its position and shape will depend upon the income consumers expect in this period, the prices of other commodities, and the relation between the price they expect in this period and the prices they expect in future periods. We can also draw a supply curve, *SS′* (the Marshallian short-period supply curve), showing how much will be produced in the period [10] at each price expected by sellers at the beginning of the period. Thus if producers expect a price of *OR*, output will be *OM*.

If we are using the disequilibrium method we can say that at the

[7] At the prices fixed.
[8] Where price adjusts itself so that the market is cleared.
[9] For a consumer good.
[10] We assume here that production plans are realized, i.e., *ex ante* output equals *ex post* output.

beginning of the period producers fix the price at *OR* and plan an output of *OM* which constitutes *ex ante* supply. Consumers learn the price and plan to buy *ON*, *ex ante* demand. During the period *OM* will be produced but, say, *ON* will be sold, the difference being made up by reduction of inventories. *Ex ante* demand exceeded *ex ante* supply by *MN; ex post* demand and supply are equal at *ON*. (By definition *ex post* demand equals *ex post* supply, since purchases are necessarily equal to sales.)

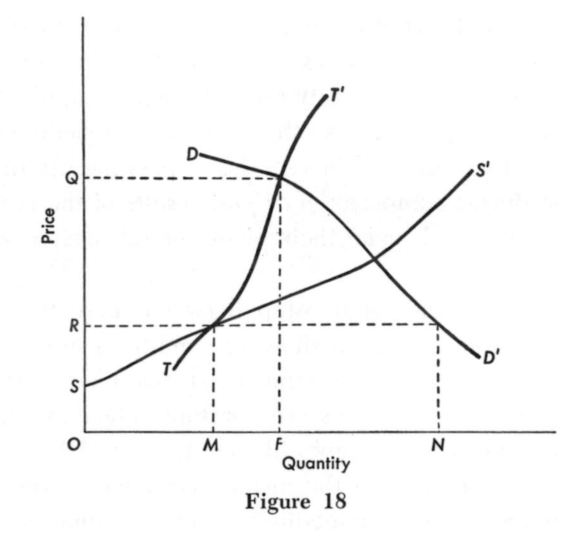

Figure 18

If we are using the equilibrium method we can say that at the beginning of the period producers expect a price of *OR*, and so plan to produce *OM*. In order to find out what price will be reached we must draw in a sales curve, *TT′*, showing how much will be sold at each price once output is fixed at *OM*.[11] We have drawn this on the assumption that producers plan to sell from inventories if price turns out to be higher than they expected, while if it is lower they prefer to add some of the period's output to inventories rather than

[11] Analogous to Marshall's market-supply curve. It will, of course, show that at a price of *OR, OM* will be sold. If price exceeds *OR*, sales will exceed output, the difference constituting a drawing-down of stocks of the product.

sell the whole output at a loss. The price will be *OQ*, and *ex post* demand (equals *ex post* supply) will be *OF*. Inventories will be reduced by *MF*.

It is evident from this that the disequilibrium method in effect assumes an infinitely elastic sales curve,[12] while the equilibrium method assumes one of less than infinite elasticity.[13] They are thus both special cases of a more general case. In spite of this, however, it is important to distinguish between them since they differ in two important respects. First, with the disequilibrium method any disappointment of expectations or nonrealization of plans, that is, any divergence of *ex post* magnitudes from *ex ante* magnitudes, will be entirely a matter of quantities not of prices.[14] With the equilibrium method, on the other hand, both quantities *and* prices may diverge from their *ex ante* values. Secondly, with the equilibrium method *ex ante* demand, supply, etc., must be treated as *schedules,* not as amounts, except on special assumptions mentioned below. With the disequilibrium method, since the price is fixed at the beginning of the period and made known to buyers, we are concerned with one point on each schedule and hence can treat *ex ante* variables as amounts.[15]

In order to see this last point more clearly, let us suppose that we are analyzing developments in a market with the use of the equilibrium method. Now if for any period buyers expect a price of $1 and plan to buy 1,000 units so that *ex ante* demand is $1,000 and if sellers expect to sell 900 units at $1.20 so that *ex ante* supply is $1,080, then we obviously have not got enough information to tell us what the *ex post* results of the period will be. We need to know

[12] Assuming that inventories are large. In the extreme case where there are no inventories the sales curve will be a point, and an excess of *ex ante* demand over *ex ante* supply will be turned into an *ex post* equality by an enforced reduction of demand due to nonavailability of the goods.

[13] In the extreme case where there are no inventories the sales curve will be a vertical line, and an excess of *ex ante* demand over *ex ante* supply will be turned into an *ex post* equality by an excess of price over what sellers expected.

[14] T. Palander, "On the Concepts and Methods of the Stockholm School," *International Economic Papers,* No. 3, p. 37.

[15] *Ibid.,* pp. 36–37.

the schedules of demand and supply to determine what price will be reached.

If, in the equilibrium method, we make the special assumption that demands and supplies are fixed in real or in money terms, that is, that the schedules have zero or unit elasticity, then it is obvious that in this special case we can treat *ex ante* demand, supply, etc., as an amount. This case and the disequilibrium method are much simpler to handle since we can express, for example, *ex ante* demand as so many dollars or so many units of the commodity.

Another advantage of the disequilibrium method is its realism as regards imperfect competition. Sellers do in fact offer certain prices and only change their offers discontinuously. An analysis of the credit market, on the other hand, would seem to demand use of the equilibrium method, since prices there move more or less continuously.

3. *THE LENGTH OF THE PERIOD*

The maximum length of the period is dictated by the requirement that a step-by-step analysis shall be possible. This means that all the events of the period must be the putting into effect of plans made at the beginning of the period, which, in its turn, is made with reference to the *ex post* results of previous periods. Thus the period must be so short that no changes in plans are made during it.

Looking at the matter the other way round, the period must not be so long that what happens toward its beginning affects what happens toward its end. If, for example, with the equilibrium method, we take the period too long, then the price reached at the beginning of the period may affect incomes and hence demand and price in the later part of the period, so that the step-by-step analysis from one period to the next is impossible.

A period must thus end when plans are changed. This does not necessarily mean that our unit period is the planning period, i.e., the length of time forward for which plans are made, though we may make that assumption if we wish. It means that it is the *plan revision period,* i.e., the interval between successive reconsideration of plans. Now plans will be revised when new information is obtained,[16] and this is of two main kinds, apart from exogenous happenings:

a. the ascertainment of results *ex post* of the period just elapsed
b. the fixing of new prices by sellers.

Note that (b) will, however, go together with (a), for any offer of a certain price will be made with respect to the experiences of the recent past as ascertained in the sellers' *ex post* calculations for recent periods. Thus the period ends when sellers and buyers calculate what has happened and revise, make, or confirm their plans for the coming period. In the disequilibrium method prices are assumed to be announced by sellers before the new period begins.[17]

The foregoing discussion raises an important problem. How do we meet the difficulty that the length of the period will differ between different parts of the economy? A farmer may reconsider his plans yearly, a milliner may reconsider hers every autumn and spring, while a wage earner will reconsider his weekly.[18] In order to obtain a unit period out of all this diversity we have to take it as the greatest length of time which will divide into the various periods of the different parts of the economy, i.e., the highest common factor of their periods. In our example this would be a week.

It is at once evident that this procedure will make applications of period analysis very complicated, so in many cases it may be worth while to do some violence to reality and assume that the periods of all the different parts of the economy are of the same length and are coincident in time. It should be noticed that this does not exclude our considering different speeds of reaction to changes, for we could, for example, say that while *A*'s plan for period t depends upon his *ex post* results in period $t-1$, *B*'s plan depends upon *B*'s *ex post* results in $t-2$ and $t-3$.

[16] Ignoring any spontaneous changes in attitude to risk, etc.

[17] The last few paragraphs are largely based on Brems, "Om Stockholmsskolens Begreber og Metoder," Sec. I, *Ekonomisk Tidskrift,* 1944.

[18] If his wage is the same he will probably not change his plan.

4. DEVELOPMENTS WITHIN A PERIOD

A theoretical analysis with the help of the period construction falls into two parts. First there is the problem of the formation of plans and expectations, i.e., the relation between the *ex ante* magnitudes for any one period and the *ex post* magnitudes of previous periods. Any general treatment of this is, of course, impossible, for there are a multitude of possible relations we could choose. Various simple treatments of expectations have been used by different authors in constructing models, for example, of inventory cycles.

The second part of period analysis is the relation between the *ex ante* magnitudes for a period and the resulting *ex post* magnitudes of that period. Professor Lindahl, in his "Algebraic Discussion of the Relations between Some Fundamental Concepts"[19] has given a systematic general treatment, and the reader is referred to that discussion. Here we shall only discuss the matter briefly in terms of the disequilibrium method.

It is obvious that if all plans are realized then *ex post* results will equal the corresponding *ex ante* magnitudes. The conditions for this are twofold. First, plans must be consistent with one another. If, for example, *A* expects to sell 200 units of his product to *B* while *B* plans to buy more or less than 200, then both their plans cannot be realized. Second, technological conditions must be correctly anticipated, for if the harvest turns out to be greater than expected, agricultural output will be greater *ex post* than *ex ante*. If, to take another example, all entrepreneurs together plan to employ more labor than is available, then *ex post* output and factor purchases will be smaller than *ex ante* output and factor purchases. Thus full equilibrium means consistency of all plans and correctness of technological expectations.

[19] Lindahl, *op. cit.*, pp. 74–136. The analysis lacks generality on one point, as Bent Hansen has pointed out in his book *A Study in the Theory of Inflation* (Allen and Unwin, London, 1951). Lindahl assumes that all purchase plans are realized, which implies that there are always large inventories and that unemployed labor is always available.

Let us now consider the effects of inconsistency (incongruence) between the *ex ante* magnitudes in a simple system[20] where there are only four enterprises: a producer of consumption goods, a producer of raw materials for consumption goods, a producer of capital goods, and a producer of raw materials for capital goods. It is evident that in this system *ex ante* divergences between purchases and sales may occur between any of the following pairs of magnitudes, while *ex post* they will necessarily be equal:

a. Consumption purchases and sales of consumption goods
b. Investment purchases and sales of capital goods
c. Raw material purchases and raw material sales
   1. For consumption goods
   2. For capital goods
d. Expenditure on factors and income of factors.

In order to see how an *ex ante* divergence is turned into an *ex post* equality we shall take each of these in turn. We do this on the assumption that there are large inventories and plenty of unemployed factors so that purchase plans can all be realized.[21] If there is an *ex ante* divergence in

a. Sales and purchases of consumer's goods, *ex post* sales of consumption goods will differ from *ex ante* sales, the difference being unintended investment or disinvestment of consumption good inventories
b. Sales and purchases of capital goods, then *ex post* sales of capital goods will differ from *ex ante* sales, the difference being unintended investment or disinvestment of capital good stocks
c. Raw material purchases and sales, then the same applies
d. Expenditure on and income of factors, then owners of the factors will earn more or less income than they had expected.

[20] Our presentation follows that of Palander, *op. cit.*, pp. 40 ff.
[21] This assumption is also made by Lindahl (see footnote 19).

In cases (a), (b), and (c) the unintended investment or disinvestment will mean that *ex post* investment will be greater or less respectively than *ex ante* investment. In case (d), the unexpected income increase or decrease will mean an excess or deficiency of savings *ex post* over savings *ex ante,* since savings *ex post* equal income *ex post* minus consumption *ex post,* and the latter, by assumption, is the same *ex post* as *ex ante.*

5. THE PROBLEM OF AGGREGATES

It is evident that if there are n markets then there will be n conditions for equilibrium, i.e., of congruency between $2n$ sets of plans, even if all technological expectations prove to be correct. In order to make analysis sufficiently simple for us to be able to handle it, we therefore have to lump together different markets. Thus we may talk of the market for consumption goods in general instead of the thousand and one markets for different consumption goods. If, then, we assume that *ex ante* demand and supply in this "aggregate" market are equal, there may well be substantial excess demands *ex ante* for some particular consumer goods if excess supplies *ex ante* of others exist. Hence our aggregative analysis ignores much that is important, and we must bear its limitations in mind.

In order to provide an important example of analysis which may be misleading because the aggregating process has been carried too far, we shall see how much difference it makes whether we lump things into two markets (a market for all currently produced goods together and a market for all factors together) or into one market. If we do the former, we can say that equilibrium exists if (a) *ex ante* demand and supply are equal in the market for currently produced goods, and (b) if *ex ante* demand and supply are equal in the market for factors. This is a double condition.

On the other hand, if we lump goods and services together with factors into only one market, we get a single equilibrium condition, namely the requirement that *ex ante* Investment equals *ex ante*

Saving. The relation between this single condition and the double condition can be seen from the following identity which relates to *ex ante* magnitudes.[22]

$$\text{Investment} - \text{Saving} \equiv (\text{Demand for Goods–Supply of Goods})^{23} + (\text{Demand for Factors–Supply of Factors}).^{24}$$

This states merely that total excess demand can be divided into excess demand for goods and excess demand for factors. In the terminology of Bent Hansen, who extended and applied this analysis: [25]

$$\text{Investment} - \text{Saving} = \text{Goods Gap} + \text{Factor Gap}.$$

The double condition for equilibrium is that both the Goods Gap and the Factor Gap shall be zero. We can now see that fulfillment of this double requirement necessarily means that Investment *ex ante* equals Saving *ex ante*. On the other hand fulfillment of the single condition, i.e., *ex ante* equality of Investment and Saving, does not guarantee equilibrium in the Goods and Factor Markets.

Suppose, for instance, that *ex ante* Investment equals *ex ante* Saving and that there is a positive Goods Gap offset by an equally large negative Factor Gap. Then *ex post,* firms will sell more than they had expected, running down stocks below the intended level to the extent of the unexpected sales of Goods. This reduction of

[22] The discussion is based on Grünbaum, "Inkongruente Forventninger og Begrebet Monetaer Ligevaegt" *Nationaløkonomisk Tidsskrift,* 1945 and Palander, *op. cit.* See also E. Schneider, "Saving and Investment in a Closed Economy," *International Economic Papers* no. 1, and Lindahl, *op. cit.*, p. 127. For a derivation of this identity see Turvey, "Some Notes on Multiplier Theory," *American Economic Review,* June 1953, p. 288.

[23] This includes both final goods (i.e., goods bought for Investment or Consumption) and intermediate goods (raw materials).

[24] This includes both contractual purchase of factor services (the rent of land, interest on loans and the wages of labor) and the transfer to households of non-contractual incomes (dividends on stock and withdrawals of profit by owners).

[25] *Op. cit.*

stocks constitutes unintended disinvestment and means that Investment *ex post* will be less than Investment *ex ante* by the amount of these unexpected sales. Thus:

ex ante Investment – *ex post* Investment = Goods Gap.

The negative Factor Gap means that households expect more income from firms (Factor sales) than firms are planning to pay them. On our assumption that purchase plans are always carried out the result of a negative Factor Gap is therefore that the incomes of households are lower than they expected. This will be reflected in their saving which will be lower than planned to the extent of the shortfall of their incomes below expectations. Thus:

ex post Saving – *ex ante* Saving = Factor Gap.

It is clear that a state of affairs where Sales of Goods turn out to exceed expectations while Sales of Factors fall short of expectations is not one of equilibrium. Thus the *ex ante* equality of Investment and Saving is not a sufficient condition for equilibrium.

There is another reason for preferring discussion to be couched in terms of the Factor and Goods Markets. The demand and supply for factors and goods are what we are directly interested in, and savings and investment are only secondary concepts. To quote Professor Ohlin: [26]

> It has thereby been shown that agreement between *planned* saving and *planned* new investment does not in itself determine economic development. It has also become obvious that an excess of planned new investment over planned saving only means that buyers intend to buy more than sellers expect to sell. . . . In these circumstances is there any reason to press the analysis of changes in the demand for consumption and business purposes and the corresponding supplies into the special form: the saving investment relation? Why not *directly* analyse income expectations and the consumption purchases based upon them—the saving decision is the

[26] "Metodfrågor inom den Dynamiska Teorin," *Ekonomisk Tidskrift,* pp. 335–336, 1941.

other side of the coin—and profit expectations and the buying and selling for business purposes based upon them? [27, 28]

The limitations of aggregative anaylsis, of which the above analysis is but one example, must be borne in mind when reading the following chapters which endeavor to show how the methods of period analysis can be used.

[27] For similar views see Schneider, *op. cit.* See also Lindahl, "Professor Ohlin om Dynamisk Teori," *Ekonomisk Tidskrift,* p. 246, 1941.

[28] We can of course, if we wish, use just the saving investment relation if we assume that factor purchase plans and factor sales expectations are consistent. Mr. Harrod does this implicitly.

Appendix to Chapter Eight

A NOTE ON FUNCTIONALS

In discussing the definition of economic dynamics in the introduction to this volume we cited part of a definition adopted by Samuelson from the work of Ragnar Frisch. At that time we found it convenient to omit part of the original statement, but we now quote the whole of it:

. . . "We may say that *a system is dynamical if its behavior over time is determined by functional equations in which 'variables at different points of time' are involved in an 'essential' way.*" [29]

The reader may observe by comparison with the earlier quotation that what has been added is the reference to functional equations. Ideally, for reasons we shall see presently, most dynamic analysis in mathematical form would involve the use of a fairly general type of what is called a functional. The following pages are designed to give an idea of the meaning of functionals in order, by contrast, to show the crude simplifications involved in period analysis. They will also be of use in view of the frequency with which functionals are referred to in the literature.

We shall not here make any attempt to describe how these functionals can be handled because of the relative difficulty of the subject. The theory of functionals is, in any case, in a relatively rudimentary state, and for this reason among others they have not been

[29] Paul A. Samuelson, *Foundations of Economic Analysis,* p. 314 (Harvard University Press, Cambridge, Mass., 1947). (The italics and single quotation marks are Professor Samuelson's.)

widely used in economic analysis. There are, however, some simple types of functionals and special problems in functionals which are relatively easily handled, and these do occasionally appear. In most of these cases the techniques have been developed and used without reference to the general theory of functionals in which we are at present interested.

Examples can be cited of sterile discussions which arose precisely because the *concept* of a functional was not employed by the protagonists.[30] Although these discussions involved attempts to determine *the* correct way in which certain problems could be handled by means of the more widely used mathematical techniques, the problems posed were of such a sort as to make the employment of functionals unavoidable in any *general* solution.

1. FUNCTIONS OF ONE AND OF SEVERAL VARIABLES

Before going into the definition of the functional it is convenient to define a concept with which the reader is likely to have some acquaintance, namely, the ordinary *function.*

We say a variable, y, is a function of another variable, x, [written $y = f(x)$] when the values of x and y are so related that for some values of x the values of y are known. An example of a function is given by the following table:

x	0	3	7	9	881
y	5	0	0	336	5

written $f(0) = 5$, $f(3) = 0$, $f(7) = 0$, $f(9) = 336$, and $f(881) = 5$; i.e., when x is equal to 0, y is equal to 5; when x is equal to 3, y is equal to 0, and so on. Note that this function is only defined for five values of x and we have no information about y when, say, x is equal to 2. Note also that even if y is a function of x there need exist no expression of the sort

$$y = x^2 \quad \text{or} \quad y = \sin(x) \quad \text{or} \quad y = x,$$

[30] See footnote 31.

although in elementary mathematics one usually thinks of a function as a formula like one of these, which gives the relationship between the variables.

Now, for example, the price of cellophane may be taken as a first approximation to be a function of the quantity offered for sale; or the price of cellophane may be taken to be a function of calendar time. Thus we may know that the wholesale price of cellophane of a certain type in New York on February 26, 1922, was $1.75 per pound, while on January 6, 1923, it rose to $2.27, and so on. Note that the price of cellophane as a function of the calendar date is not given for any date such as 1783 before cellophane was invented.

When we have a function of the form $y = f(x)$ we say y is a function of a single variable. y may also be a function of several variables, say x_1, x_2, and x_3 [written $y = f(x_1, x_2, x_3)$]. This will be the case when for some values of x_1, x_2, and x_3 the value of y is completely determined, e.g., if we know that when $x_1 = 5$, $x_2 = 3$, and $x_3 = 779$, $y = 37$, and so forth. Thus the price of cellophane may depend not only upon the quantity of cellophane offered for sale but also on the prices of each of the possible substitutes for cellophane, and it will then be a function of several variables.

2. *FUNCTIONALS*

We may define a *functional* simply as a function of an infinite number of variables. An example of a functional relationship may be developed by an examination of the factors determining the output of shoes today. The magnitude of that output depends not only on how much of various types of work is done today but also on how much and what type of work was done on shoe machinery previously and on how those machines were used or misused previously. That in turn depends on the labor that was put into the mining of coal to produce the steel for the shoe industry, and so on. Thus, today's output of shoes may be said to depend on the magnitude of the various types of input employed every second, indeed every "instant," before today. Even if we are prepared to ignore everything that happened more than twenty years ago, there are still an infinite number of "instants" in twenty years, and current output of shoes is therefore a function of an infinite number of variables.

Let us try and get a somewhat more detailed picture. There is a particular type of functional, which has been called "a function of a line," which is helpful for our purpose. We proceed again with the aid of an example. Picture a ramp of a given length down which a ball is rolled. The length of time which it takes the ball to get down the ramp depends on the shape of the ramp. If, when we look at it from the side the ramp is straight (as shown by line *AB* in Fig. 19), the ball may get down more or less quickly than if the ramp is shaped like *A′B′* in Figure 20. Thus the length of time, *t*, it takes the ball to get down the ramp is a function of the shape of the line *AB*.

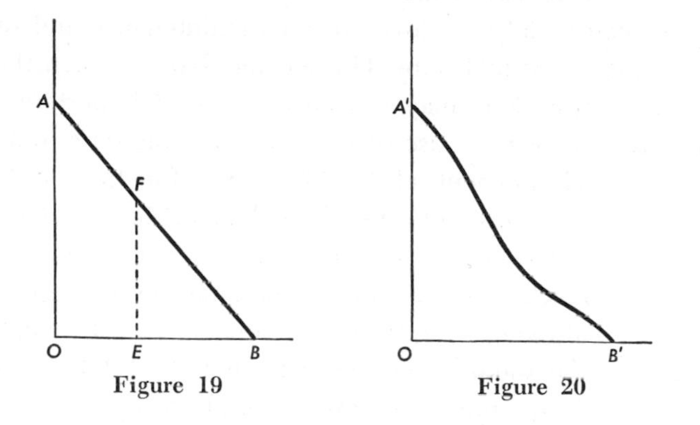

Figure 19 Figure 20

This may also be expressed by saying that the time the ball takes to reach the ground depends on the height, *EF*, of the ramp at every point, *E*, between the point *O* above which the ball starts to roll and the point *B* at which the ramp reaches the ground. Since there are an infinite number of points between *O* and *B*, it follows that this time, *t*, is a functional as we have defined it. Now write y for the height *EF* of the ramp at point *E*, and write x for the distance *OE* of the point *E* from the point *O*. We can then express the height, y, of the ramp at point *E* as a function of the distance, x, of point *E* from point *O* and write $y = f(x)$. But t, the time the ball takes to descend, depends on the value of y for every point E between O and B, that is to say, on the value of y for every x between $x = 0$ and $x = OB$. In other words, t depends on the shape of the line given by $y = f(x)$ between the points $x = O$ and $x = OB$. We express all this symbolically by writing

$$t = F\begin{bmatrix} OB \\ f(x) \\ O \end{bmatrix}.$$

Let us now go back to our problem of today's shoe output and try to formulate that type of relationship more explicitly. Let us say that on May 26, 1950, the condition of equipment in the shoe factory we are considering depends on how intensively that machinery has been used since it was installed on December 27, 1941, and on the number of hours that was devoted to its maintenance and repair at different times since that date. The specific date at which the maintenance work was done may obviously be most important. Let us represent the intensity of use of the machine (the daily output per machine at each moment of its life) as a function of time by $u = f(t)$, where t represents the chronological time, and represent the amount invested in maintenance and repair at every moment of the life of the machine (as a function of time) by $m = g(t)$. If we assume then that today's output of shoes depends on the condition of machinery in the factory and on the amount of labor expended today (adequate quantities of raw materials being provided) and represent this quantity (the number of labor hours expended, assuming only one type of work is done) by L, then today's output of shoes may be represented as

$$S = \begin{bmatrix} \text{26 May '50} & \text{26 May '50} & \\ f(t), & g(t), & L \\ \text{27 Dec. '41} & \text{27 Dec. '41} & \end{bmatrix}.$$

This is to be taken to mean that the output of shoes on May 26, 1950, depends on the labor devoted to shoe production today and on the use and maintenance of the machinery since the date of its installation. The reader may readily see how relationships involving more complicated functionals may be found in the economy.[31]

3. THE APPLICATION TO DYNAMICS

Since in dynamic analysis we are concerned with an analysis of the relationship between present and past events, or more generally between events and the happenings in the economy preceding these events, the applicability of functional analysis to dynamics should be obvious. Today's output depends on investment over the past, say, fifty years; the future prices a seller expects for his commodity depend on the prices he has experienced over the years in the past during which he has been in business, and so on. Unless we are able to describe the functional relationships involved and operate with them, our analysis can never be complete.

In practice, as has been said, such a complete analysis is very difficult if not impossible. The reader need only consider the problems involved in formulating a precise relationship between the seller's price expectations and his knowledge of the history of past prices (the relationship itself may even change from moment to moment). Moreover, if we assume a relationship whose precise form is not known, just as we assume that there is a demand curve for butter though we may not know its shape precisely, we can get

[31] We can now see how it is that economists following Böhm Bawerk were misled into trying to find an "average period of production" to which current output could be related. As we have seen, current output depends partly on how much has been invested in production (purchase) and maintenance of capital equipment at each moment over a period of time. As a result (output being of the nature of a functional) it is not possible to relate current output to any single magnitude representing investment and maintenance over the entire period. Ultimately the problem is an index-number problem, for it amounts to a search for an index number which will represent the course of investment through time. Such an index number (which is what the average period of production was meant to serve as) is, of course, possible. But like all index numbers it does not tell us everything about the situation. Thus the search for "the correct" average period of production must necessarily be as futile as the search for an ideal index number. Failure to recognize this has led to confusion and sometimes to error in capital theory. This is one of the arguments of Victor Edelberg's unpublished Ph.D. thesis.

results only in relatively simple cases or on so high a level of generality that they are not very interesting and informative.

For that reason various types of assumptions about reality involving convenient oversimplifications are employed. We assume, for example, that prices change only once every so often, once a week, or more generally once a period; or we assume that expected price depends not on all past prices but on the prices experienced in the past two periods, and so on. In other words, we seek approximate relationships whereby current economic phenomena may be described as ordinary functions of a few variables.

The way in which this is done and some of the more rudimentary techniques for dealing with these cases will be considered in the next chapters, where examples of some of the results achieved will be examined as we proceed.

Part IV

SINGLE EQUATION MODELS

Chapter Nine

FIRST-ORDER DIFFERENCE EQUATIONS

Since reality is, for the most part, too complex for us to be able to analyze it in all its details, at least with existing techniques, we must adopt more modest objectives. We therefore consider hypothetical systems which are sufficiently simple for us to be able to subject them to a fairly thorough analysis but which are nevertheless a fair enough approximation to reality to give us information about the world in which we live. These hypothetical systems or models are not merely a feature of economic dynamics; in most branches of science the consideration of the interrelation of all phenomena is no more than an ideal, and it is therefore a common practice to proceed by ignoring the less important relationships.

1. A SIMPLE TYPE OF DIFFERENCE EQUATION

One of the simplest kinds of relationship which we can assume in a dynamic model is obtained by taking the magnitude of one of the variables to depend only upon the magnitude of that same variable at one or more dates in the recent past. If, for example, we know that for some reason the national income is rising at a steady rate of 10 per cent per week, then we need only know last week's national income in order to be able to determine that of this week.

In itself, of course, this relation explains very little; we want to know its rationale, which may involve consideration of many other variables such as investment, consumption, etc. If, however, we can show that such a relation (income growing 10 per cent each week) does exist, then, as we shall see, the analysis of the situation may turn out to be quite simple.

As an example of a fairly general form which such a relationship may take, we give

$$y(t) = 5y(t-1) + 73y(t-2) - 18y(t-3) + 10 \qquad (1)$$

where $y(t)$ is the national income accruing during any period, t, and, for example, $y(t-5)$ is the national income accruing five periods previously. The equation says, in effect, that current national income depends upon the income levels of the past three periods. Thus if we know that in periods $t-1$, $t-2$, and $t-3$ national income was 2, 1, and $1\frac{1}{2}$ (in $100 billion) respectively, then we can obtain income during t:

$$y(t) = (5 \times 2) + (73 \times 1) - (18 \times 1\tfrac{1}{2}) + 10 = 66.$$

The Path of y *Through Time*

A more important feature of such a relationship is that, given the national income of periods $t-1$, $t-2$, and $t-3$, we know not only the income of period t but also the income of every period thereafter. Recourse to our example of income increasing 10 per cent in every period will make this clear. If income were 100 in some given week, we would not only know that in the following week income would be 110 but we would also know that it would be 121 in the week after that, and so on. By making 55 such calculations we could determine what the level of income would be 55 weeks after that week when income was 100, and to do this we require no more information than is contained in the statement, "Income was 100 in the first week and increased by 10 per cent each week thereafter."

Similarly, given the relationship stated in Eq. (1) and given the values of income in periods $t-1$, $t-2$, and $t-3$, we can determine the income not only of period t but also of every subsequent period. Since Eq. (1) holds for any four consecutive periods and since we found income in period t to be 66, we have, for period $t+1$;

$$y(t+1) = 5y(t) + 73y(t-1) - 18y(t-2) + 10$$

or $y(t+1) = (5 \times 66) + (73 \times 2) - (18 \times 1) + 10 = 468.$

In the same way we can now calculate $y(t+2)$, and so on. It is thus clear that a relationship such as (1), together with information about the situation in a number of consecutive periods, contains implicitly all the facts about the course of national income thereafter.

The purpose of this chapter is to see how relationships of the above type have been obtained in some of the models that have been constructed. We shall also describe techniques which permit us to obtain explicit data about the future from the information which is only implicit in the system. In sum we shall examine the relationship between the past and the present in some simple situations and see how, given the initial situation, things may be expected to develop. This is exactly what we have defined to be the problem of economic dynamics.

Definitions

Equation (1) is called a *third-order linear* difference equation with *constant* coefficients. It is said to be of the third order because the situation in period t depends partly on the situation three periods previously and not on the situation of any earlier period. It is called linear because it involves only terms such as $73y(t-2)$ and no more complicated terms such as $15[y(t-1)]^2$ or $\log [55y(t-3)]$.[1] The equation is said to have constant coefficients

[1] The reader may know that the usual linear equation represented by a straight-line graph is of the form $y = ax + b$ and that for a plane it is of the form $y = ax + bz + c$, where x, y, and z are variables and a, b, and c are constants. If we set $y(t) = y$, $y(t-1) = x$, and $y(t-2) = z$, these are first- and second-order linear difference equations of the sort we are considering.

(5, 73, and −18) because its coefficients have the same values in all periods.[2]

The general nth order linear difference equation with constant coefficients may be written

$$y(t) = a_1 y(t-1) + a_2 y(t-2) + \cdots + a_n y(t-n) + b \quad (2)$$

where $a_1, a_2, \cdots, a_n$ and b are constants and a_n is not equal to zero (for otherwise the last term would drop out and the equation be of order less than n). The initial conditions for this equation can be written

$$y(1) = C_1 \quad \text{(i.e., income in the initial period was } C_1\text{)}$$
$$y(2) = C_2 \quad \text{(i.e., income in the next period was } C_2\text{)}$$
$$\cdot$$
$$\cdot$$
$$\cdot$$
$$y(n) = C_n \quad \text{(income in the } n\text{th period was } C_n\text{)}$$

where $C_1, C_2, \cdots, C_n$ are all constants. We refer to an *nth* order equation together with its n initial conditions as an nth order system.

We can, of course, take any n consecutive periods as the initial periods and see what happens from then onward. By substituting the values for income in those periods into (2) we can, as we have seen, find out income during period $n+1$, and with the aid of this we can find out the income of period $n+2$, and so on.

Our task is now to find a formula which will enable us to calculate the income (or whatever variable is under consideration) of any period without the tedious task of computation step by step from the initial periods. As an example of what is meant by such a formula, which is called a *solution* of a difference equation, consider the simple system given by the first-order equation

$$y(t) = 2y(t-1) + 4$$

and the initial condition

$$y(1) = 14.$$

[2] If the coefficients were of the form, e.g., of $9t$, $13t^3$, or $4 \sin t$, they would be called variable coefficients and our relationship would change in successive periods. Many of the propositions which are developed below are valid also for the variable coefficients case.

Then, as the reader can easily verify, the incomes of the next few periods coincide with the values of $y(t)$ given by

$$y(t) = 9(2)^t - 4.$$

We shall presently show that this expression is the solution of the system and holds for the indefinite future.

Properties of the Solution

We shall consider the derivation of the solution later. For the present we shall just note some of its properties. First, it must give the correct initial values. In our example for the initial date $t = 1$,

$$y(1) = 9(2)^1 - 4 = 18 - 4 = 14.$$

Second, the solution must satisfy the requirements of the difference equation. Thus our example requires

$$y(t) = 2[y(t-1)] + 4.$$

Now the solution is

$$y(t) = 9(2)^t - 4$$

so that

$$y(t-1) = 9(2)^{t-1} - 4.$$

To see why this value of $y(t-1)$ satisfies our difference equation we substitute it into the equation to see if in fact the terms add up to $9(2)^t - 4 = y(t)$ as the equation requires. Making the substitution for $y(t-1)$ we obtain

$$\begin{aligned} 2[y(t-1)] + 4 &= 2[9(2)^{t-1} - 4] + 4 \\ &= 2 \times 9 \times 2^{t-1} - 2 \times 4 + 4 \\ &= 9 \times 2^t - 4 \\ &= y(t) \end{aligned}$$

so that these values of $y(t)$ and $y(t-1)$ satisfy the equation.

In short, we may say that the two requirements of a solution are

(a) that it satisfy the initial conditions, and (b) that it satisfy the difference equation. More precisely:

(a) A formula which we symbolize by $y^*(t)$ satisfies the n initial conditions given above if substituting 1 for t in the formula gives $y^*(1) = C_1$, if substituting 2 for t gives $y^*(2) = C_2$, and so on, for all numbers up to and including n (for an nth order system).

(b) A formula symbolized by $y^*(t)$ satisfies the difference Eq. (2) if we substitute $y^*(t-1)$ for the unknown $y(t-1)$, $y^*(t-2)$ for $y(t-2)$, and so on, up to and including $y^*(t-n)$ for $y(t-n)$ and can show that the resulting expression

$$a_1y^*(t-1) + a_2y^*(t-2) + \cdots + a_ny^*(t-n) + b$$

actually adds up to $y^*(t)$.

Any formula which satisfies these two requirements is a solution since, as we have seen, the future values of the variable under consideration are completely determined by the difference equation and the initial values. This gives us:

PROPOSITION ONE: Any formula which gives a set of values satisfying both the difference equation and the initial conditions is a solution.

PROBLEMS

1. Give the order of the following equations:

   a) $y(t) = 5y(t-1) + 16y(t-2) + 33y(t-3) - 5$
   b) $y(t) = ay(t-1) + by(t-2) + c$
   c) $y(t) = ay(t-1) + by(t-2)$
   d) $y(t) = by(t-2)$
   e) $y(t) = 5y(t-1) + 33y(t-3) - 5$
   f) $y(t) = 5y(t-1) + 33y(t-503) - 5$
   g) $y(t) = 5y(t-1) + 33y(t-n) - 5$

2. How many initial conditions are required to complete the system in each of the above equations?
3. Compute y for the first five periods after the initial periods given:

   a) $y(t) = 2y(t-1), y(0) = 1$
   b) $y(t) = -2y(t-1), y(0) = 1$

c) $y(t) = 2y(t-1) - y(t-2), y(0) = 1, y(1) = 2$
d) $y(t) = 2y(t-2), y(0) = 1, y(1) = 2$
e) What can you compute in case (d) if you are given only $y(0) = 1$, i.e., only one initial condition?

4. Compute y for the first four periods after the initial periods with

$y(t) = 2y(t-1) + y(t-2)$ given:
a) $y(0) = 1, y(1) = 2$
b) $y(1) = 2, y(2) = 5$
c) $y(1) = 1, y(2) = 2$

Why do (a) and (b) give the same results? What is the relation between the results of (a) and (c)?

5. Show that $y(t) = 5y(t-1)$ is satisfied by

a) $y^*(t) = 5^t$
b) $y^*(t) = 7 \times (5)^t$

6. Show that $y(t) = 5y(t-1) + 7y(t-2) - 15y(t-3) + 8$ is satisfied by $y^*(t) = 2$.
7. Show that $y(t) = 5y(t-1) - 6y(t-2)$ is satisfied by

a) $y^*(t) = 2^t$
b) $y^*(t) = 5 \times 2^t$
c) $y^*(t) = 5 \times 2^t + 2 \times 3^t$

2. SIMPLE FIRST-ORDER SYSTEMS

An Economic Example

Before examining the method of finding a solution we may turn back to economics for a moment. How do we obtain a neat difference-equation system from an economic problem? It is no use learning how to deal with such systems before we can find them.

As a matter of fact, we have already formulated a difference-equation system in an earlier chapter, though without considering it in that light. In discussing Mr. Harrod's dynamic system we saw that it was based on two premises: (a) The community's saving (investment) during any period, *t*, is a constant proportion, *s*, of the income of that period, i.e.,

$$S(t) = sy(t)$$

(b) Entrepreneur's desired investment during that period, $I(t)$, equals a constant, g, times the increase of the income of that period over the income of the previous period, i.e.,

$$I(t) = g[y(t) - y(t-1)].$$

From this we saw that if investors' desires are to be satisfied we must have

$$I(t) = S(t)$$

that is, $$sy(t) = g[y(t) - y(t-1)]$$

or, subtracting $gy(t)$ from both sides and changing signs (multiplying by -1),

$$(g - s)y(t) = gy(t-1).$$

Dividing throughout by $g - s$ gives

$$y(t) = \frac{g}{g-s}\,y(t-1)$$

and this is an ordinary first-order difference equation with the constant coefficient $g/(g-s)$, which tells us how income must behave from period to period if entrepreneurs' investment desires are to be satisfied, i.e., it gives the "warranted" course of income. Given the initial situation the equation enables us to compute the warranted income for any future period. If we can find the solution we will, by the use of the present approach, have obtained some new information.

The Method of Solution: Preliminary

In order to find the general solution let us denote the fraction $g/(g-s)$ by K. To provide a numerical illustration we shall assume that $g = 2/3$ and $s = 1/2$ so that $K = 4$. We therefore have the general[3] and specific first-order equations

$$y(t) = Ky(t-1) \quad (3) \qquad\qquad y(t) = 4y(t-1) \quad (3a).$$

[3] We postpone consideration of the more general form $y(t) = Ky(t-1) + B$ (where B is a constant) until later.

Let the initial situation be given by $y(0) = C_0$ and in the numerical example take C_0 to be 3; that is to say that income in the initial situation, period 0, was 3 (hundred billion).

We can now proceed by a method of trial and error, trying various formulas and seeing whether they satisfy both the difference equation and the initial condition. *Note that this method is completely justified by Proposition One.*

First of all, we may work out the income of the first few periods step by step and see if that gives us any clue to a correct formula. For period 1 we have from our equation

$$y(1) = Ky(0) = KC_0 \qquad y(1) = 4y(0) = 4 \times 3$$

and similarly for periods 2, 3, and 4 we have

$$y(2) = Ky(1) = K \times KC_0 = K^2C_0$$
$$y(3) = Ky(2) = K^3C_0$$
$$y(4) = Ky(3) = K^4C_0$$
$$y(2) = 4y(1) = 4 \times 4 \times 3$$
$$y(3) = 4y(2) = 4 \times 4 \times 4 \times 3$$
$$y(4) = 4y(3) = 4 \times 4 \times 4 \times 4 \times 3.$$

The alert reader will no doubt be able to guess the solutions we are coming to, but it may pay us to approach the result in several steps nevertheless, since in more complicated work the slower approach is convenient.

The Method of Solution: Continued

It is apparent that our solution may involve something of the form M^t for the tth period, so let us try as an approximation

$$y(t) = M^t \tag{4}$$

where M is a number to be determined. Now if this is to satisfy Eqs. (3) and (3a), we must have

$$M^t = KM^{t-1} \quad \text{or} \quad M = K \qquad M^t = 4M^{t-1} \quad \text{or} \quad M = 4$$

so as a further approximation we try

$$y(t) = K^t \quad (5) \qquad\qquad y(t) = 4^t \quad (5a)$$

and observe the following:

(a) This approximation does satisfy (3) and (3a), for

$$Ky(t-1) = K \times K^{t-1} = K^t = y(t) \qquad 4y(t-1) = 4 \times 4^{t-1} = 4^t$$

(b) In *general,* (5) and (5a) do not satisfy the initial conditions

$$y(0) = C_0 \quad (6) \qquad\qquad y(0) = 3 \quad (6a)$$

for (5) and (5a) give[4] $y(0) = 1$ for period 0, which is *only* the result we desire if $C_0 = 1$.

The Solution and the Initial Condition

In order to see how we can extend our result to make it satisfy both (3) and (3a) and the initial conditions (6) and (6a), we must digress for a moment to state the following:

PROPOSITION TWO: If $f(t)$ is any formula [such as (4) or (5)] which satisfies a difference equation [such as (3)], then

$$f^*(t) = Af(t) \quad (7)$$

also satisfies that equation, where A is any arbitrarily chosen number.

Proof. It will be recalled that, by definition, the statement that $f(t)$ satisfies (3) and (3a) means that

$$Kf(t-1) = f(t) \quad (8) \qquad\qquad 4f(t-1) = f(t) \quad (8a)$$

so that, multiplying both sides of (8) and (8a) by A

$$KAf(t-1) = Af(t) \qquad\qquad 4Af(t-1) = Af(t)$$

or

$$Kf^*(t-1) = f^*(t) \qquad\qquad 4f^*(t-1) = f^*(t)$$

which shows us that $f^*(t) = Af(t)$ satisfies our equations if $f(t)$ does, where A is any arbitrary number, and this is the result we wanted to prove.

[4] For any number, n, by definition, $n^0 = 1$, $n^1 = n$, $n^{-k} = 1/n^k$.

We are now ready to obtain a solution to our system. As in (a) above we showed that (5) and (5a) satisfy (3) and (3a), we now see that by Proposition Two

$$y(t) = AK^t \qquad (9) \qquad\qquad y(t) = A4^t \qquad (9a)$$

also satisfy them. In addition we want (9) and (9a) to satisfy the initial conditions (6) and (6a), i.e., we want

$$C_0 = y(0) = AK^0 = A \qquad\qquad 3 = y(0) = A4^0 = A$$

so that if we take the formulas

$$y(t) = C_0K^t \qquad (10) \qquad\qquad y(t) = 3 \times 4^t \qquad (10a)$$

we see that they satisfy both the difference equations (3) and (3a) and the initial conditions (6) and (6a). Proposition One then tells us that (10) and (10a) are the expressions we are looking for; they give us the general result for the future course of income (or any other quantity represented by y). They agree, of course, with the results we obtained for the first four periods by direct computation.

PROBLEMS

1. Solve:

   a) $y(t) = 5y(t-1)$, $y(0) = 3$
   b) $y(t) = -2y(t-1)$, $y(0) = 5$
   c) $y(t) = y(t-1)$, $y(0) = -1$
   d) $y(t) = Ly(t-1)$, $y(0) = M$
   e) $y(t) = 5y(t-1)$, $y(1) = 15$
   f) $P(t) = 5P(t-1)$, $P(0) = 3$

2. Is there really any difference between (e) and (a)? Between (f) and (a)?

3. CONSIDERATION OF THE RESULTS

The general form of the solution of our first-order difference equation is

$$y(t) = AM^t$$

where A and M are numbers. We shall now consider the meaning of the solution for all possible values of M and A.

The Influence of M *on the Time Path of* y

1. *M* POSITIVE

a. $M = 1$. Then $M^2 = 1$, $M^3 = 1$, etc., so that $y(t)$ will equal A for all future periods, t. In other words the value of y is stationary, y never changes. The course of y over time will be of the form shown by AA' in Figure 21.

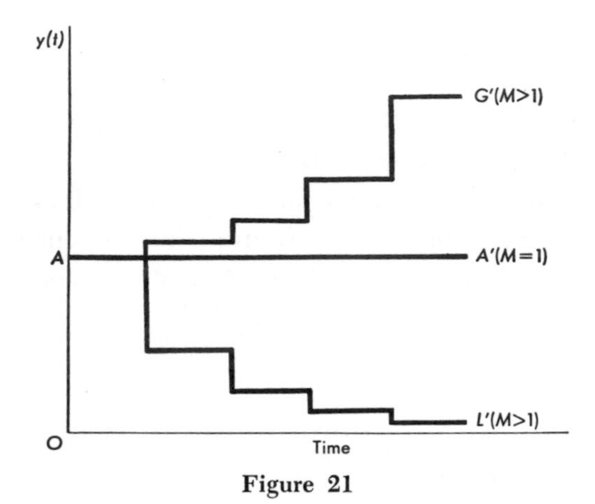

Figure 21

b. $M > 1$. There are three more propositions which we must state in connection with this case.

PROPOSITION THREE: If M is greater than unity, M^2 is greater than M, M^3 is greater than M^2, and so on.[5] The reader can easily check this by numerical examples.

PROPOSITION FOUR: For any specific number, n, however large, there is a number, t, for which M^t is greater than n.[6]

[5] *Proof.* We have $M > 1$. Therefore, multiplying both sides of the inequality by M^n we have $M^{n+1} > M^n$.

[6] *Proof.* $M > 1$ means $\log M > 0$. Therefore, for any n, we can choose t so great that $t > (\log n / \log M)$. This means (multiplying through by $\log M$) that $t \log M > \log n$, i.e., $M^t > n$.

PROPOSITION FIVE: M^t increases by ever-increasing amounts as t increases.[7]

These propositions tell us that in this case $(M > 1)$, $y(t)$ will increase over time without bounds and by ever-increasing amounts. The course of y over time will be of the form shown by AG' in Figure 21.

c. $M < 1$. Similar propositions with analogous proofs hold. $y(t)$ will continually decrease over time by ever-decreasing amounts. The course of y over time will be of the form shown by AL' in Figure 21.

2. *M* NEGATIVE

Say $M = -5$. Then M^2 will be positive (25), M^3 will be negative (−125), M^4 positive, and so on. In other words, $y(t) = AM^t$ will behave exactly as if M were positive, except that $y(t)$ will be positive one period, negative the next, and so on, changing sign each

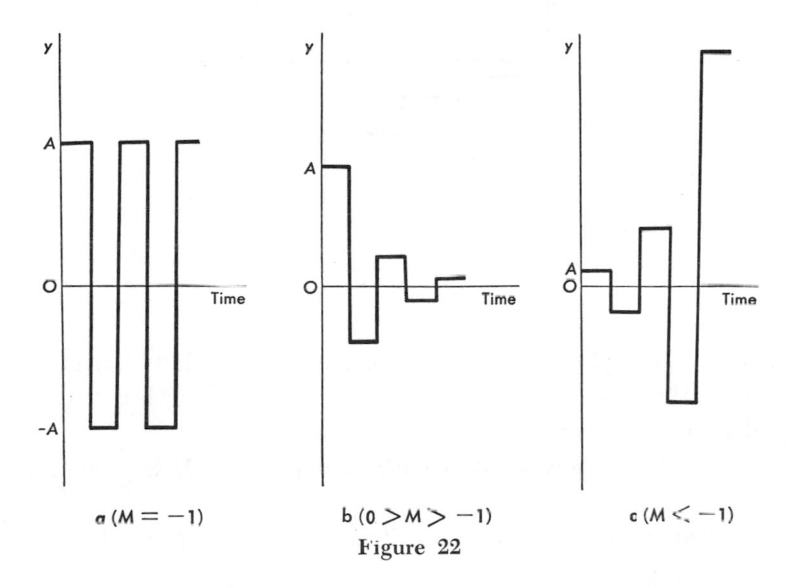

Figure 22

[7] *Proof.* $M > 1$, i.e., $M > (M - 1)/(M - 1)$. Therefore, multiplying both sides by $M - 1$, $M^2 - M > M - 1$. Multiplying both sides by M^n, $M^{n+2} - M^{n+1} > M^{n+1} - M^n$.

period. Analogously to when M is negative we have the three cases:

$$M = -1 \text{ (see Fig. 22a)}$$
$$M > -1 \text{ (see Fig. 22b)}$$
$$M < -1 \text{ (see Fig. 22c)}$$ [8]

The Influence of A *on the Time Path of* y

All these results hold if A is positive. If it is negative, everything that was positive will now become negative, and vice versa. For example, the results illustrated in Figure 21 will now be changed to look like those shown in Figure 23.

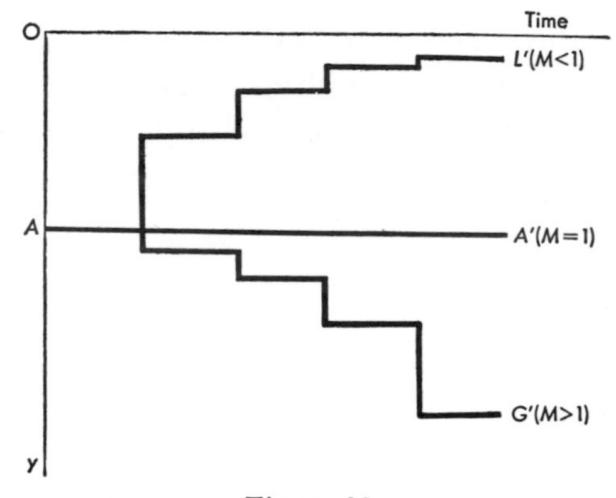

Figure 23

We can sum up as follows:

a. $y(t)$ will explode (shoot off to plus or minus infinity), decrease toward nothing, or stay constant as M is greater than, less than, or equal to, 1 in absolute value.[9]

b. $y(t)$ will move without or with oscillations as M is positive or negative.

c. A change in the sign of A will turn the results upside down.

[8] Note that the three diagrams employ different vertical scales. Why?

[9] The absolute value or modulus of a negative number, n, is defined to be $-n$; the absolute value (modulus) of a positive number, p, is defined to be p. Thus the absolute value of both 5 and -5 is 5.

PROBLEM

1. Describe the time path of y in the following cases:

   a) $y(t) = y(t-1)$
   b) $y(t) = \frac{1}{2}y(t-1)$
   c) $y(t) = -5y(t-1)$
   d) $y(t) = 3y(t-1)$

4. USE OF THE RESULTS

Let us compare these results with the first-order system given by the difference Eq. (3) and the initial condition (6); i.e.,

$$y(t) = Ky(t-1) \quad \text{and} \quad y(0) = C_0.$$

We saw that the solution of this system was

$$y(t) = C_0K^t \tag{10}$$

so that when we took $y(t) = AM^t$ as our general solution in Section 3, we had $A = C_0$ (given by our initial condition) and $M = K$ (given by our difference equation from Section 2). For any such case, whether $y(t)$ will or will not fluctuate and whether it will explode, taper off, or do neither depends, according to the results (a) and (b) given at the end of Section 3, only upon the value of K. In other words, without having any information about the initial condition we can look at our difference equation and tell at once what will happen. This is perhaps to be expected, for what happens depends on the relationship between consecutive values of y, and that is given by the difference equation. On the other hand, result (c), whether $y(t)$ is positive or negative and whether it is rising and falling, will sometimes depend partly on C_0, the initial condition. Again this is intuitively clear, for, necessarily, y in the initial period will be positive or negative as C_0 is positive or negative.

Mr. Harrod's Model Again

A considerable effort was required to obtain our results, but now that we have them they can be of considerable help in the analysis of further problems. Let us return to Mr. Harrod's model and see what we can say about it. We had the basic equation

$$y(t) = \frac{g}{g-s} y(t-1)$$

so that $K = g/(g-s)$. Both g and s may be taken to be positive, since saving will rise with income and entrepreneurs will want to increase their capital equipment when output increases. Now if g is greater than s, as we may expect for reasons given above (Chapter Four, Section 6), $g - s$ will be positive. Since it is less than g, K must be positive and greater than 1. Thus from the results (a) and (b) stated at the end of the last section we can see that this means that the path of income over time will be explosive and nonoscillating. Further, if $y(0) = C_0$ is positive, and this must surely be the case, income will be positive.

This, of course, is the same result as we obtained before without the use of difference-equation technique. We can now, however, see a possibility which was not apparent before: If s were greater than g, $K = g/(g-s)$ would be negative and Mr. Harrod's warranted income would oscillate in perpetuity, jumping from positive to negative one year and from negative to positive the next year. This queer case is of little economic significance, first because, as has already been said, g will almost certainly be greater than s, and second because (as will be seen in problem 1 below) the model may easily be modified to eliminate this peculiar possibility. The example merely serves to indicate that in many cases the difference-equation technique can be very helpful in indicating various possibilities which would not otherwise have been observed.

PROBLEM

1. Suppose saving is in proportion to income of the preceding period and not to that of the current period, so that $S(t) = sy(t-1)$ and not $S(t) = sy(t)$ as before. Suppose, however, that we still have $I(t) = g[y(t) - y(t-1)]$. Show that in this case the warranted rate of growth of $y(t)$ given by $I(t) = S(t)$ permits of no oscillations if s and g are both positive. The assumption $S(t) = sy(t-1)$ implies that the public bases its saving decisions on the experience of the recent past.

5. *ANOTHER ILLUSTRATIVE PROBLEM*

Now that we have the technique of analysis, let us see how to use it in another simple problem. We shall consider the simple multiplier analysis. The argument is that if, in a certain period, 0, the government spends an amount I on public works, then in the next period the people who receive I as income will spend a constant proportion, c, of it. This in turn provides income in the following period, the recipients of this second expenditure will spend the same proportion of it, and so on. Thus the initial expenditure, I, will cause expenditure in subsequent periods, and our problem is to find out the amount of this expenditure due directly to I in, say, the nth period. Let $E(t)$ be this expenditure in period t. Then we have the difference equation

$$E(t) = cE(t-1).$$ [10]

We also have the initial condition

$$E(0) = I.$$

We can obtain the solution at once by substituting $I = C_0$ and $c = K$ into Eq. (10), giving

$$E(t) = I(c^t)$$

so that if the marginal propensity to consume is 1/2 and the initial investment expenditure 5 (million) we have

$$E(t) = 5\left(\frac{1}{2}\right)^t.$$

From what we know about the behavior of such systems we can see that, since I is positive and c is positive but less than unity (since people save some part of their income), the expenditure directly induced by the initial expenditure will always be positive and will gradually taper off with time. In the peculiar case where c is greater

[10] c is the marginal and average propensity to consume and $E(t)$ the multiplier effect in period t of the initial dose of investment I.

than unity, that is to say, where a rise in earnings induces people to increase their consumption by more than that increase, $E(t)$ will explode with time. Thus in this case a small initial expenditure will cause income to expand indefinitely and may (though this is not the way the term is ordinarily used) be called pump priming with a vengeance!

PROBLEM

Formulate the cobweb model (Chapter Seven, Section 1) as a first-order linear difference equation.

Chapter Ten

HIGHER-ORDER DIFFERENCE EQUATIONS

1. SECOND-ORDER SYSTEMS

An Economic Example

We now proceed to examine slightly more complicated cases involving second-order difference equations. We shall consider Professor Samuelson's Multiplier Acceleration Principle model.[1] This differs from Harrod's model in that it concerns what will actually happen to income (net national production) rather than what ought to happen if the Scylla of overproduction and the Charybdis of underproduction are to be avoided.

The magnitude of national output in any period will, apart from such acts of God as earthquakes and bad harvests, depend upon the decisions of producers with respect to that period. We may assume that they will plan to produce such an output as they expect to be able to sell at current prices. (We shall ignore the possibility of price changes so that the money value of output can be taken as an index of physical production.) We shall separate their demand estimates (and production plans) into two parts: those concerning consumer

[1] Paul A. Samuelson "Interactions between the Multiplier Analysis and the Principle of Acceleration," *Review of Economic Statistics,* 1939, and reprinted in *Readings in Business Cycle Theory* (The Blakiston Company, Philadelphia and Toronto, 1944).

goods and those concerning producer goods.[2] We assume that producers expect demand for the first type of good to be proportional to income and that they expect demand for the second type to depend on the rate of increase of income (output), i.e., they work on the hypothesis of the acceleration principle. Since they cannot know the income of a period at its beginning when they are making their plans, we take it that they form their estimates on the basis of the most recent information available and expect the income of the period to be equal to the income of the previous period.[3]

These assumptions may be written in the following form:

$$y(t) = C(t) + I(t) \tag{11}$$

which means that national output (income), $y(t)$, will be the sum of estimated consumer demand, $C(t)$, and estimated investment demand, $I(t)$. We also have

$$C(t) = cy(t-1) \tag{12}$$

where c is the marginal and average propensity to consume, say $c = 1/4$. Finally we have

$$I(t) = B[y(t-1) - y(t-2)] \tag{13}$$

where B is a constant (the "acceleration coefficient") say $B = 5$.

If we substitute $C(t)$ and $I(t)$ from (12) and (13) into (11) we get

$$y(t) = cy(t-1) + B[y(t-1) - y(t-2)]$$

which equals

$$y(t) = (c+B)y(t-1) - By(t-2) \tag{14}$$

[2] These two types of goods need not differ as regards their physical characteristics; as well as being a consumer good a pair of shoes can be a producer good if shopkeepers are building up stocks.

[3] We do not, of course, mean to imply that producers base their individual demand estimates on figures for the national income. We assume only that consumers' expenditure is proportional to their incomes in the previous period, that investment expenditure is proportional to the rate of growth of output, and that sellers estimate the demand for their goods in any period with approximate correctness.

i.e., we get

$$y(t) = 5\tfrac{1}{4}y(t-1) - 5y(t-2) \tag{14a}$$

thus obtaining a second-order difference equation with constant coefficients which gives us the relationship between national income (output) in any period and the national income (output) of the preceding two periods. To make the system complete we take as our initial conditions

$$y(0) = C_0 = 3$$

$$y(1) = C_1 = 6\tfrac{1}{2}.$$

Before proceeding we shall, for convenience in future operations set $(c + B) = -A$ in (14), giving us as our more general equation

$$y(t) = -Ay(t-1) - By(t-2) \tag{15}$$

whose solution we shall now consider.

2. SOLUTION OF THE SECOND-ORDER EQUATION

Since the solution of linear difference equations with constant coefficients and of order higher than second is in principle similar to the solution of second-order linear difference equations, we shall give the more general results and their derivations in footnotes as we proceed.

Solution of the Equation Ignoring Initial Conditions

Once again, as in the first-order case, we may commence by trying as a first approximation a solution of the form

$$y(t) = x^t. \tag{16}$$

Substituting this into (15) and (14a) to see whether it satisfies them we get

$$x^t = -Ax^{t-1} - Bx^{t-2} \quad (17) \qquad x^t = 5\tfrac{1}{4}x^{t-1} - 5x^{t-2}. \quad (17a)$$

This obviously holds for any x for which

$$x^2 = -Ax - B \qquad (18) \qquad\qquad x^2 = 5\tfrac{1}{4}x - 5 \qquad (18a)$$

since given any such x we need only multiply (18) and (18a) by x^{t-2} to obtain (17) and (17a).[4]

Now if we add $Ax + B$ to both sides of (18) and (18a) we get the so-called characteristic equation of (14a) and (15):

$$x^2 + Ax + B = 0 \qquad\qquad x^2 - 5\tfrac{1}{4}x + 5 = 0$$

and this is the familiar quadratic equation to which, as is well known, there are two solutions:

$$x_1 = \frac{-A + \sqrt{A^2 - 4B}}{2} = \frac{5\frac{1}{4} + \sqrt{27\frac{9}{16} - 20}}{2} = \frac{5\frac{1}{4} + \sqrt{7\frac{9}{16}}}{2}$$

$$= \frac{5\frac{1}{4} + \sqrt{\frac{121}{16}}}{2} = \frac{5\frac{1}{4} + \frac{11}{4}}{2} = \frac{8}{2} = 4$$

and

$$x_2 = \frac{-A - \sqrt{A^2 - 4B}}{2} = \frac{5\frac{1}{4} - \sqrt{27\frac{9}{16} - 20}}{2} = \frac{5\frac{1}{4} - \frac{11}{4}}{2}$$

$$= \frac{2\frac{1}{2}}{2} = 1\frac{1}{4}.$$

[4] Similarly, (16) satisfies the nth order equation $y(t) = a_1y(t-1) + a_2y(t-2) + \cdots + a_ny(t-n)$ for any x for which $x^t = a_1x^{t-1} + a_2x^{t-2} + \cdots + a_nx^{t-n}$, i.e., for any x which satisfies the ordinary polynomial equation of degree n in x: $x^n = a_1x^{n-1} + a_2x^{n-2} + \cdots + a_n$, the characteristic equation of our difference equation. For the roots of such an equation we have no general formula of the type used for $n = 2$ in the text, for n greater than 4. We do, however, know that any such nth degree equation has n roots which we shall call $x_1, x_2, \cdots, x_n$, any one of which must satisfy the equation. In any specific equation there are methods for finding numerical values for the roots to any desired degree of approximation so that we can obtain the roots to any desired number of decimal places. Thus we could find a number which is within 1/100, 1/1,000, or 1/1,000,000 for that matter, of the true value of, say, x_5 in the equation $x^5 = 44x^4 + 2x^3 + 37\frac{1}{2}x^2 - x + 15$. See Chapter Twelve.

Since, as the reader may satisfy himself, either x_1 or x_2 satisfy (18) and (18a) we have as solutions

$$y(t) = x_1^t \quad (19) \qquad y(t) = 4^t \quad (19a)$$

or

$$y(t) = x_2^t \quad (20) \qquad y(t) = (1\tfrac{1}{4})^t \quad (20a)$$

and it can be seen that these satisfy (15) and (14a). The reader will also readily see that our initial conditions

$$y(0) = C_0 = 3 \qquad y(1) = C_1 = 6\tfrac{1}{2} \quad (21)$$

are *not* generally satisfied by these results;[5] for example, we have $y(0) = (4)^0 = (1\tfrac{1}{4})^0 = 1 \neq 3$.

Modification of the Solution to Take Account of the Initial Conditions

To arrive at a solution, called the *general solution*, satisfying both our difference equation and our initial conditions we must first state:

PROPOSITION SIX: If $y_1(t)$ and $y_2(t)$ are any two formulas, both satisfying our difference equation, then it will also be satisfied by $ay_1(t) + by_2(t)$, where a and b are arbitrary constants;[6] that is, they are any numbers we care to choose.

[5] Similarly, any expression $y(t) = x^t$, where x is one of the roots of the characteristic equation in footnote 4, will satisfy that equation. But it will in general not satisfy the n initial conditions $y(0) = C_0$, $y(1) = C_1, \cdots, y(n-1) = C_{n-1}$, where $C_0, C_1, \cdots C_{n-1}$ are constants.

[6] *Proof.* If we substitute this new expression for $y(t-1)$ and $y(t-2)$ in (15) we get

$$-A[ay_1(t-1) + by_2(t-1)] - B[ay_1(t-2) + by_2(t-2)] \quad (22)$$

which we want to show equal to $ay_1(t) + by_2(t)$. Now (22) equals:

$$a[-Ay_1(t-1)] + b[-Ay_2(t-1)] + a[-By_1(t-2)] + b[-By_2(t-2)]$$

which equals

$$a[-Ay_1(t-1) - By_1(t-2)] + b[-Ay_2(t-1) - By_2(t-2)]. \quad (23)$$

But since $y_1(t)$ and $y_2(t)$ are assumed to satisfy our difference equation we have $-Ay_1(t-1) - By_1(t-2) = y_1(t)$ and $-Ay_2(t-1) - By_2(t-2) = y_2(t)$ and substituting these results into the square brackets in (23) gives: $ay_1(t) + by_2(t)$ as we required. $ay_1(t) + by_2(t)$ is thus a solution of our difference equation if $y_1(t)$ and $y_2(t)$ are solutions. Similarly, if $y_1(t), y_2(t), \cdots, y_n(t)$, are all solutions of our nth order difference equation, where n is any whole number, then $b_1y_1(t) + b_2y_2(t) + \cdots + b_ny_n(t)$ is also a solution, where $b_1, b_2, \cdots, b_n$ are any arbitrary numbers.

The Numerical Solution

We now proceed as follows: We know that (19), (19a), (20), and (20a) satisfy our difference equations so, by Proposition Six, they are also satisfied by

$$y(t) = a(x_1)^t + b(x_2)^t \quad (24) \quad y(t) = a(4)^t + b(1\tfrac{1}{4})^t \quad (24a)$$

where a and b are any numbers we like to choose. In order that our initial conditions (21) be satisfied we thus require

$$y(0) = a + b = C_0 = 3$$
$$y(1) = ax_1 + bx_2 = 4a + 1\tfrac{1}{4}b = C_1 = 6\tfrac{1}{2}.$$

It is clear that any a and b which satisfy these conditions will satisfy both our difference equation and our initial conditions. These two conditions are two ordinary equations which may be solved simultaneously for a and b; thus

$$a + b = 3$$
$$4a + 1\tfrac{1}{4}b = 6\tfrac{1}{2}.$$

Multiplying the top equation by 4 gives

$$4a + 4b = 12$$

and subtracting the bottom equation from this we obtain

$$2\tfrac{3}{4}b = 5\tfrac{1}{2}$$

i.e.,
$$b = 2.$$

From the top equation $a + b = a + 2 = 3$ so that $a = 1$. Then by (24a) the general solution of equation (14a) is

$$y(t) = 4^t + 2(1\tfrac{1}{4})^t.$$

The reader should verify directly that this expression gives the required results.[7]

[7] From the proposition stated in footnote 6 it follows that $b_1(x_1)^t + b_2(x_2)^t + \cdots + b_n(x_n)^t$ is a solution of our nth order equation where $b_1, b_2, \cdots, b_n$ are arbitrary constants and $x_1, x_2, \cdots, x_n$ are the roots of the characteristic

PROBLEMS

1. Solve the following second-order systems:

 a) $y(t) = 4y(t-1) - 3y(t-2), y(0) = 2, y(1) = 4$
 b) $y(t) = 6y(t-1) - 8y(t-2), y(0) = 8, y(1) = 22$
 c) $y(t) = 5y(t-1) - 6y(t-2), y(0) = -3, y(1) = -4$
 d) $y(t) = 3y(t-1) + 10y(t-2), y(0) = 8, y(1) = -2$
 e) $y(t) = 8y(t-1) - 12y(t-2), y(0) = 57, y(1) = 334$
 f) $y(t) = 4y(t-2), y(0) = 8, y(1) = -4$

2. Why doesn't the given method work for

 a) $y(t) = 6y(t-1) - 9y(t-2)$
 b) $y(t) = 3y(t-1) - 10y(t-2)$?

3. *THE NONHOMOGENEOUS EQUATION WITH A CONSTANT TERM*

An Economic Example

Suppose that in our multiplier acceleration principle model we assume that as well as acceleration investment there is another part of investment which is independent of the level of income (e.g., government demand for armaments) and which, for the time under consideration, is fixed. Let this quantity be given by L, say, $L = 3$. Then equation (13) becomes

$$I(t) = B[y(t-1) - y(t-2)] + L \tag{25}$$

i.e., investment demand is estimated to be the sum of acceleration investment demand plus government investment demand, L. Substituting (25) and (12) into (11), Eqs. (15) and (14a) become

$$y(t) = -Ay(t-1) - By(t-2) + L \tag{26}$$

$$y(t) = 5\tfrac{1}{4}y(t-1) - 5y(t-2) + 3. \tag{26a}$$

---

equation $x^n = a_1x^{n-1} + \cdots + a_n$ obtained in footnote 4. The general solution can then be obtained by setting $y(0) = C_0$, $y(1) = C_1 \cdots y(n-1) = C_{n-1}$, and solving simultaneously for $b_1, b_2, \cdots, b_n$, where $C_0, C_1, \cdots, C_{n-1}$ are given by the initial conditions of footnote 5.

We shall assume that our initial conditions are given this time by

$$y(0) = D_0 = 9 \qquad (27) \qquad\qquad y(1) = D_1 = 18\tfrac{1}{2} \quad (27a)$$

Such a system with a constant term, L, is often encountered in this sort of analysis. It is referred to as a nonhomogeneous equation in contrast with the equation with no constant term encountered earlier.

Difference equations can also be rendered nonhomogeneous by a *variable* term such as $5t^2$ or 2^t, that is, by any term which is not of the form $ay(t-k)$. But for the present the discussion is confined to the case where the nonhomogeneous term is a constant. However, some material on the variable term case is found in Chapters Fourteen and Fifteen. Note also that the method of solution in the nonhomogeneous case is valid for equations of any order.

The Method of Solution

In order to obtain our result we must state:

PROPOSITION SEVEN: If $X(t)$ is any expression which satisfies the homogeneous nth order equation

$$y(t) = a_1y(t-1) + a_2y(t-2) + \cdots + a_ny(t-n) \qquad (28)$$

and $Z(t)$ is any expression which satisfies

$$y(t) = a_1y(t-1) + a_2y(t-2) + \cdots + a_ny(t-n) + \mathrm{b} \quad (29)$$

which is obtained by adding the constant term b to the right-hand side of (28), then $X(t) + Z(t)$ also satisfies (29).[8]

[8] *Proof.* We substitute $X(t) + Z(t)$ in the right side of (29), getting:

$$a_1[X(t-1) + Z(t-1)] + \cdots + a_n[X(t-n) + Z(t-n)] + b$$

and try to show that this equals $X(t) + Z(t)$. By multiplying out and rearranging terms we get $[a_1X(t-1) + \cdots + a_nX(t-n)] + [a_1Z(t-1) + \cdots + a_nZ(t-n) + b]$. Now since $X(t)$ satisfies (28), the expression in the first bracket equals $X(t)$ and similarly since $Z(t)$ satisfies (29) the expression in the second bracket equals $Z(t)$; their sum equals $X(t) + Z(t)$ as desired. *Note that nowhere in the proof do we require that b be a constant.* Thus we may employ an approach similar to that here developed for handling an equation with a constant term to handle equations with simple variable terms.

Returning to homogeneous equations (15) and (14a) we see that they are equations (26) and (26a) with the constant term, $L = 3$, removed. Thus (15) and (14a) correspond to (28) while (26) and (26a) correspond to (29) in Proposition Seven.

The Particular Solution

Why do we want a solution $X(t) + Z(t)$ to (29) if we already know $Z(t)$ is a solution? As before we will need two undetermined constants which we can choose in such a way that our final solution satisfies the initial conditions. But Proposition Seven permits us to obtain our arbitrary constants directly by employing as $X(t)$ the solutions (24) and (24a) which had previously been obtained for (15) and (14a):

$$X(t) = a(x_1)^t + b(x_2)^t \qquad X(t) = a(4)^t + b(1\tfrac{1}{4})^t.$$

This gives us two undetermined constants which, as before, we can choose in such a way that our final solution satisfies the initial conditions. To this we must add (with no need to worry about arbitrary constants) an expression $Z(t)$, called a *particular solution,* which satisfies our nonhomogeneous equation (26). Indeed we shall try to find the simplest function, i.e., a constant term, $z = Z(t)$, which satisfies it. For this to be the case we must have by (26)

$$z = -Az - Bz + L \qquad z = 5\tfrac{1}{4}z - 5z + 3$$

$$(1 + A + B)z = L \qquad z - 5\tfrac{1}{4}z + 5z = 3$$

$$z = \frac{L}{1 + A + B} \quad (30) \qquad z = 4. \quad (30a)$$

The reader may check for himself that this satisfies (26) and (26a).

But by Proposition Seven a solution is also given by

$$y(t) = X(t) + Z(t) = a(x_1)^t + b(x_2)^t + z \quad (31)$$

$$= a(4)^t + b(1\tfrac{1}{4})^t + 4 \quad (31a)$$

so that in order that our initial conditions be satisfied we proceed as before to find appropriate values for a and b. We require

$$y(0) = a + b + z = D_0$$

$$y(1) = ax_1 + bx_2 + z = D_1$$

$$y(0) = a + b + 4 = 9$$

$$y(1) = 4a + 1\tfrac{1}{4}b + 4 = 18\tfrac{1}{2}.$$

These may be solved simultaneously to give appropriate values to a and b. In the numerical example we subtract 4 from both sides of the equations to get

$$a + b = 5$$

$$4a + 1\tfrac{1}{4}b = 14\tfrac{1}{2}.$$

Multiplying the upper equation by 4 gives

$$4a + 4b = 20$$

and subtracting the second equation from this leaves

$$2\tfrac{3}{4}b = 5\tfrac{1}{2}$$

i.e.,
$$b = 2.$$

Substituting this into the first equation we obtain

$$a + 2 = 5$$

i.e.,
$$a = 3$$

so that the final solution of our numerical example is

$$y(t) = 3(4)^t + 2(1\tfrac{1}{4})^t + 4.$$

4. *EXAMPLES OF THE SOLUTION OF DIFFERENCE-EQUATION SYSTEMS*

EXAMPLE 1

Let us now see how we can proceed directly to solve a difference-equation system without having to detour and explore as we did above. Suppose that we have somehow obtained the system

$$y(t) = 2y(t-1) + 3y(t-2) + 8$$

$$y(0) = 6 \qquad y(1) = 2$$

and that we wish to solve it. To start with, we find the solution of the homogeneous equation obtained by dropping the constant term,[9] 8.

$$y(t) = 2y(t-1) + 3y(t-2).$$

We try a solution of the form $X(t) = x^t$, and substituting we get

$$x^t = 2x^{t-1} + 3x^{t-2} \quad \text{or} \quad x^t - 2x^{t-1} - 3x^{t-2} = 0.$$

Dividing by x^{t-2} gives our characteristic equation

$$x^2 - 2x - 3 = 0$$

which has the roots

$$x_1 = \frac{2 + \sqrt{4+12}}{2} = \frac{2+\sqrt{16}}{2} = \frac{6}{2} = 3$$

and

$$x_2 = \frac{2 - \sqrt{4+12}}{2} = \frac{2-4}{2} = -1.$$

These values and equation (24) give us

$$X(t) = a(3)^t + b(-1)^t.$$

We must now find $Z(t) = z$ which satisfies our initial equation by substituting z for $y(t)$, $y(t-1)$, and $y(t-2)$:

$$z = 2z + 3z + 8$$

$$z - 2z - 3z = 8$$

$$-4z = 8$$

$$z = -2.$$

[9] Professor Samuelson has called this the "reduced equation."

The general solution of our equation is then given by (31) with these results substituted into it, i.e., by

$$y(t) = X(t) + Z(t) = a(3)^t + b(-1)^t - 2.$$

To find values of a and b satisfying the initial conditions we substitute this into the initial conditions, obtaining

$$a + b - 2 = 6$$

$$3a - b - 2 = 2$$

i.e.,

$$4a - 4 = 8, \; 4a = 12, \qquad a = 3.$$

Substituting this into the first equation we have

$$3 + b - 2 = 6,$$

i.e.,

$$b = 5.$$

The final solution is thus

$$y(t) = 3(3)^t + 5(-1)^t - 2.$$

EXAMPLE 2

Let us now return to first-order systems and take a case where the difference equation has a constant term. Such an equation can arise in a problem of the following sort. A man invests I (say, \$5,000) per period in bonds paying 5 per cent per period. Then in any period the total amount he has will be the amount he had in the previous period, $P(t-1)$, plus the interest on that amount, $iP(t-1) = 0.05P(t-1)$ plus his new investment $I = 5{,}000$. This gives us the first-order difference equation

$$P(t) = P(t-1) + iP(t-1) + I$$

$$= (1+i)P(t-1) + I$$

or

$$P(t) = 1.05P(t-1) + 5{,}000.$$

As our initial condition relating to the first period when he started investing we have

$$P(0) = 5{,}000 = I.$$

We start by solving the reduced homogeneous equation

$$P(t) = 1.05P(t-1).$$

Its solution, (10) is

$$X(t) = a(1.05)^t$$

where a is an undetermined constant.

To find the solution $Z(t) = z$ of our original equation we substitute z for $P(t)$ and $P(t-1)$, getting

$$z = 1.05z + 5{,}000$$

$$-0.05z = 5{,}000$$

$$z = -100{,}000.$$

Our solution [Eq. (31)] is then

$$P(t) = a(1.05)^t - 100{,}000.$$

To find the valuc of a satisfying the initial condition we substitute $P(0)$ in the initial condition

$$P(0) = a - 100{,}000 = 5{,}000$$

so that

$$a = 105{,}000$$

and the final solution of our first-order system is

$$P(t) = 105{,}000\,(1.05)^t - 100{,}000.$$

PROBLEMS

1. Solve the following systems:

   a) $y(t) = 5y(t-1) - 8, y(0) = 5$
   b) $y(t) = 6y(t-1) - 8y(t-2) - 9, y(0) = 5, y(1) = 19$
   c) $y(t) = 3y(t-1) + 10y(t-2) - 12, y(0) = 9, y(1) = -1$
   d) $y(t) = 4y(t-2) + 90, y(0) = -32, y(1) = -14$

2. Compare the results and initial conditions in problems (b), (c), and (d) with those of problems (b), (d), and (f) of Problem 1, Section 2.
3. Why doesn't our method of solution work for

$$y(t) = 4y(t-1) - 3y(t-2) + 5?$$

5. A SPECIAL PROBLEM [10]

Cases Where the Given Method for Finding the Particular Solution Fails

Consider the nonhomogeneous difference equation

$$y(t) = y(t-1) + 7.$$

Here we cannot obtain a solution of the form $Z(t) = z$, for substitution gives

$$z = z + 7$$

or

$$7 = 0.$$

This is obviously nonsense. Similarly, with the equation

$$y(t) = 5y(t-1) - 4y(t-2) + 88$$

there is no so-called "particular" solution of the form $Z(t) = z$, since substitution gives

$$z = 5z - 4z + 88$$

or

$$88 = 0.$$

More generally, if we take the general nth order difference equation (29) and try to find the particular solution $Z(t) = z$, on substituting into (29) we obtain

$$z = a_1 z + a_2 z + \cdots + a_n z + b$$

or

$$z - a_1 z - a_2 z - \cdots - a_n z = b$$

i.e.,

$$z(1 - a_1 - a_2 - \cdots - a_n) = b. \tag{32}$$

If the sum of the coefficients

$$1 - a_1 - a_2 - \cdots - a_n \tag{33}$$

[10] This and the following sections should be omitted on the first reading. The reader should note that throughout, by $z(t)$ we mean the constant z multiplied by t and not some unspecified function of t. Thus e.g., $z(t-1) = zt - z$.

is not equal to zero, we can divide both sides of (32) by (33) and get

$$z = \frac{b}{1 - a_1 - a_2 - \cdot \cdot \cdot - a_n} = Z(t)$$

as our particular solution. But if, on the other hand, (33) equals zero, (32) becomes $b = 0$, contrary to hypothesis. Thus wherever the sum of the coefficients (33) is zero, the particular solution $Z(t)$ cannot have the form z, where z is a constant.

A Particular Solution in These Cases

When this happens we can generally use a particular solution of the form $Z(t) = zt$, where z is a constant. Trying this result in (29) gives

$$zt = a_1z(t-1) + a_2z(t-2) + \cdot \cdot \cdot + a_nz(t-n) + b$$

or

$$zt = a_1zt + a_2zt + \cdot \cdot \cdot + a_nzt - a_1z - 2a_2z - \cdot \cdot \cdot - na_nz + b$$

i.e.,

$$zt(1 - a_1 - a_2 - \cdot \cdot \cdot - a_n) + z(a_1 + 2a_2 + \cdot \cdot \cdot + na_n) = b.$$

Now the expression in parentheses (33) on the left-hand side is equal to zero by hypothesis (for otherwise we could take $Z(t) = z$), so we have

$$z(a_1 + 2a_2 + \cdot \cdot \cdot + na_n) = b \qquad (34)$$

which, if

$$a_1 + 2a_2 + \cdot \cdot \cdot + na_n \qquad (35)$$

is not equal to 0 can be solved to give

$$z = \frac{b}{a_1 + 2a_2 + \cdot \cdot \cdot + na_n}.$$

If, however, both (33) and (35) are zero, then again we get the nonsense result $b = 0$, so that we can use neither $Z(t) = z$ nor

$Z(t) = zt$. In this unusual case we can generally use $Z(t) = zt^2$, for on substituting this into (29) we get

$$\begin{aligned} zt^2 &= a_1 z(t-1)^2 + \cdots + a_n z(t-n)^2 + b \\ &= a_1 z(t^2 - 2t + 1) + \cdots + a_n z(t^2 - 2nt + n^2) + b \\ &= zt^2(a_1 + a_2 + \cdots + a_n) - 2zt(a_1 + 2a_2 + \cdots \\ &\qquad + na_n) + z(a_1 + 2^2 a_2 + \cdots + n^2 a_n) + b \end{aligned}$$

so that

$$zt^2(1 - a_1 - a_2 - \cdots - a_n) + 2zt(a_1 + 2a_2 + \cdots + na_n) + z(-a_1 - 2^2 a_2 - \cdots - n^2 a_n) = b.$$

But the expressions in the first two sets of brackets are (33) and (35) and equal to zero, so the last equation becomes

$$z(-a_1 - 2^2 a_2 - \cdots - n^2 a_n) = b$$

which can be solved for z unless the expression in brackets is equal to zero. If so, we try $Z(t) = zt^3$ in a similar manner and if this too fails we try $Z(t) = zt^4$, and so on. If all others fail, it can be shown that the particular solution $Z(t) = zt^n$ must satisfy the nth order difference equation.

Thus a particular solution of the form $Z(t) = zt^g$ can be found where g is not greater than the order of the equation under consideration.

EXAMPLES

We can now solve the two difference equations given at the beginning of this section. We shall not concern ourselves with the initial conditions since these can be handled as before.

First we take $y(t) = y(t-1) + 7$. The solution of the reduced equation is, by (10), clearly

$$y(t) = a(1)^t = a$$

and the particular solution $Z(t) = zt$ is given by

$$zt = z(t-1) + 7$$

i.e., $$zt - zt + z = 7$$

$$z = 7$$

so that the solution of the equation, by Proposition Seven, is

$$y(t) = X(t) + Z(t) = a + 7t$$

where a is an arbitrary constant to be determined by the initial conditions.

Secondly, we wish to solve

$$y(t) = 5y(t-1) - 4y(t-2) + 88.$$

We obtain the solution of the reduced equation by trying $X(t) = x^t$, which gives

$$x^t = 5x^{t-1} - 4x^{t-2}$$

or $$x^2 = 5x - 4$$

i.e., $$x^2 - 5x + 4 = 0$$

which has the roots

$$x_1 = \frac{5 + \sqrt{25 - 16}}{2} = \frac{5 + \sqrt{9}}{2} = \frac{8}{2} = 4$$

$$x_2 = \frac{5 - \sqrt{25 - 16}}{2} = \frac{5 - 3}{2} = 1$$

so that, by (24),

$$X(t) = a(4)^t + b(1)^t = a(4)^t + b.$$

To obtain the particular solution $Z(t)$ to our difference equation, we substitute

$$zt = 5z(t-1) - 4z(t-2) + 88$$

$$= 5zt - 5z - 4zt + 8z + 88$$

$$= zt + 3z + 88$$

so that $$z = \frac{-88}{3}.$$

The solution to the difference equation is thus

$$y(t) = a(4)^t + b - \frac{88}{3}t.$$

PROBLEM

1. Find $Z(t)$ for the following:

   a) $y(t) = 4y(t-1) - 3y(t-2) + 5$
   b) $y(t) = -7y(t-1) + 8y(t-2) - 3$
   c) $y(t) = -7y(t-1) - 8y(t-2) - 3$
   d) $y(t) = 3y(t-1) - 3y(t-2) + y(t-3) + 6.$

6. ANOTHER SPECIAL PROBLEM: MULTIPLE ROOTS

EXAMPLE

Consider the difference-equation system

$$y(t) = 4y(t-1) - 4y(t-2)$$

with initial conditions

$$y(0) = 5 \qquad y(1) = 6.$$

To find the solution we proceed as usual and substitute x^t for $y(t)$ which gives

$$x^t = 4x^{t-1} - 4x^{t-2}$$

or

$$x^2 = 4x - 4$$

which has the roots

$$x_1 = \frac{4 + \sqrt{16 - 16}}{2} = \frac{4}{2} = 2$$

$$x_2 = \frac{4 - \sqrt{16 - 16}}{2} = \frac{4}{2} = 2$$

so that $x_1 = x_2 = 2$. This is a case of "multiple roots," and the root in this case is said to have multiplicity 2. If, say, 5 of the 7 roots of a seventh-degree equation are equal, these roots are said to be of multiplicity 5.

In the case under consideration, if we try to use solution (24) we get

$$y(t) = a(x_1)^t + b(x_2)^t$$
$$= a(2)^t + b(2)^t = (a+b)(2)^t = d(2)^t$$

where, since a and b are any two numbers we like, d is any number we like. Thus we have lost an arbitrary constant somewhere, and this solution will not satisfy the initial conditions. We want

$$y(0) = d = 5$$

but we also want $y(1) = 2d = 6$, i.e., $d = 3$, and d cannot equal both 5 and 3 at the same time.[11]

The General Solution in the Multiple-Roots Case

In order to obtain a solution which does satisfy the initial conditions in a case of multiple roots we must state:

PROPOSITION EIGHT: If a second-order difference equation involves double roots, $x_1 = x_2$, so that $y(t) = (x_1)^t$ satisfies it, then $y(t) = t(x_1)^t$ also satisfies it.[12]

[11] Similarly, in the nth order case where the roots are of multiplicity m, so that we may take $x_1 = x_2 = \cdots = x_m$, the solution given in footnote 6 becomes, on adding the first m terms, $y(t) = c(x_1)^t + b_{m+1}(x_{m+1})^t + \cdots + b_n(x_n)^t$. There are now only $n - m + 1$ arbitrary constants, and if we proceed as in footnote 7 to substitute the above equation into the initial conditions so as to determine the arbitrary constants so that these initial conditions are satisfied, we will find that it is in general impossible, since we have n equations and only $n - m + 1$ unknowns to determine.

[12] *Proof.* If $x^2 + bx + c = 0$ has two equal roots, $x_1 = (-b + \sqrt{b^2 - 4c})/2 = x_2 = (-b - \sqrt{b^2 - 4c})/2$, we must obviously have $\sqrt{b^2 - 4c} = 0$, or $b^2 = 4c$, and $x_1 = x_2 = -b/2$. Thus since $c = b^2/4$, the left-hand side of the equation must be of the form $x^2 + bx + b^2/4$. Hence if a second-order difference equation is to involve multiple roots it must be of the form $y(t) = -by(t-1) - (b^2/4)y(t-2)$. (We ignore any constant term since we are here only concerned with the solution of the reduced equation.) In order to show that $t(x_1)^t = t(-b/2)^t$ satisfies the equation, we must show that

$$y(t) = t(-b/2)^t = -by(t-1) - (b^2/4)y(t-2)$$

Combination of this proposition with Proposition Six tells us that a second-order difference equation with double roots, $x_1 = x_2 = a$, will be satisfied by [13]

$$y(t) = ba^t + cta^t. \tag{36}$$

EXAMPLE 1

With the help of (36) we can now proceed to solve a system with multiple roots for values of b and c satisfying the initial conditions. We may first take the system given at the beginning of this section:

$$y(t) = 4y(t-1) - 4y(t-2)$$

$$y(0) = 5 \qquad y(1) = 6.$$

We already know that this equation involves the double root $x_1 = x_2 = 2$, so from (36) the solution is

$$y(t) = b(2)^t + ct(2)^t.$$

---

but the right-hand side of this equation equals

$$-b\left(-\frac{b}{2}\right)^{t-1}(t-1) - \frac{b^2}{4}\left(-\frac{b}{2}\right)^{t-2}(t-2)$$

$$= 2\left(-\frac{b}{2}\right)\left(-\frac{b}{2}\right)^{t-1}(t-1) - \left(-\frac{b}{2}\right)^2\left(-\frac{b}{2}\right)^{t-2}(t-2)$$

$$= \left(-\frac{b}{2}\right)^t(2t - 2 - t + 2)$$

$$= t\left(-\frac{b}{2}\right)^t$$

as we required. Thus $y(t) = t\left(-\frac{b}{2}\right)^t$ satisfies our difference equation.

It can also be shown that if a is a root of multiplicity m of an nth order equation, that equation will be satisfied by any one of the following expressions: $a^t, ta^t, t^2a^t, \cdots, t^{m-1}a^t$.

[13] Similarly, a solution of the nth order equation with one root of multiplicity m is given by:

$$y(t) = b_1a^t + b_2ta^t + b_3t^2a^t + \cdots + b_mt^{m-1}a^t + b_{m+1}(x_{m+1})^t + \cdots + b_n(x_n)^t$$

where we write $x_1 = x_2 = \cdots = x_m = a$ and where $b_1, b_2, \cdots, b_n$ are arbitrary constants. The result may be readily extended to the case where there is more than one set of multiple roots.

To find values of b and c satisfying the initial conditions, we set

$$y(0) = 5 = b$$

and
$$y(1) = 2b + 2c = 6$$

so that
$$10 - 6 = -2c$$

$$c = -\ 2.$$

The solution is thus

$$y(t) = 5(2)^t - 2t(2)^t.$$

EXAMPLE 2

Secondly, let us solve the system

$$y(t) = 2y(t-1) - y(t-2) + 12$$

$$y(0) = 5 \qquad y(1) = 9.$$

We shall see that this system involves both the special problems considered up to now.

In order to find $X(t)$ satisfying

$$X(t) = 2X(t-1) - X(t-2)$$

we get $x^t = 2x^{t-1} - x^{t-2}$, which gives us the characteristic equation

$$x^2 - 2x + 1 = 0$$

which has the roots

$$x_1 = \frac{2 + \sqrt{4-4}}{2} = 1$$

$$x_2 = \frac{2 - \sqrt{4-4}}{2} = 1$$

so that we have the double root $x_1 = x_2 = 1$. Thus by (36) we have

$$X(t) = a(1)^t + bt(1)^t = a + bt.$$

Since the original equation also has a constant term, 12, we require in addition an expression $Z(t)$ satisfying it. We first try $Z(t) = z$, and by substitution obtain

$$z = 2z - z + 12 \quad \text{or} \quad 12 = 0$$

a nonsense result, so we try instead $Z(t) = zt$, getting

$$zt = 2z(t-1) - z(t-2) + 12 = 2zt - 2z - zt + 2z + 12$$

which again gives $12 = 0$. From Section 5 we know that $Z(t) = zt^2$ is the next possibility, so we substitute, getting

$$\begin{aligned} zt^2 &= 2z(t-1)^2 - z(t-2)^2 + 12 \\ &= 2z(t^2 - 2t + 1) - z(t^2 - 4t + 4) + 12 \\ &= 2zt^2 - 4zt + 2z - zt^2 + 4zt - 4z + 12 \\ &= zt^2 - 2z + 12 \end{aligned}$$

i.e.,

$$z = 6$$

so that we have $Z(t) = zt^2 = 6t^2$, and the solution of our equation is

$$y(t) = X(t) + Z(t) = a + bt + 6t^2.$$

For the initial conditions to be satisfied we require

$$y(0) = a = 5$$

$$y(1) = a + b + 6 = 9$$

so

$$b = -2.$$

The final solution is thus

$$y(t) = 5 - 2t + 6t^2.$$

PROBLEM

1. Solve:

   a) $y(t) = -6y(t-1) - 9y(t-2)$
   b) $y(t) = 10y(t-1) - 25y(t-2)$

7. IMAGINARY AND COMPLEX ROOTS

EXAMPLE

Consider the difference equation

$$y(t) = 2y(t-1) - 5y(t-2).$$

To solve this we proceed as usual, taking $y(t) = x^t$ and getting

$$x^t = 2x^{t-1} - 5x^{t-2}$$

or

$$x^2 = 2x - 5$$

i.e.,

$$x^2 - 2x + 5 = 0$$

which has as its roots

$$x_1 = \frac{2 + \sqrt{4-20}}{2} = \frac{2 + \sqrt{-16}}{2} = \frac{2 + 4\sqrt{-1}}{2} = 1 + 2\sqrt{-1}$$

$$x_2 = \frac{2 - \sqrt{4-20}}{2} = \frac{2 - \sqrt{-16}}{2} = \frac{2 - 4\sqrt{-1}}{2} = 1 - 2\sqrt{-1}$$

so that the solution $y(t) = a(x_1)^t + b(x_2)^t$ is

$$y(t) = a(1 + 2\sqrt{-1})^t + b(1 - 2\sqrt{-1})^t.$$

This result may seem very strange. What does $\sqrt{-1}$ mean? By definition, it is the number which, when multiplied by itself gives -1; i.e., if $i = \sqrt{-1}$, then $i^2 = -1$. But we know that the square of either a positive or a negative number is positive and the square of zero is zero, so that, for example, $5^2 = (-5)^2 = 25$. How then can there be any number, i, whose square is negative?

Imaginary and Complex Numbers

This problem seems first to have been met by the Italian mathematicians of the early renaissance who called i such things as an absurd, fictitious, or imaginary number. This last name has stuck; we call any number such as $4\sqrt{-1} = 4i$ or $773\frac{1}{2}i$ an imaginary number.

This still tells us nothing about such numbers. It will help in understanding the interpretation given below if we first recall that not until the middle ages were negative numbers (or, for that matter, zero) accepted as *bona fide* numbers. It is true that the Greeks conceded a meaning to -4 in the process $5 - 4$, but they saw no sense in the operation $3 - 4$. Only when in India during the middle ages it was realized that a man in debt, for example, could be considered to be in possession of a negative sum of money, did negative numbers begin to be accepted.

An interpretation of this sort for imaginary numbers did not appear until much more recent times. As we shall see, that interpretation is extremely important for our problem. First, however, we may point out that a number such as $1 + 2\sqrt{-1} = 1 + 2i$, the sum of the "real" number 1 and the imaginary number $2i$, is called a complex number. Other complex numbers are $5 - 57.25i$, $333 - i$, and $-4 + 4i$.

In Figure 24 take the point A whose horizontal distance from the origin is one unit and whose vertical distance from the origin is two units. Let us represent horizontal distance by real numbers and vertical distance by imaginary numbers. Then the point A will be

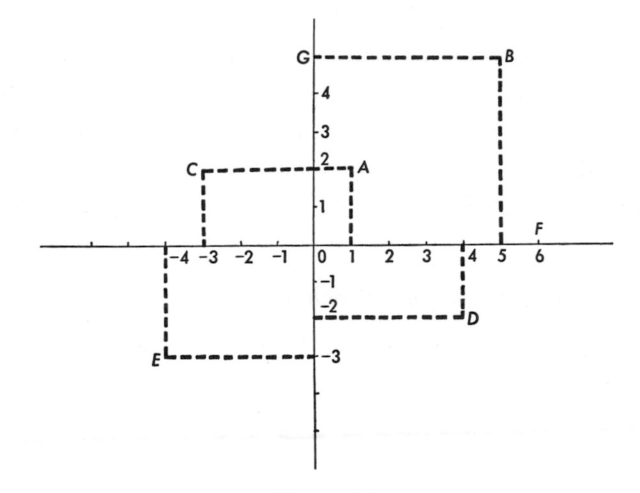

Figure 24

represented by $1+2i$ and, conversely, $1+2i$ will be represented by point A since no other point on the graph corresponds to $1+2i$. Similarly, therefore, point B will be $5+5i$, point C will be $-3+2i$ (since horizontal distance to the left of the origin is taken to be negative), point D will be $4-2i$ (since vertical distance below the origin is taken to be negative), point E will be $-4-3i$, and point F will be $6-0i=6$, so that all points on the x axis represent real numbers; while point G will be $0+5i=5i$, so that all points on the y axis represent imaginary numbers.

Before we can use this geometric interpretation of imaginary and complex numbers it is necessary to know some simple definitions and results of trigonometry, and we now turn to these.

Trigonometric Definitions

To start with, we give a general definition of the sine of an angle. Draw a horizontal line as an x axis and a vertical line as a y axis. Then draw a line from the origin forming an angle, Q, with the portion of the x axis to the right of the origin, and let R be any point on this line. We can consider OR as the hand of a clock starting from position OR' and moving counter clockwise around O as Q increases. Thus in Figure 25a an angle of 45° ($Q=45°$) is represented, 135° in Figure 25b, 225° in Figure 25c, and 315° in Figure 25d. Now there is no reason why we should stop the hand once it has made the full circle. It can go on to its position in Figure 25a making an angle of 405°, and further on to its position in Figure 25b making an angle of 495°, and so on *ad infinitum*. Thus the starting line involves angles of 0°, 360°, 720°, etc., for each complete successive circle of the clock

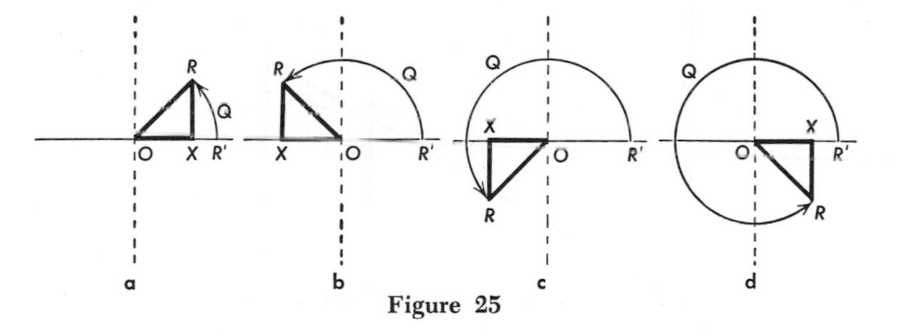

Figure 25

hand. We can also go back and see what happens before it reached the starting position and say that OR' involves angles of $-360°$, $-720°$, etc. For each complete counter clockwise movement 360° is added. Similarly, the clock hand vertical above the origin involves angles of 90°, 450°, 810°, etc., and of $-270°$, $-630°$, etc.

Drop a perpendicular from point R on the clock hand to X on the x axis. We can now define [14] the sine of angle Q (written $\sin Q$) and the cosine of angle Q (written $\cos Q$) thus:

$$\sin Q = \frac{XR}{OR} \qquad \cos Q = \frac{OX}{OR}.$$

The sine of Q is thus the ratio between the vertical distance of R above the origin to the length of the clock hand, while the cosine is the ratio between the horizontal distance of R from the origin to the length of the clock hand.[15]

[14] The definition given here may appear strange to the reader if he remembers the sine of an angle to be defined in terms of a right angled triangle as the ratio of the length of the side opposite the angle to the length of the hypotenuse. Careful consideration will show, however, that this definition corresponds to that given above for angles of less than 90°, while it cannot apply to angles greater than 90°. Our definition is thus more general.

[15] Note that the actual numerical value of $\sin Q$ and $\cos Q$ is not affected by which point on the clock hand we choose to call R. Thus in terms of the figure let us see what happens if we take, say, OR' instead of OR as the length of our clock hand. Now the triangles $OX'R'$ and OXR must be similar, since they each have a right angle and since they have angle Q in common. Therefore, because the corresponding sides of similar triangles are proportional $XR/OR = X'R'/OR'$ and $OX/OR = OX'/OR'$; i.e., we get the same values for $\sin Q$ and $\cos Q$, whichever point on the clock hand we take as R.

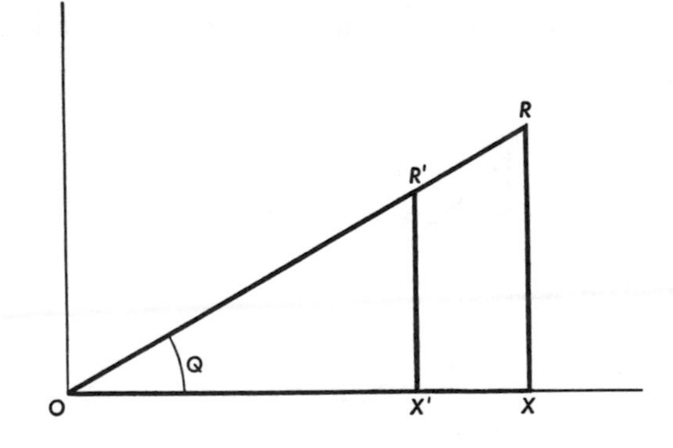

We take OX to be positive if X lies to the right of the origin and negative if X lies to the left of it. Similarly, we take XR to be positive if it is above the horizontal axis and negative if it is below it. OR, however, we always by convention take to be positive. Thus in Figure 25b, XR is positive and OX is negative, so that $\sin Q = XR/OR$ is positive, but $\cos Q = OX/OR$ is negative. The reader may verify that in Figure 25a they are both positive, that in Figure 25c they are both negative, and that in Figure 25d $\sin Q$ is negative while $\cos Q$ is positive.

Periodic Trigonometric Functions

We define the sine function and cosine function as

$$y = \sin Q \text{ and } y = \cos Q$$

respectively, i.e., the values of $\sin Q$ and $\cos Q$ corresponding to every angle Q. By way of illustration we give the following table of values which the reader may easily verify:

Degrees	0	90	180	270	360	450	540	630	720	etc.
$\sin Q$	0	1	0	−1	0	1	0	−1	0	
$\cos Q$	1	0	−1	0	1	0	−1	0	1	

To see how we obtain these figures, suppose that $Q = 0$, which means that the hand is at its starting point. Since the hand coincides with the x axis, the vertical distance of point R above the origin is nil, while its horizontal distance from the origin, OX, equals OR. Hence we have

$$\sin Q = \frac{XR}{OR} = \frac{0}{OR} = 0 \qquad \cos Q = \frac{OX}{OR} = \frac{OR}{OR} = 1.$$

When Q is 90° the hand is vertical so that the vertical distance above the origin of R equals OR, while the horizontal distance of R from the origin is zero. Substituting this information into the formulae gives the information shown in the table.

We note that these values repeat themselves every 360°, because after each complete revolution the clock hand returns to its original position. We therefore call the sine and cosine functions *periodic.* Their graphs look something like Figure 26. Note that since the sine and cosine of an angle repeat themselves every 360° we cannot tell from the sine or cosine of an angle what that angle is unless we

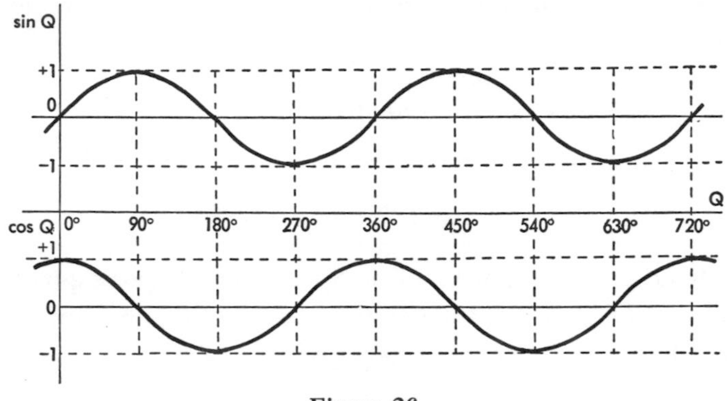

Figure 26

know, say, that it lies between zero and 360°. When we have no other information we always, by convention, assume this to be the case. But even so, given just cos Q (say cos $Q = 0$) we cannot tell what Q is since obviously from Figure 25, $\cos Q = \cos(360 - Q) = \cos(-Q)$, e.g., ($\cos 90 = \cos 270 = 0$), and similarly, given just sin Q (say $\sin Q = 0$), we cannot tell what Q is since $\sin Q = \sin(180 - Q)$. Thus it is only from a knowledge of both sin Q and cos Q that we can ascertain the value of Q.

Since sin Q and cos Q repeat themselves regularly every 360° it should be intuitively obvious that so does

$$e \cos Q + f \sin Q \tag{37}$$

where e and f are any constants. More rigorously, we may state:

PROPOSITION NINE: $e \cos(Q + 360) + f \sin(Q + 360) = e \cos Q + f \sin Q$ since $\sin(Q + 360) = \sin Q$ and $\cos(Q + 360) = \cos Q$.

We shall employ this result presently, but first we must state another trigonometric result:

PROPOSITION TEN: [16] Given $y = a[\cos Q + i \sin Q]$, where $i = \sqrt{-1}$, then any integral power, y^n of y is given by

$$y^n = a^n[\cos (nQ) + i \sin (nQ)]. \qquad (38)$$

Note that while the coefficient a is raised to the power n nothing happens to i and Q becomes nQ.

A Trigonometric Expression for Complex Numbers

We can now return to our graphic representation of complex numbers. Consider for example the complex number $1 + 2i$ represented by point A in Figure 24. Draw a line from O to A and take Q to be the angle made by OA with the x axis. Let X be the point directly below A on the x axis. If we consider OA to be the clock

[16] *Proof.* If there is any number, $m - 1$, for which the formula for y^{m-1} is as stated, then it follows that the formula is also valid for the next higher number, m. For

$$y^m = y^{m-1} \cdot y = \{a^{m-1} \cos [(m-1)Q] + a^{m-1}i \sin [(m-1)Q]\}$$
$$(a \cos Q + ai \sin Q) = a^m \cos [(m-1)Q] \cos Q + a^m i \cos [(m-1)Q] \sin Q$$
$$+ a^m i \sin [(m-1)Q] \cos Q + a^m i^2 \sin [(m-1)Q] \sin Q$$

But since $i^2 = (\sqrt{-1})^2 = -1$, we have, by collecting terms

$$y^m = a^m \{\cos [(m-1)Q] \cos Q - \sin [(m-1)Q] \sin Q\}$$
$$+ a^m i \{\cos [(m-1)Q] \sin Q + \sin [(m-1)Q] \cos Q\}.$$

But it is a well-known result of elementary trigonometry that the expression in the first bracket is equal to $\cos (mQ)$ and that in the second bracket is equal to $\sin (mQ)$, so that we have $y^m = a^m \cos (mQ) + a^m i \sin (mQ)$. Thus if our formula holds for any integral value, $m - 1$, of n, then it holds for the next integer, m. But we can see at once that the formula holds for $n = 1$, since for that value of n,

$$a^n \cos (nQ) + a^n i \sin (nQ) = a \cos Q + ai \sin Q = y.$$

From what we have just proved it follows that since the formula holds for $n = 1$, that it must be true for $n = 2$, and if it is true for $n = 2$ it must be true for the next integer $n = 3$, and so on. Thus eventually it is true for any finite integer greater than 1. Proposition Ten is called De Moivre's theorem.

hand of our foregoing discussion, we can see that

$$\cos Q = \frac{OX}{OA} = \frac{1}{OA}$$

or, multiplying by OA,

$$OA \cos Q = OX = 1.$$

Similarly,

$$\sin Q = \frac{XA}{OA} = \frac{2}{OA}$$

or, multiplying by OA,

$$OA \sin Q = XA = 2.$$

This gives $1 + 2i = OA \cos Q + OAi \sin Q$. We know, moreover, that the length of the clock hand, OA (taken to be constant), is the hypotenuse of the right-angled triangle OXA, and so, by Pythagoras' theorem,

$$\begin{aligned} OA &= \sqrt{(OX)^2 + (AX)^2} \\ &= \sqrt{1^2 + 2^2} \\ &= \sqrt{5} \end{aligned}$$

so that $1 + 2i = \sqrt{5} \cos Q + i\sqrt{5} \sin Q$.

In the same manner we can write any complex number, $c + di$, in the form

$$\sqrt{c^2 + d^2}\,(\cos R + i \sin R)$$

where R is some angle which we can find in any table of sines or cosines by looking up

$$\cos R = \frac{c}{\sqrt{c^2 + d^2}} \quad \text{and} \quad \sin R = \frac{d}{\sqrt{c^2 + d^2}}.$$

$\sqrt{c^2 + d^2}$ is called the modulus of the complex number $c + di$.

Consider now what we call the "complex conjugate" of $c + di$, namely, $c - di$. Thus, for example, the complex conjugate of

$1-2i$ is $1+2i$, and that of $-5-4i$ is $-5+4i$. $c-di$ may analogously be represented by

$$\sqrt{c^2+(-d)^2}\,(\cos S+i\sin S)=\sqrt{c^2+d^2}\,(\cos S+i\sin S)$$

where
$$\cos S=\frac{c}{\sqrt{c^2+d^2}}=\cos R$$
$$\sin S=\frac{-d}{\sqrt{c^2+d^2}}=-\sin R.$$

Thus

$$c+di=\sqrt{c^2+d^2}\,(\cos R+i\sin R) \tag{39}$$
$$c-di=\sqrt{c^2+d^2}\,(\cos R-i\sin R). \tag{40}$$

A Trigonometric Expression for the Solution With Complex Roots

Let us write $D=\sqrt{c^2+d^2}$, the modulus of $c+di$ and of $c-di$, and consider how we can rewrite the expression $a(c+di)^t+b(c-di)^t$, an example of which is the solution to the difference equation given at the beginning of this section:

$$\begin{aligned} y(t) &= a[1+2\sqrt{(-1)}]^t+b[1-2\sqrt{(-1)}]^t \\ &= a(1+2i)^t+b(1-2i)^t. \end{aligned}$$

Substitution from (39) and (40) gives

$$a(c+di)^t+b(c-di)^t=a[D(\cos R+i\sin R)]^t + b[D(\cos R-i\sin R)]^t$$

or, from our example,

$$a(1+2i)^t+b(1-2i)^t=a[\sqrt{5}\,(\cos R+i\sin R)]^t + b[\sqrt{5}(\cos R-i\sin R)]^t.$$

From Proposition Ten we can compute the expressions in brackets raised to the tth power. We get

$$aD^t[\cos(tR)+i\sin(tR)]+bD^t[\cos(tR)-i\sin(tR)]$$

and

$$a(\sqrt{5})^t[\cos(tR)+i\sin(tR)]+b(\sqrt{5})^t[\cos(tR)-i\sin(tR)].$$

Multiplying through and rearranging terms gives

$$D^t[(a+b)\cos(tR)+i(a-b)\sin(tR)]$$

$$(\sqrt{5})^t[(a+b)\cos(tR)+i(a-b)\sin(tR)].$$

Since a and b are completely arbitrary we may without loss of generality write

$$(a+b)=e \qquad i(a-b)=f$$ [17]

so that the above two formulas become

$$D^t[e\cos(tR)+f\sin(tR)]$$

$$(\sqrt{5})^t[e\cos(tR)+f\sin(tR)].$$

Generalizing, we state:

PROPOSITION ELEVEN: The solution of the second-order difference equation involving complex conjugate roots $c+di$ and $c-di$ can be written

$$y(t)=(\sqrt{c^2+d^2})^t[e\cos(tR)+f\sin(tR)]+Z(t) \qquad (41)$$

where $Z(t)$ is a particular solution of the unreduced (nonhomogeneous) equation and e and f are constants to be determined in accordance with the initial conditions.[18]

Fortunately, whenever one of the roots is complex or imaginary, the other will *always* be its complex conjugate, so that wherever complex roots appear, (41) will apply. This can be seen as follows:

$$x_1=\frac{-A+\sqrt{A^2-4B}}{2}=\frac{-A}{2}+\frac{\sqrt{A^2-4B}}{2}$$

$$x_2=\frac{-A}{2}-\frac{\sqrt{A^2-4B}}{2}$$

[17] The reader may feel that we are cheating by writing f for $i(a-b)$, thereby getting rid of i. But since a and b are completely arbitrary, they may well be imaginary, so that it is possible for $i(a-b)$ to be real. For example, if we suppose $a=5+2i$ and $b=5-2i$, then $e=a+b=10$ and $f=i(a-b)$ $=i(5+2i-5+2i)=i(4i)=4i^2=-4$. The reader may verify in this way that we can always make e and f real by choosing a and b to be any pair of complex conjugate numbers.

[18] Note again that $\sqrt{c^2+d^2}$, the modulus of $c+di$ and of $c-di$, is the length of our clock hand and is always taken to be positive.

so that if we write $A^2 - 4B = -g$ where g is a positive number, we have

$$x_1 = \frac{-A}{2} + \frac{\sqrt{g}}{2} i$$

$$x_2 = \frac{-A}{2} - \frac{\sqrt{g}}{2} i$$

and these are obviously complex conjugates.[19]

Example 1

We shall now apply the tools developed above to the solution of the following second-order system involving complex roots:

$$y(t) = -y(t-2) + 12$$

$$y(0) = 11 \qquad y(1) = 5.$$

This is a second-order system although the equation has no term including $y(t-1)$, since the definition of an nth order equation requires only that the coefficients of $y(t)$ and $y(t-n)$ shall be other than zero. We could have written the equation as

$$y(t) = 0y(t-1) - y(t-2) + 12.$$

In order to solve the equation we must first find $Z(t)$. Trying with $Z(t) = z$ gives

$$z = -z + 12$$

i.e.,

$$z = 6$$

so we have $Z(t) = 6$.

[19] It may be noted that complex roots involved in higher order equations also always occur in conjugate pairs. Cf. L. Dickson, *A First Course in the Theory of Equations* (John Wiley and Sons, New York, 1922), p. 19. Thus if in the solution to the nth order equation in footnote 7, x_1 and x_2 are conjugate complex roots, by an extension of Proposition Eleven, the solution may be rewritten as $D^t(b_1 \cos Qt + b_2 \sin Qt) + b_3 x_3^t + \cdots + b_n x_n^t$, where $b_1, b_2, b_3, \cdots, b_n$ are arbitrary constants and where D and Q are found from x_1 and x_2 as in the text. This can be extended to the case of any number of pairs of complex roots in the solution.

Next we want the solution $X(t)$ of the reduced equation

$$y(t) = -y(t-2)$$

and we substitute x^t for $y(t)$, getting

$$x^t = -x^{t-2}$$

i.e.,

$$x^2 = -1$$

or

$$x^2 + 1 = 0.$$

In this simple case we can see directly that this has the complex conjugate roots

$$x_1 = \sqrt{-1} = i = 0 + i$$

$$x_2 = -\sqrt{-1} = -i = 0 - i$$

so we have

$$X(t) = D^t[e \cos(tR) + f \sin(tR)]$$

where $D = \sqrt{0^2 + 1^2} = 1$ and where R is given by

$$\sin R = \frac{1}{D} = 1$$

and $\cos R = 0/D = 0$. From our tables of sines and cosines we see that if $\sin R = 1$ and $\cos R = 0$, R is 90°. Thus we have

$$X(t) = [e \cos(t90) + f \sin(t90)]$$

and the complete solution of the difference equation is

$$y(t) = X(t) + Z(t) = [e \cos(t90) + f \sin(t90)] + 6.$$

In order that the initial conditions be satisfied, we set

$$y(0) = 11 = e \cos(0) + f \sin(0) + 6.$$

Since our table shows $\cos(0) = 1$ and $\sin(0) = 0$, this becomes

$$y(0) = 11 = e + 6$$

i.e.,

$$11 - 6 = e$$

$$e = 5.$$

From the other initial condition we get

$$y(1) = 5 = e \cos(90) + f \sin(90) + 6.$$

By the table this becomes

$$5 = f + 6$$

i.e.,

$$5 - 6 = f$$

$$f = -1.$$

The final solution of the system is therefore

$$y(t) = 5 \cos(t90) - \sin(t90) + 6.$$

Example 2

Let us now take a more complicated system:

$$y(t) = -6y(t-1) - 25y(t-2) + 64$$

$$y(0) = 7 \qquad y(1) = -21.$$

To find $Z(t)$, try $Z(t) = z$. This gives

$$32z = 64$$

$$z = 2.$$

To find $X(t)$, substitute $X(t) = x^t$ into the reduced (homogeneous) equation. We get

$$x^t = -6x^{t-1} - 25x^{t-2}$$

or

$$x^2 + 6x + 25 = 0$$

so that

$$x_1 = \frac{-6 + \sqrt{36 - 100}}{2} = \frac{-6 + \sqrt{-64}}{2} = \frac{-6 + 8i}{2} = -3 + 4i$$

$$x_2 = \frac{-6 - \sqrt{36 - 100}}{2} = \frac{-6 - 8i}{2} = -3 - 4i.$$

Our formula then gives us

$$X(t) = (\sqrt{3^2+4^2})^t[e \cos (tQ) + f \sin (tQ)].$$

Now $\cos Q$ is given by $c/\sqrt{c^2+d^2} = -3/\sqrt{3^2+4^2} = -3/5 = -0.6$, and $\sin Q$ is given by $d/\sqrt{c^2+d^2} = 4/\sqrt{3^2+4^2} = 4/5 = 0.8$. The reader will observe that the cosines and sines given in most trigonometric tables lie between zero and plus one and are all positive. Thus we can look up $\sin Q$ without any difficulty, but since $\cos Q$ is negative we will not find it in the trigonometric table. But we do know that $\cos Q = -\cos (180 - Q)$. This follows at once from the definition and the diagrams, since in the figures we have $\cos Q = OX/OR$, and if OX for angle Q is, say, positive, OX for $(180 - Q)$ is equal to that for Q, but negative, i.e., it lies to the left of the origin. Similarly we have $\sin Q = -\sin(-Q)$, although we do not require this for the solution of our present problem.

We now have

$$\cos (180 - Q) = -\cos (Q) = 0.6$$

and looking this up in the trigonometric tables we have

$$0.6 = \cos (180 - Q) = \cos 53.1 \text{ (approximately)}$$

i.e.,

$$180 - Q = 53.1 \quad \text{or} \quad Q = 180 - 53.1 = 126.9^\circ \text{ (approximately)}.$$

To check this we note that $\sin Q = \sin (180 - Q)$ [just as $\cos(-Q) = \cos Q$ and $\sin (126.9) = \sin (180 - 126.9) = \sin (53.1) = 0.8$ (approximately)] as required by our problem.

We now have

$$y(t) = X(t) + Z(t) = 5^t[e \cos (126.9t) + f \sin (126.9t)] + 2.$$

To find values for e and f we set

$$y(0) = e \cos 0 + f \sin 0 + 2 = e + 2 = 7$$

i.e.,

$$e = 5$$

$$y(1) = 5(5 \cos R + f \sin R) + 2$$

$$= 25\left(-\frac{3}{5}\right) + 5f\frac{4}{5} + 2 = -21$$

i.e.,

$$-15 + 4f + 2 = -21$$

$$4f = 15 - 2 - 21$$

$$= -8$$

$$f = -2.$$

The final solution is thus

$$y(t) = 5^t[5 \cos (t\,126.9°) - 2 \sin (t126.9°)] + 2.$$

PROBLEMS

1. Put the solutions of the following in trigonometric form

   a) $y(t) = -12y(t-1) - 100y(t-2) + 226, y(0) = 4, y(1) = 14$
   b) $y(t) = 24y(t-1) - 225y(t-2), y(0) = 5, y(1) = 69$
   c) $y(t) = 12y(t-1) - 100y(t-2) + 89, y(0) = 3, y(1) = 37$
   d) $y(t) = -24y(t-1) - 225y(t-2), y(0) = 5, y(1) = -69$
   e) $y(t) = -y(t-2), y(0) = 16, y(1) = -7$
   f) Find $y(t)$ for $t = 10$ in problems (a), (c), and (e).

2. Graph the time path of $y(t)$ for the first ten periods in problem (e). Note that the cycles are somewhat "lopsided."

Chapter Eleven

INTERPRETATION OF DIFFERENCE EQUATION MODELS

1. INTERPRETATION OF THE SECOND-ORDER SOLUTIONS

The Roots of the Characteristic Equation and the Time Path of y

We are now in a position to solve all second-order systems and to interpret the solutions in terms of the time sequences which result. For the present ignoring the case of multiple roots and the case where $Z(t)$ is not a constant, we know that the solution will always take the form

$$y(t) = a(x_1)^t + b(x_2)^t + z$$

where a, b, and z are constants, and where x_1 and x_2 are the roots of an equation of the form

$$x^2 + bx + c = 0.$$

On the basis of what we have seen in the last few sections we can classify the various possibilities as follows.

Both Roots Real and Positive (or Zero)

a. If both x_1 and x_2 are less than unity, then both $a(x_1)^t$ and $b(x_2)^t$ will gradually taper off to zero, so that $y(t)$ will approach z

asymptotically roughly as in Figure 27 but presumably in discontinuous steps.

b. If one root, say x_1, is equal to 1 while the other root is less than 1, then $y(t)$ will gradually taper off to $a + z$, since we have $y(t) = a(1)^t + b(x_2)^t + z = a + b(x_2)^t + z$, and the second term will taper off to nothing. Similarly, if $x_2 = 1$ and x_1 is less than 1, $y(t)$ will gradually approach $b + z$.

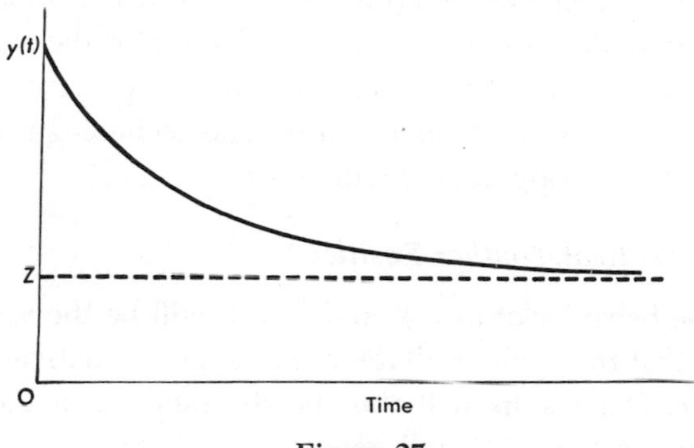

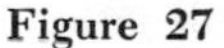
Figure 27

c. If either or both roots exceed unity, $y(t)$ will explode. Thus if x_1 is greater than unity and a and b are positive, $a(x_1)^t$ will (as we saw before) eventually surpass any given finite magnitude and so, therefore, will $y(t)$. If a is negative, then $a(x_1)^t$ will explode downwards. If a is negative and b is positive, the result depends on which of x_1 *and* x_2 is greater, and what eventually happens will be very little affected by the smaller root. Indeed, supposing that x_1 is the larger, $y(t)$ will behave approximately as though it were $y(t) = a(x_1)^t$.

This statement may usefully be generalized into:

PROPOSITION TWELVE: In an expression of the form $y(t) = a(x_1)^t + b(x_2)^t$, where the absolute value [1] of, say, x_2 is less than that of x_1,

[1] Defined in footnote 9, Chapter Nine.

then eventually, i.e., for high values of t, $b(x_2)^t$ will become a very small percentage of the entire expression $y(t)$.[2]

In applying this result the economist must exercise extreme caution in interpretation. Above all he should not place *too* much confidence in the system's predictions as to what will happen eventually. "Eventually" may turn out to be a very long time away; indeed, it may be so far away that before the foreseen outcome materializes, changing conditions may render our original difference-equation system completely inapplicable to the real world. We may thus legitimately describe trends and tendencies of the system, but we must not be surprised if "exogenous causes" prevent their fruition, much as the advent of birth control and technological advance upset the classical population predictions.

Both Roots Real, Neither Positive

Here the behavior of $a(x_1)^t$ and $b(x_2)^t$ will be the same as before, except that they will oscillate, each being alternatively positive and negative. Our results will thus be the same as in the positive roots case, except that $y(t)$ will generally oscillate.

a. If both x_1 and x_2 are less than unity in absolute value (i.e., lie between 0 and -1), $y(t)$ will oscillate about z and the oscillations will eventually die out.

b. If one of the two roots equals -1 while the other is less than 1 in absolute value, the oscillations will tend to sink to the oscillations of, say, $a(x_1)^t$ if $x_1 = -1$. This is a special case of Proposition Twelve: $y(t)$ will tend toward $a(x_1)^t + z = a(-1)^t + z$, and its

[2] We give the proof only for the case where a, b, x_1, and x_2 are all positive. The extension to the general case involves no special difficulties. Since $x_1 > x_2$, we may write $x_1 = kx_2$, where k is a number greater than unity. The proportion, P, of $b(x_2)^t$ to $y(t)$ is

$$P = \frac{b(x_2)^t}{a(x_1)^t + b(x_2)^t} = \frac{b(x_2)^t}{a(kx_2)^t + b(x_2)^t} = \frac{b(x_2)^t}{ak^t(x_2)^t + b(x_2)^t} = \frac{b}{ak^t + b}.$$

Since only ak^t in this last expression depends on t and since it gets larger and larger as t increases, the whole expression gets smaller and smaller, eventually approaching zero. Thus the proportion of $b(x_2)^t$ to $y(t)$ will eventually become negligible.

course over time will be as shown in Figure 28. The amplitude of the fluctuations thus tends toward $2a$; that is, at the upper points $y(t)$ tends toward $z + a$ and at its lower points it tends toward $z - a$.

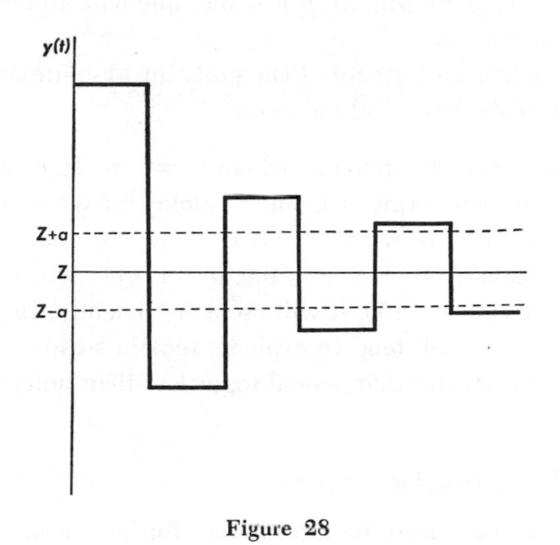

Figure 28

c. Where either root is greater than 1 in absolute value there will be explosive oscillations, since the term with the smaller absolute value will eventually exert only a negligible influence.

One Root Positive, the Other Negative

What will happen here depends on whether the root with the greatest absolute value is positive or negative since, by Proposition Twelve, the influence of the other root eventually becomes negligible. Suppose that, in absolute value, x_1 is the larger root. Then $y(t)$ will ultimately approximate $a(x_1)^t + z$, so that any of the following six cases may ultimately arise:

a. (x_1 positive and less than unity) $y(t)$ will approach z as in Fig. 27
b. ($x_1 = 1$) $y(t)$ will approach the steady level $a + z$
c. (x_1 positive and greater than unity) $y(t)$ will explode

d. (x_1 negative and less than unity in absolute value) $y(t)$ will tend to oscillate about z, and the oscillations will gradually die down
e. ($x_1 = -1$) $y(t)$ will, after a while, fluctuate forever between $z + a$ and $z - a$
f. (x_1 negative and greater than unity in absolute value) $y(t)$ will oscillate explosively about z.

The troublesome case remains where $x_1 = -x_2$. Here we can give no general results in terms of x_1 and x_2 alone, for what happens will depend upon a and b, which are determined by the initial conditions. If $x_1 = 2$ and $x_2 = -2$, $a = 100$, $b = 1$, $y(t)$ will not oscillate, while if $a = 1$ and $b = 100$, it will oscillate violently. In general we may say that $y(t)$ will tend to explode, remain steady, or level out as the roots are greater than, equal to, or less than unity in absolute value.

Complex or Imaginary Roots

This case may easily be interpreted, for, as we have seen, the solution to the difference equation may be written in the form

$$y(t) = D^t[e \cos (tR) + f \sin (tR)] + z \tag{41}$$

where the roots are $c + di$ and $c - di$ and where $D = \sqrt{c^2 + d^2}$ and is positive.

From Proposition Nine it will be seen that the expression in square brackets in (41) will repeat itself every 360°, i.e., each time tR increases by 360°. This means that $y(t)$ will undergo a cycle of length $t = 360/R$. Sin R is given by d/D, so we can find R and hence the length of the cyclical movement from trigonometric tables. If, for example, we find R to be 60°, then the length of the cyclical movement will be six periods.

Some caution is required here, however. It must be remembered that we are dealing with period analysis. We can, in these terms, discuss the situation only once, say, at the end of every period. We can speak of employment at $t = 4$ and $t = 5$, but there is no meaning to the expression "employment at $t = 4.2$" in terms of our present frame of reference. This is because our equation is of such a form as to predict the value of the variable in question at some particular moment or period, t, in terms of its value at $t - 1$, $t - 2$, etc. But there is no information required or implied about the situation at, say, $[(t-1) - (t-2)]/2$.[3]

Now suppose we have $R = 50°$. In this case it is tempting to argue that the expression in square brackets in (41) will repeat itself every $7.2 = 360/50$ periods. But we have seen that this assertion is meaningless in terms of our present analysis. Instead we can say only that the expression in question may be expected to come close to repeating itself every seven periods.[4] In this case, then, where R does not divide 360 exactly, the expression in question will undergo a movement which is only approximately cyclical.

In either case it will be seen that with complex roots we have an element in the solution which fluctuates more or less cyclically and that the length of the cycle varies from case to case. This is much more interesting than the two-period oscillations we encountered earlier.

Another word of caution is called for here. The drawings of the sine and cosine curves in Figure 26 may suggest that a graph of the bracketed expression in (41) would exhibit more or less symmetric cycles. However, because we are now dealing with a difference equation *period* analysis the peak of the smooth graph of (41) which is obtained by letting t vary continuously may not fall at the beginning or middle of a period. In that case the upswing may contain a different number of periods than does the downswing, and the resulting cycles may look "lopsided" as illustrated in Figure 29.

[3] Note that this is what permits us to choose as our angle any one of the angles R, $R + 360$, $R + 720$, etc., where $0 \leqq R < 360°$. For in fact, e.g., $\sin (R + 360)t$ does not behave like $\sin Rt$ *within a period*. Only when t is an integer do the two coincide. If n is any integer, $\sin (R + n\,360)t$, repeats itself n times every period!

[4] We may add, however, that the expression will repeat itself exactly every $36 = 5 \times 360/50$ periods. But the number theorist will note that when $360/R$ is an irrational number (roughly, a nonterminating decimal) the time path will never repeat itself precisely. Moreover, in the mathematician's sense almost all numbers are irrational!

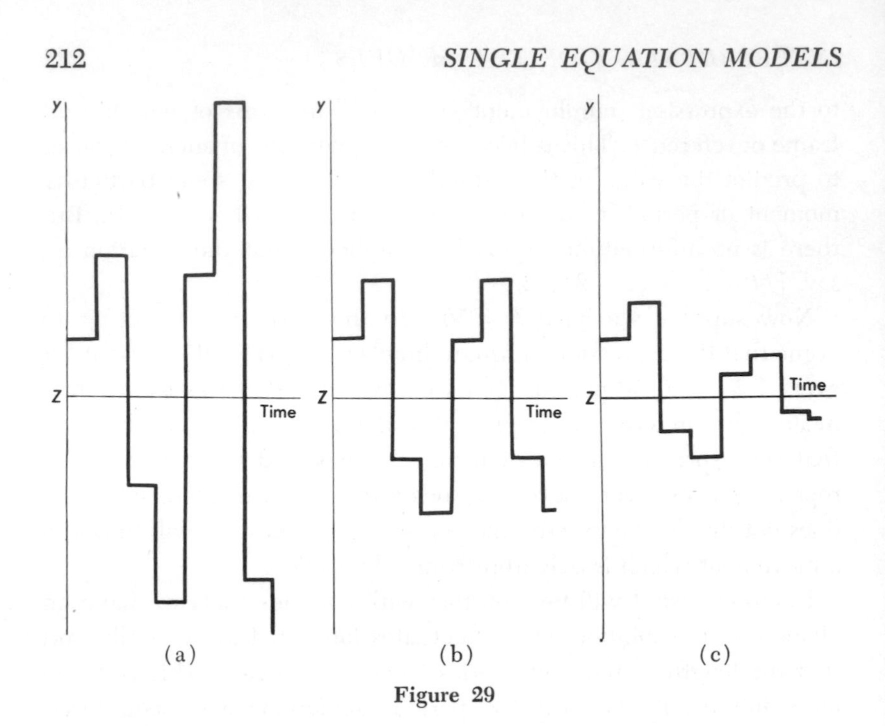

Figure 29

While the factor in brackets in (41) repeats itself more or less periodically in perpetuity, neither dying down nor exploding, it is multiplied by the *t*th power of the modulus of the complex roots, D, which is always positive. There are three cases (cf. Fig. 29):

a. $D > 1$, so D^t explodes, intensifying the fluctuations

b. $D = 1$, so D^t is constant and will have no influence

c. $D < 1$, so D^t will die down, damping the fluctuations.[5]

[5] It is not very difficult to extend these interpretations to cover many of the higher order cases. We need only point out that, where we have the complex root $c + di$, its absolute value is defined to be its modulus, $D = \sqrt{c^2 + d^2}$ (indeed, the words "modulus" and "absolute value" are usually used synonymously). We can then state the following extension of Proposition Twelve: Let A be the greatest of the absolute values of the roots involved in the solution $y(t)$ of the *n*th order equation

$$y(t) = b_1(x_1)^t + b_2(x_2)^t + \cdots + b_n(x_n)^t + z.$$

Then if the absolute value (modulus) of any root, x_r is less than A, the effect of the term $b_r(x_r)^t$ will eventually become negligible. We can thus conclude that, if all roots are less than 1 in absolute value, $y(t)$ will eventually approach z. If

2. EQUILIBRIUM AND STABILITY

Equilibrium and the Stationary Equilibrium Definition

We are now in a position to examine more carefully the central problem of Chapter Seven, that of equilibrium and stability in a dynamic system.

Suppose we are given a first-order equation, $y(t) = ay(t-1) + b$, and we find that there exists some constant z such that if $y(t-1) = z$, then $y(t) = az + b = z$. In other words for this value of y we always have $y(t) = y(t-1)$. In this case we define z as a stationary equilibrium value of y because if y takes on this value during one period, then in the absence of any disturbance from outside the system y will take on that value period after period—forever.

More generally for the nth order equation (29) we define a stationary equilibrium value of y as follows. Let z again be a constant, and take as our initial conditions $y(t-1) = y(t-2) = \cdots = y(t-n) = z$ where t represents any specific date. Then if on substituting these values into (29) we also obtain $y(t) = z$, i.e., if

$$a_1z + a_2z + \cdots + a_nz + b = z \qquad (42)$$

we say that z is the equilibrium value of y.

---

the root of greatest modulus value is equal to unity in absolute value, $y(t)$ will neither approach z nor explode, while if any root is greater than 1 in absolute value, $y(t)$ will explode. If there is only one root or pair of conjugate complex roots of modulus A, then the system will fluctuate, oscillate, or do neither as this root is complex, real and negative, or real and positive. When, however, there is more than one root whose absolute value is A, and these roots are not all of the same sort, e.g., some are real and others complex, we run into trouble again, and here the results will depend on the magnitudes of $b_1, b_2, \cdots, b_n$, which in turn depend on the initial conditions.

The words "oscillate" and "fluctuate" are not used in any precise sense. Our working definition is that an oscillation is necessarily two periods in length and is what we expect to result from negative roots, while a fluctuation is generally over two periods in length and is what we expect to result from complex roots. We might not expect oscillations to occur in economic problems as frequently as do fluctuations in the sense in which the terms are here used.

Stationary Equilibrium and the Particular Solution

But we shall show now that this z is also the particular solution of our difference equation (29), i.e., it is the constant term in the first equation of this chapter or in equation (41). For it will be remembered that to find the particular solution we substitute throughout the equation the constant $Z(t) = z$ for $y(t)$, and solve for z. But this means that we are finding a particular solution z such that $y(t) = y(t-1) = \cdots = y(t-n) = z$ so that z is a stationary equilibrium value of y as defined above.[6]

We have thus defined a stationary equilibrium value of our variable and identified it as the term in the solution which represents the constant particular solution of the nonhomogeneous equation. It follows incidentally that zero is a stationary equilibrium value of the variable of a homogeneous equation. For in such an equation the constant term, b, is always zero, and setting $b = 0$ in (42) we find that $z = 0$ is a particular (equilibrium) value of y.

Stability: Definition

We turn to the second central concept of Chapter Seven—that of stability. It is now easily defined. The solution of a difference equation is stable if, whenever the variable does not start out at equilibrium (i.e. the initial conditions are not $y(t) = y(t-1) = \cdots = y(t-n) = z$), the value of the variable converges toward its equilibrium value z.

For example, Figures 27 and 29c represent the time paths of *stable* solutions because the value of $y(t)$ approaches closer and closer to z and if we are willing to wait long enough $y(t)$ will approach as close to z as we like. On the other hand neither Figures 28, 29a nor 29b represent a stable equilibrium. Without outside interference, waiting until doomsday will not permit us to see y coming close to z.

[6] Indeed, substitution of $Z(t) = z$ for every y in (29) yields the equation $a_1z + \cdots + a_nz + b = z$ which appears as equation (42) in the definition of the equilibrium of y above. In other words the equilibrium value of y in (29) and the particular solution for that equation are found by solving the same equation (42) for the value of z.

The reader should have noted already that we have merely defined stability as the damped class of solutions of a difference equation. We may conclude at once from the material of the preceding section that the solution is stable if and only if *every one* of the roots of the characteristic equation is less than unity in absolute value. For otherwise the solution will either explode or approach a constant value (or a cycle of constant amplitude).

We may note that in the stable case, except for the particular solution z, every one of the terms in the solution of the difference equation approaches zero asymptotically. These terms are therefore sometimes referred to as the *transient* part of the solution.

Multiple Roots and Non-Constant Particular Solutions: Moving Equilibrium

In this section we shall do no more than state the results since their proofs are a bit beyond the level of difficulty of this discussion. In the cases now considered there will be multiple roots terms in the solution of the form

$$at^r(x)^t$$

where a is a constant and r a positive whole number, or a particular solution term

$$bt^r$$

where b is a constant.[7]

Consider first the influence of terms like bt^r. It will be recalled from the preceding chapter that such a term will occur only when there is no constant z which satisfies the difference equation. In other words such an equation does not permit its variable to take any stationary equilibrium value. In such a case we speak of bt^r as

[7] Where the multiple roots are complex (this requires an equation of the fourth or greater order), the solution includes terms of the form $t^rD^t[e \cos Qt + f \sin Qt]$, and the interpretation of the result can be inferred by the reader from the interpretation of t^rD^t and that of $e \cos Qt + f \sin Qt$, both of which have been given in the text.

a *moving equilibrium*.[8] It is clear that this term imparts an upward trend to the solution. This is a straight-line trend when $r = 1$ and explosive when $r > 1$. Thus where there is such a term the results illustrated in Figure 29b will be changed to those shown in Figures 30a and 30b, as $r = 1$ or $r = 2$ respectively. Observe that the upward trend may transform small downward movements (crises?) into upward movements, as can be seen by comparing the change from $y(6)$ to $y(7)$ in Figures 29b and 30b.

Second, let us consider the influence of terms like $at^r(x)^t$. If x is greater than unity in absolute value, then the term is explosive in any event and the presence of the factor t^r will not make much difference; in the long run the violence of the explosion of $(x)^t$ will overshadow its effect.

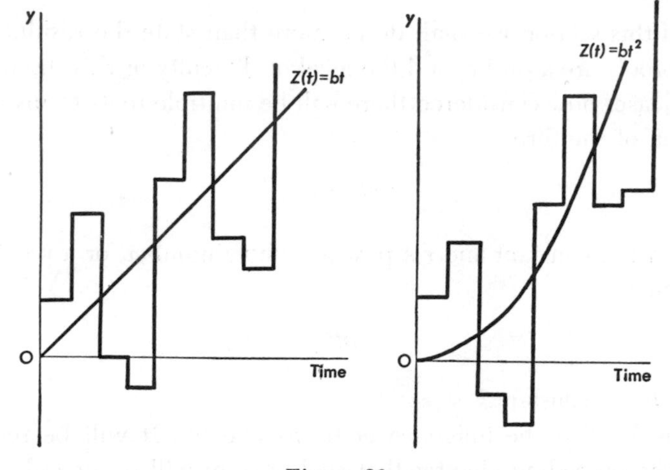

Figure 30

Where $x = 1$, then $at^r(x)^t = at^r(1)^t = at^r$ and we have the same result as has just been considered. If $x = -1$, then $at^r(x)^t = at^r(-1)^t$, and this term will behave just as at^r does, except that its values will oscillate, being alternatively positive and negative.

[8] Such a moving equilibrium will also generally apply when the nonhomogeneous term in a difference equation is itself some variable function of time, $f(t)$. See the differential equation case discussed in Chapter Fourteen, Section 8.

Finally, where x is less than unity in absolute value, so that $a(x)^t$ will die down to zero, it might be supposed that this tendency could sometimes be offset by the explosive tendency of t^r. Here, however, we have the remarkable result that no matter how great r is, t^r will never be able to offset the damping effect of $(x)^t$. A term $at^r(x)^t$, where x is less than unity in absolute value, will thus always die down to zero.

3. QUALITATIVE ANALYSIS IN THE FIRST- AND SECOND-ORDER CASES

A First-Order Case

With first- and second-order systems, since we have convenient formulas for the roots in the second-order case and since the root is obvious in the first-order case, we can obtain more general results than is possible simply with the help of specific numerical problems.

In Section 2 of Chapter Nine we obtained

$$y(t) = y_0 \left(\frac{g}{g - s}\right)^t$$

as the solution to the first-order system, giving Mr. Harrod's warranted rate of growth, so that $g/(g - s)$ was the relevant root. We know that six general types of behavior are possible: $y(t)$ may explode, stay constant, or it may move in a stable manner toward its zero equilibrium value, and it may or may not oscillate.

Thus if, for example, $y(t)$ is to be constant without oscillations, the relevant root must be unity, i.e.,

$$\frac{g}{g - s} = 1 \quad \text{or} \quad g = g - s \quad \text{or} \quad s = 0.$$

The condition for this result is thus that the average propensity to save will be zero.

We can also determine the conditions in which the other four types of behavior will result. The results may be summarized graphically as shown in Figure 31.

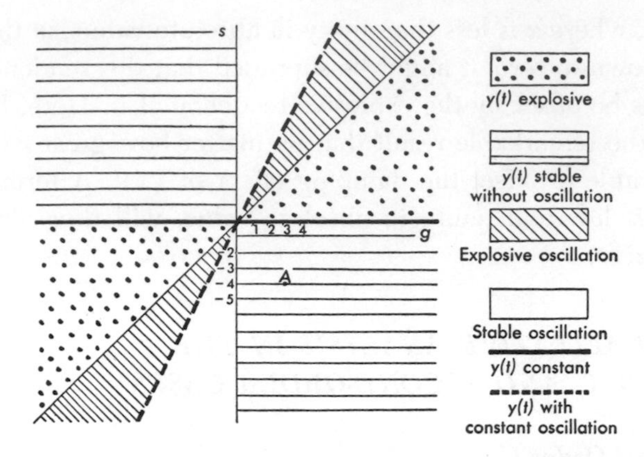

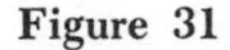
Figure 31

In Figure 31 plot g on the horizontal axis and s on the vertical axis. Then for $s = 2g$, the heavy dotted line, there will be oscillations which neither explode nor die down. Similarly, for $s = 0$, the x axis, $y(t)$ will be steady. The diagram will also be divided by the conditions

$\frac{g}{g-s} > 1$: $y(t)$ will explode $\qquad -1 < \frac{g}{g-s} < 0$: stable oscillations in $y(t)$

$0 < \frac{g}{g-s} < 1$: $y(t)$ stable $\qquad \frac{g}{g-s} < -1$: explosive oscillations in $y(t)$.

Let us see how we find the conditions in which each of these types of behavior will result. For the explosive case, i.e., for $g/(g-s) > 1$, we have two subcases:

a. If g is greater than s so that $g - s$ is positive we require $g > g - s$ or $0 > -s$; i.e., $s > 0$.

b. On the other hand, if g is less than s so that $g - s$ is negative we require [9] $g < g - s$ or $0 < -s$; i.e., $s < 0$.

[9] It must be remembered that, if $a > b$ and c is negative, $ca < cb$. For example, $5 > 4$ and with $c = -2$ we have $-2 \times 5 = -10$ and $-2 \times 4 = -8$, so that $-2 \times 5 < -2 \times 4$.

Thus $y(t)$ will be explosive if s is positive and g is greater than s, and if s is negative and g is less than s.

The conditions in which each of the other three types of behavior will result can be determined similarly.

To see the significance of the diagram let us see, for example, what will occur when $g = 3$ and $s = -4$. We look at the point representing this (point A) and see that it lies in the horizontally shaded area, which shows that $y(t)$ will be stable.

The Second-Order Case

The same sort of classification of results by this kind of analysis is also possible in second-order systems. Consider, for example, the Samuelson model (Section 1, Chapter Ten). There we obtained the difference equation

$$y(t) = (c + B)y(t-1) - By(t-2) \tag{14}$$

whose solution involves the roots of

$$x^2 - (c + B)x + B = 0$$

i.e.,

$$x_1 = \frac{c + B + \sqrt{(c+B)^2 - 4B}}{2} \qquad x_2 = \frac{c + B - \sqrt{(c+B)^2 - 4B}}{2}.$$

If the system is to involve fluctuations, these roots must be complex or imaginary, which requires that $(c + B)^2 - 4B$ be negative, i.e.,

$$(c + B)^2 < 4B.$$

Similarly, we can find the combinations of c and B from which each type of behavior of $y(t)$ through time will result, and, if we wish, we can summarize our results diagrammatically.[10]

The following four basic simple rules may help in qualitative

[10] Professor Samuelson has done this in his "Interactions Between the Multiplier Analysis and the Principle of Acceleration," *The Review of Economic Statistics,* May 1939, reprinted in *Readings in Business Cycle Theory* (The Blakiston Company, Philadelphia and Toronto, 1944). The system presented here differs from Samuelson's presentation in some unimportant respects.

analysis: If we write our second-order difference equation in the form

$$y(t) + by(t-1) + cy(t-2) + d = 0$$

then

a. If b is negative and c is positive neither of the roots of the characteristic equation will be negative [apply this to (14)]
b. If both b and c are positive, neither of the roots will be positive[11]
c. If c is negative, both roots will be real and one will be positive and the other negative[12]
d. If $b^2 < 4c$ so that the roots are complex, then the modulus (absolute value) of the roots is $\sqrt{c}$ and the solution will be stable if and only if $c < 1$.[13]

[11] More generally the equation

$$x^n - b_1x^{n-1} + b_2x^{n-2} - b_3x^{n-3} + \cdots = 0$$

where $b_1, b_2, \cdots, b_n$ are all positive, has no negative roots. For x^n, x^{n-1}, x^{n-2}, etc., are alternately positive and negative if x is negative, e.g., $(-2)^4 > 0$, $(-2)^3 < 0$, $(-2)^2 > 0$, etc. Therefore, all the terms on the left-hand side of the equation will be positive or all the terms will be negative, and so they cannot possibly add up to zero. E.g., in the expression $x^2 - 3x + 4$ we have for $x = -2$: $(-2)^2 - 3(-2) + 4$ all of whose terms are positive.

Similarly, the equation $x^n + b_1x^{n-1} + b_2x^{n-2} + \cdots + b_n = 0$ cannot have a positive root, since for x positive all the terms on the left-hand side of the equation would be positive and so could not add up to zero.

[12] The first part of the statement is obvious, since the roots of the equation are $\frac{-b + \sqrt{b^2 - 4c}}{2}$ and $\frac{-b - \sqrt{b^2 - 4c}}{2}$ so that if c is negative $b^2 - 4c$ must be positive and so $\sqrt{b^2 - 4c}$ must be real. The second part follows from the observation that with c negative we have $\sqrt{b^2 - 4c} > \sqrt{b^2}$ = the absolute value of b. Therefore, the first root listed in the initial sentence of this footnote must be positive and the second must be negative. More general results on the relation between polynomial coefficients and roots can be obtained from the so-called factor theorem of algebra. This states that $a_1, a_2, \cdots, a_n$ are the n roots of $x^n + b_1x^{n-1} + \cdots + b_n = 0$, if and only if $(x - a_1)(x - a_2) \cdots (x - a_n) = x^n + b_1x^{n-1} + \cdots + b_n$. For examples of such results see any introductory text on the theory of equations. It is with the aid of the factor theorem that we "cooked up" the problems.

[13] *Proof*. The modulus of the complex root $r + si = -\frac{b}{2} + i\frac{\sqrt{4c - b^2}}{2}$ is $\sqrt{r^2 + s^2} = \sqrt{\frac{b^2}{4} + \frac{4c - b^2}{4}} = \sqrt{c}$.

Using these results and the sort of reasoning employed in constructing Figure 31 we can derive the following diagram which is the analogue of Figure 31 for our general second order equation:

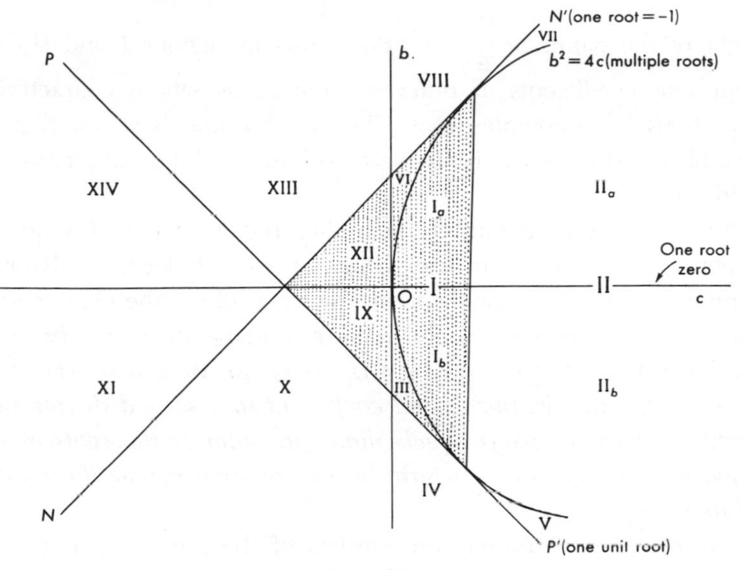

Figure 32

This figure shows what sorts of time path of the variable follow from different values of the coefficients b and c of the difference equation. It will be noted that the diagram has been divided into fourteen regions each of which corresponds to a different type of time path. For example we have:

I. stable fluctuation (complex roots, absolute value less than unity)
II. explosive fluctuation (complex roots, absolute value greater than unity)
III. stable without oscillation (both roots positive, less than unity)
IV. ultimately explosive without oscillation (both roots positive, one greater, the other less than unity)
V. explosive without oscillation (both roots greater than unity)
VI. stable oscillation (both roots negative, less than unity in absolute value) and so on.

This diagram is derived as follows:

Regions I and II: complex roots occur if and only if $(b^2 - 4c) < 0$ so that all points with c greater than $\frac{b^2}{4}$, i.e., all points which lie to the right of the parabola $\frac{b^2}{4} = c$ (the points in regions I and II) will represent coefficients of difference equations whose characteristic equations have complex roots. The border line between region I (stable) and region II is the vertical line $c = 1$ (by observation d. above).

For the mapping out of remaining regions we first require a theorem fundamental in the theory of second degree polynomial equations. By the factor theorem (footnote 12) if the characteristic equation $x^2 + bx + c$ has the roots r_1 and r_2, then $x^2 + bx + c = (x - r_1)(x - r_2) = x^2 - (r_1 + r_2)x + r_1r_2$ so that $b = -(r_1 + r_2)$ and $c = r_1r_2$ that is, *the second coefficient in a second degree polynomial equation always equals minus the sum of the roots of that equation and the constant term in the equation equals the product of its roots.*[14]

We can now determine the borders of the remaining regions in Figure 32. Let us show that region III contains the coefficients of all equations both of whose roots are positive and less than unity. We do this in several steps tracing out each of the borderlines of region III in turn.

i. (Positive roots occur in the southeast quadrant as does region III.) Since both roots are positive we must have $c = r_1r_2 > 0$ and $b = -(r_1 + r_2) < 0$ so that all points in region III must lie below the c axis and to the right of the b axis, i.e., they must all lie in the southeast quadrant of the figure.[15]

[14] For a generalization of this theorem see Proposition 6a of Chapter Sixteen, Section 4, below.

[15] Conversely, by observation b. above, if coefficient b is negative and c is positive the equation can have no negative roots. Hence, at every point in this quadrant both roots are either positive or complex and so any such point which is not in region I or II must represent the coefficients of an equation both of whose roots are positive.

ii. (Positive roots both less than unity occur above line PP'.)[16] Since both roots are less than unity the expressions $1 - r_1$ and $1 - r_2$ are both positive and so is their product. Hence we have

$$0 < (1 - r_1)(1 - r_2) = 1 - (r_1 + r_2) + r_1 r_2 = 1 + b + c,$$

i.e.,

$$b > -c - 1.$$

Thus any point in region III must have a b value greater than $-c - 1$, i.e., it must lie above the line $b = -c - 1$ which is the line PP' in the diagram.

iii. (Positive roots both less than unity occur to the left of $c = 1$.) Since r_1 and r_2 are both less than unity, $c = r_1 r_2$ is less than unity.

iv. Summary: we have now proved that region III (the region of stable non-oscillation, i.e., with both roots positive and less than unity) is as shown in the diagram. For region III must not include any of regions I or II in which the roots are complex. It must lie in the southeast quadrant to the left of $c = 1$ and above the line PP'. This is the region shown in the diagram.[17]

An important use of Figure 32 is for the analysis of the effects of changes in the coefficients of the difference equation on the behavior of the system. Frequently such an investigation yields surprising results. For example, policies which are plausibly alleged always to increase the stability of a dynamic system sometimes are shown to

[16] To locate the borderline PP' in the first place we note that the region in question ends when one of the roots becomes unity. Thus set, say, $r_1 = 1$. This gives $b = -r_1 - r_2 = -1 - r_2$ and $c = r_1 r_2 = r_2$ so that $b = -1 - r_2 = -1 - c$.

[17] We have thus proved that less than unit positive roots will occur only at points in region III. But we have not proved the converse, that every point in region III corresponds to this type of roots. How do we know, for example, that some point involving roots greater than unity has not sneaked into region III? The answer is that this will be taken care of automatically as each type of root is confined to a different region of the figure. For example, we have already seen that all complex root points occur in regions I and II and so none of these can be in region III. Similarly, each other type of root (other than less than unit positive roots) can one by one be shown to belong in other regions. Hence the converse follows automatically: no root of any other type can possibly occur in region III.

do so only under rather special circumstances. If the policy in question can be examined with the aid of a second-order difference equation model we need only see whether it moves the point in Figure 32 which represents the coefficients b and c of the equation, toward the origin of the diagram so that the roots must become smaller in absolute value (cf. footnote 12, above). Similarly, the diagram can be used to examine the effects of the proposed change on the other characteristics of the system, e.g., what it would do to the frequency with which cycles will occur in the system. Methods by means of which the last question can be investigated are indicated in problem 7 below.

PROBLEMS

1. Complete the computations required in drawing Figure 31.
2. The equations

$$S(t) = sy(t-1)$$
$$I(t) = g[y(t) - y(t-1)]$$

for $S(t) = I(t)$ give the difference equation

$$y(t) = \frac{s+g}{g} y(t-1).$$

Draw the graph corresponding to Figure 31 for this equation. Compare the problem at the end of Section 4 of Chapter Nine.

3. Prove that regions IV, V and VI in Figure 32 are as described in the text.
4. What type of roots correspond to each of regions VII to XIV in Figure 32? Give proofs.
5. Derive Chart 2 in Samuelson, *op. cit.*
6. Use Figure 32 to show that in the Samuelson model a simultaneous decrease in the accelerator coefficient B and in the marginal propensity to consume, c [equation (14)] is stabilizing.
7. a) Show that, in the complex roots case the greater is the value of R in equation (41) the more frequently will new cycles occur, i.e., the shorter will be their duration.

   b) Noting that R and $\cos R$ vary inversely for $O \leq R \leq 90°$ (cycles no shorter than four periods) discuss within this range how the frequency of the cycle varies with the values of the coefficients

b and c of our difference equation. [Hint: recall that for complex roots $r + si$ we have (page 198) $\cos R = r/\sqrt{r^2 + s^2}$ so that by footnote 13, above, $\cos R = -b/(2\sqrt{c})$].

c) In Figure 32 draw in several "iso frequency curves" [equations: $-b/(2\sqrt{c}) =$ constant] and discuss their significance.

d) How would "iso stability curves" be constructed?

4. EXPECTATIONS

Although all the models discussed in the preceding part of this book are examples of period analysis, we have said very little about *ex ante* and *ex post* magnitudes. These two concepts are nevertheless implicit in our analysis as can easily be shown. Let us, for example, consider the simple multiplier analysis in Section 5, Chapter Nine in terms of the factor market.

When, in period 0, I is spent, the income was not expected and so has no effect on consumption. Income *ex post* is greater than income *ex ante*, and the difference, I, constitutes unintended (*ex post*) saving. In the following period, if expected income equals the *ex post* income of the preceding period, income *ex ante* will be $I[= E(0)]$, so that *ex ante* consumption (and *ex post* consumption) will be $cE(0)$ and *ex ante* saving will be $(1 - c)E(0)$. Income *ex post*, however, will equal only $cE(0)$ since investment is now zero and is thus equal to consumption so that saving *ex post* is zero. Again, investment and saving are equal *ex post*. The reader will see that statement in these terms merely involves application of the concepts developed in the chapter on period analysis. In the simple multiplier analysis little is gained by this, but the understanding of more complicated problems is considerably facilitated if the distinction between *ex ante* and *ex post* magnitudes is used.

In any period analysis some assumption must be made concerning expectations of income, prices, and so on. It is obviously reasonable to suppose that, say, the price expected at any time depends to a considerable extent upon present and recent prices. Now obviously expectations of what price will be in the future are rather indefinite, and their determination must be a matter of great complexity. If, however, we are to construct any dynamic models at all a crude assumption must be made. A useful and simple one is that the price expected for any period equals the price of the previous period plus some proportion, B, of the price change of that period. Thus if we write P for price we have

$$\text{Expected } P(t) = P(t-1) + B[P(t-1) - P(t-2)].$$[18]

If we take $B = 0$, then we have the special case where present prices are expected to continue unchanged. This is the assumption which we have made in most of the models presented in this book. In many cases, however, interestingly different results can be obtained if B is taken as positive or negative. If B is positive that means that people expect price to go on rising (falling) if it has been rising (falling) recently and to remain constant if it has not changed recently. If B is negative then people expect recent price changes to be partly or wholly reversed.

The immense simplifications involved in the formula suggested are self-evident, and it will therefore suffice here to point out only the two most important factors other than recent price changes which may affect expected price. First, if the idea of some normal price is strong, the position of actual price relative to this normal price will have an influence on expectations. Second, consideration of the factors determining price will play a share. Thus if farmers expect a good harvest and general depression they will be pessimistic in their price expectations.

The reader may at this point ask what is the connection between B (which may be called the "coefficient of expectation") and the Hicksian concept of the elasticity of expectations. The answer is that they are quite different, as can be seen by comparing our formula above with the formula for the elasticity of expectations:

$$\frac{\text{Proportional change in expected price}}{\text{Proportional change in present price}}.$$

[18] See Metzler, "The Nature and Stability of Inventory Cycles," *Review of Economic Statistics*, 1941.

This does not tell us what expected price *is* but merely *how it changes* when present price changes. Thus its field of application lies entirely within comparative statics, and it is of no use for period analysis.[19]

[19] It is often incorrectly interpreted as

$$\frac{\text{Expected proportional change in price}}{\text{Proportional change in present price}}$$

i.e.,

$$\frac{\left(\dfrac{\text{Expected future price} - \text{present price}}{\text{Present price}}\right)}{\text{Proportional change in present price}}.$$

This concept can be used in period analysis, but it must be clearly distinguished from the Hicksian concept. Metzler, *op. cit.*, indicates the relationship between the coefficient of expectation and this sham elasticity in a footnote on p. 119.

Chapter Twelve

COMPUTATION IN HIGHER ORDER SYSTEMS

1. REVIEW

We have already described much of the technique needed to solve higher order linear difference equations. This is shown by the following illustrations:

Example 1

Solve

$$y(t) = y(t-1) + 10y(t-2) + 8y(t-3) + 36$$

with initial values $y(0) = -15$, $y(1) = 26$ and $y(2) = -30$. First, to find a particular solution, $Z(t)$, we try a constant $Z(t) = z$ and get

$$z = z + 10z + 8z + 36.$$

Thus $z = -2 = Z(t)$. Next we find the solution $X(t)$ of the reduced equation

$$y(t) = y(t-1) + 10y(t-2) + 8y(t-3).$$

This involves the roots of

$$x^t = x^{t-1} + 10x^{t-2} + 8x^{t-3} \quad \text{or} \quad x^3 = x^2 + 10x + 8$$

i.e.,

$$x^3 - x^2 - 10x - 8 = 0.$$

We have so made up the problem that this equation has the roots $x_1 = 4$, $x_2 = -2$, and $x_3 = -1$, as the reader may verify by trying them. Thus we have

$$X(t) = a(4)^t + b(-2)^t + c(-1)^t$$

where a, b, and c are arbitrary constants. Hence, the solution to our difference equation is

$$y(t) = X(t) + Z(t) = a(4)^t + b(-2)^t + c(-1)^t - 2.$$

In order that the initial conditions be satisfied we substitute this result into the equations giving those conditions, and we get

(a) $a + b + c - 2 = -15$, or $a + b + c = -13$

(b) $4a - 2b - c - 2 = 26$, or $4a - 2b - c = 28$

(c) $16a + 4b + c - 2 = -30$, or $16a + 4b + c = -28$.

Adding (b) successively to (a) and (c) we get

(1a) $5a - b = 15$
(1b) $20a + 2b = 0$.

Multiplying (1a) through by 2 we get

(2a) $10a - 2b = 30$

which when added to (1b) gives

(3a) $30a = 30$, or $a = 1$.

This result substituted in (1a) gives $5 - b = 15$, or $b = -10$, and these results for a and b, when substituted into (a), give $1 - 10 + c = -13$, or $c = -4$. Thus the final result is given by $y(t) = (4)^t - 10(-2)^t - 4(-1)^t - 2$. Thus $y(t)$ will oscillate at first, since $x_2 = -2$ and $x_3 = -1$ are negative and since their coefficients, $a = -10$ and $b = -4$, are so great in absolute value as to outweigh the influence of the first term in the beginning. But since the root of greatest absolute value, $x(1) = 4$, is positive, we know that ultimately its influence will predominate, so that after a while oscillations will disappear and $y(t)$ will explode upwards.

Example 2

Solve

$$y(t) = 3y(t-1) - 7y(t-2) - 71y(t-3) - 24y(t-4) + 100y(t-5).$$

This involves the roots of

$$x^t = 3x^{t-1} - 7x^{t-2} - 71x^{t-3} - 24x^{t-4} + 100x^{t-5}$$

i.e., of

$$x^5 = 3x^4 - 7x^3 - 71x^2 - 24x + 100.$$

This is another "cooked-up" problem, and we know that the roots are $x_1 = 3 + 4i$, $x_2 = 3 - 4i$, $x_3 = -2$, $x_4 = -2$, and $x_5 = 1$. This involves two complex roots and one pair of multiple roots, and the reader can verify that the solution of the difference equation will be of the form

$$y(t) = [\sqrt{(3)^2 + (4)^2}]^t[e \cos (tR) + f \sin (tR)] + a(-2)^t + bt(-2)^t + c(1)^t$$

and since $\sqrt{(3)^2 + (4)^2} = \sqrt{9 + 16} = 5$ and is greater than 1, the complex roots will be the roots of greatest absolute value, so that we know that ultimately the time path of $y(t)$ must involve explosive fluctuations.

2. *THE ROLE OF THE CHARACTERISTIC EQUATION*

Roots of Higher Degree Polynomial Equations

The major difficulty which arises in solving higher-order difference equations is encountered when one seeks the roots of the characteristic equation.[1] In other respects the method of solution is a simple extension of the second-order procedure as the preceding illustrations show. But, for example, solution of the fifth-order equation $y(t) = 3y(t-1) - 7y(t-2) - 71y(t-3) - 24y(t-4) +$

[1] We shall see that this problem also arises in the solution of simultaneous difference and differential equation systems. See below, Chapters Fifteen and Sixteen.

$100y(t-5)$ requires us to find the five roots of the fifth degree polynomial equation

$$x^5 = 3x^4 - 7x^3 - 71x^2 - 24x + 100$$

and this is no straightforward matter.

Quadratic (second degree) polynomial equations can, as we know, be solved by application of a very simple formula. Third and fourth degree equations of this variety can also be solved by algebraic methods although the procedure is considerably more complex than that which applies in the second degree case. However, except in some special cases fifth and higher degree polynomial equations cannot be solved by algebraic methods. Indeed, it has been proved that it is impossible to find an algebraic expression which represents the general solution of such a higher degree polynomial!

Approximation Methods

There do however exist methods which can give us both qualitative and quantitative information about the roots of any such equation. Even where the value of such a root cannot be found precisely, it can, given enough time and effort, be located to any desired degree of approximation; that is, we can find a number which differs by no more than any arbitrarily chosen tolerance limit such as 0.0001 from the root whose true value we seek.

A detailed introduction to the art of numerical computation is beyond the scope of this book. But we shall illustrate the methods sufficiently to offer the reader some idea of the techniques which are involved. It is also hoped that this discussion can serve as an introduction to those who wish to do some numerical computation and permit them to follow up the details by themselves.

3. QUALITATIVE INFORMATION ON REAL ROOTS

Information Provided by Sturm's Method

As we have seen, the nature of the time path of the variable is heavily dependent on the location of the roots. We know a great deal about the history of the variable when we have found out how many roots are real, how many are positive, how many negative, how many are greater than unity, how many less than -1, etc. In this section we describe a very powerful and ingenious procedure (Sturm's method) for answering such qualitative questions. We shall see that the method is also an essential step in quantitative procedures which find numerical approximations to the roots of the equations.

Sturm's method is designed to indicate the number of distinct[2] real roots of an equation which lie between any two specific values of the variable. For example, it can tell us how many roots lie between $x = 3.7$ and $x = 77.0$. Such a computation will take us a long way toward finding the number of roots of each type—our central qualitative problem. One proceeds by translating each of our original questions into corresponding questions which can be answered directly by Sturm's method. Thus, to find the number of real roots we compute the number of roots which lie between "minus infinity" $(-\infty)$ and "plus infinity" $(+\infty)$.[3] Similarly, to find the number of positive roots we use Sturm's method to compute the number of roots between 0 and $+\infty$. To determine the number of roots which are less than unity in absolute value we can calculate the number of roots between -1 and $+1$, and so on.

[2] Direct application of Sturm's method counts multiple roots only once so that if there are two simple roots and one double root between -1 and $+3$, direct use of the theorem will indicate that three (and not four) roots lie between these limits. This is discussed further in Section 5 below.

[3] If the characteristic equation is of (say) degree 7, and even if only 6 roots are shown by Sturm's method to lie between $-\infty$ and $+\infty$ we can be sure that all 7 of the roots are real because complex roots always come in conjugate pairs so that the single unidentified seventh root cannot possibly be complex. The explanation of the discrepancy between the true number of real roots and the smaller number found by Sturm's method is that there must in this case be one pair of multiple (double) roots which Sturm's method counts as a single root (see the preceding footnote). If, however, in our seventh degree equation only five or fewer roots are shown to lie between $-\infty$ and $+\infty$, we cannot be sure without further investigation whether the remaining roots are complex roots or multiple roots. However, this equation can be settled by direct examination of the Sturm's method computations as is shown in Section 5 below.

The Sturm Functions

We first describe Sturm's method mechanically and without any attempt at explanation. Only after we have shown what the method is will we be able to explain its workings. Suppose the polynomial whose roots we are seeking is

$$0 = f(x) = a_0x^n + a_1x^{n-1} + \cdots + a_{n-1}x + a_n \tag{43}$$

$$0 = x^3 - 3x^2 - 6x + 4. \tag{43a}$$

We now derive a set of polynomials from our original polynomial $f(x)$, and shall find that these new made up polynomials will permit us to locate the real roots of $f(x)$.

The first of these new polynomials, $f_1(x)$ is simply the first derivative of $f(x)$[4]:

$$f_1(x) = \frac{df}{dx} = na_0x^{n-1} + (n-1)a_1x^{n-2} + \cdots + a_{n-1}$$

$$f_1(x) = 3x^2 - 6x - 6.$$

The next of these polynomials, $f_2(x)$, is derived from $f(x)$ and $f_1(x)$ by a process of long division. We divide $f_1(x)$ into $f(x)$ and $f_2(x)$ is defined to be the remainder *multiplied by minus one* (-1). Similarly, $f_3(x)$ is obtained by dividing $f_2(x)$ into $f_1(x)$ and designating as $f_3(x)$ the quantity minus one times the remainder, and so on. For example, let us go through the computation for equation (43a). We start by dividing $f(x)$ by $f_1(x)$ thus:

$$\begin{array}{r|l} & \frac{1}{3}x - \frac{1}{3} \\ 3x^2 - 6x - 6 & x^3 - 3x^2 - 6x + 4 \\ & x^3 - 2x^2 - 2x \\ \hline & -x^2 - 4x + 4 \\ & -x^2 + 2x + 2 \\ \hline & -6x + 2. \end{array}$$

[4] It is assumed that the reader knows that the first derivative of $ax^n = nax^{n-1}$ so that, e.g., $d5x^3/dx = 15x^2$. See also the first footnote of Chapter Fourteen.

Since the remainder is $-6x + 2$, we designate $f_2(x) = -1(-6x + 2) = 6x - 2$.

Now, to find $f_3(x)$ we divide $f_1(x)$ by the $f_2(x)$ which we have just constructed, to obtain

$$\begin{array}{r}
\frac{1}{2}x - \frac{5}{6} \\
6x - 2\overline{)3x^2 - 6x - 6} \\
\underline{3x^2 - 1x } \\
-5x - 6 \\
\underline{-5x + 5/3} \\
-7\tfrac{2}{3}
\end{array}$$

so that $f_3 = -(-7\tfrac{2}{3}) = 7\tfrac{2}{3}$.

We can summarize these successive long divisions as follows:

$$\left.\begin{aligned}
f(x) &= g_1(x)f_1(x) - f_2(x) \\
f_1(x) &= g_2(x)f_2(x) - f_3(x) \\
&\cdots\cdots\cdots\cdots \\
f_{n-2}(x) &= g_{n-1}(x)f_{n-1}(x) - f_n(x)
\end{aligned}\right\} \tag{44}$$

$$\left.\begin{aligned}
(x^3 - 3x^2 - 6x + 4) &= \left(\frac{1}{3}x - \frac{1}{3}\right)(3x^2 - 6x - 6) - (6x - 2) \\
(3x^2 - 6x - 6) &= \left(\frac{1}{2}x - \frac{5}{6}\right)(6x - 2) - (7\tfrac{2}{3})
\end{aligned}\right\} \tag{44a}$$

so that Sturm's polynomials in our numerical case are

$$f(x) = x^3 - 3x^2 - 6x + 4$$

$$f_1(x) = 3x^2 - 6x - 6$$

$$f_2(x) = 6x - 2$$

$$f_3(x) = 7\tfrac{2}{3}.$$

Note that each of these polynomials is one degree lower than that which precedes it, and that the last "polynomial" is simply a constant.

The Sturm Criterion

How do these functions help us locate the roots of $f(x)$? Only one more simple step is required. For example, to find the number of real roots of (43a) which lie between zero and plus one we first determine the signs of these functions for $x = 0$ and then for $x = 1$ as shown in the following table.

	$x = 0$		$x = 1$	
Function	*Value*	*Sign*	*Value*	*Sign*
$f(x)$	$0^3 - 3(0)^2 - 6(0) + 4 = 4$	$+$	$(1)^3 - 3(1)^2 - 6(1) + 4 = -4$	$-$
$f_1(x)$	$3(0)^2 - 6(0) - 6 = -6$	$-$	$3(1)^2 - 6(1) - 6 = -9$	$-$
$f_2(x)$	$6(0) - 2 = -2$	$-$	$6(1) - 2 = 4$	$+$
$f_3(x)$	$7\frac{2}{3} = 7\frac{2}{3}$	$+$	$7\frac{2}{3} = 7\frac{2}{3}$	$+$
	number of variations in consecutive signs	2		1

Note that at $x = 0$ f is positive, f_1 negative, f_2 negative, and f_3 is positive. Thus there are two changes in sign as we proceed down the list of functions—one between f and f_1, and the other change between f_2 and f_3. We write $V(0) = 2$, meaning that there are two such variations in sign when $x = 0$. When $x = 1$ we have $V(1) = 1$ since there is only one variation in sign which occurs between f_1 (negative) and f_2 (positive).

We now state that the number of real roots of (43a) which lie between $x = 0$ and $x = 1$ is equal to $V(0) - V(1) = 1$, i.e., one real root of that equation lies in this interval. More generally we state (without yet having attempted to justify the assertion)

STURM'S THEOREM: if $f(x)$ is a polynomial which has no multiple roots, and $a < b$ are any two real numbers, then the number of real roots of $f(x)$ which lie between $x = a$ and $x = b$ is equal to $V(a) - V(b)$, i.e., to the number of variations in sign of the Sturm functions *when x takes its lower value,* minus the number of variations in sign when x takes the higher of the two values.

Let us see how this rule is applied by finding out some more about the roots of our numerical equation (43a). To find the total number of the real roots of this equation we consider the interval between $x = -\infty$ and $x = +\infty$. Since at "infinity" and "minus infinity" a polynomial is defined to take on the sign of its term of highest degree,[5] the sign of $f(x) = x^3 - 3x^2 - 6x + 4$ as x approaches $-\infty$ will be the same as the sign of x^3 and hence it will be negative since the cube of a negative number is negative. Similarly, the sign of $f_1(x) = 3x^2 - 6x - 6$ at $x = -\infty$ is the same as that of $3x^2$ which is positive since the square x^2 of any real number is positive. Proceeding on in this way we obtain

$$f(-\infty) < 0, \quad f_1(-\infty) > 0, \quad f_2(-\infty) < 0,$$
$$f_3(-\infty) > 0 \text{ so that } V(-\infty) = 3,$$

and for similar reasons

$$f(+\infty) > 0, \quad f_1(+\infty) > 0, \quad f_2(+\infty) > 0,$$
$$f_3(+\infty) > 0 \quad \text{so that} \quad V(+\infty) = 0.$$

We conclude that the number of real roots of $f(x)$ is $V(-\infty) - V(+\infty) = 3$, i.e., that all three roots of $f(x)$ are real, Similarly the number of *positive* real roots of $f(x)$ is given by $V(0) - V(+\infty) = 2 - 0$ so that our function has two positive roots. We already know that one of these lies between zero and unity so that the other must be greater than unity. Hence we know that $f(x)$ cannot be the characteristic equation of a stable difference equation since one of the roots is greater than unity.

Thus we have almost completed the qualitative analysis of the difference equation

$$y(t) = 3y(t-1) + 6y(t-2) - 4y(t-3)$$

[5] The reason for this convention is really quite straightforward. Consider, e.g., the polynomial $x^4 - 2x - 5$. For low positive values of x this will be negative, e.g., for $x = 1$ it will equal -6. But eventually when x grows sufficiently large (x approaches $+\infty$) it will become positive and stay positive because for large x the large positive value of x^4 will outweigh the negative value of $-2x - 5$. Similarly, as x takes on larger and larger negative values (x approaches $-\infty$) this expression will again take on and keep the (positive) sign of the x^4 term which will once more ultimately swamp the other terms.

whose characteristic equation is our numerical $f(x)$. We know that there are no complex roots, one negative root, and at least one root greater than unity in absolute value, so that the time path of $y(t)$ will be explosive and it may involve some oscillation but no fluctuation (complex roots).

PROBLEMS

1. Compute for equation (43a)
   a) $V(-2)$
   b) $V(-1)$
   c) $V(+2)$
2. From the answer to question 1, and the result $V(-\infty) = 3$, $V(\infty) = 0$, show whether the negative root or the larger of the two positive roots will be greater in absolute value.
3. Compute Sturm's functions for
   a) $x^3 - 3x^2 - 3x - 1 = 0$
   b) $x^3 - 3x + 1 = 0$
4. Show by use of Sturm's method that *all* of the roots of the equation in the preceding problem are real. Prove that this holds for any $f(x)$ each of whose Sturm polynomials has a positive coefficient to its term of highest degree.

4. THE MECHANISM OF STURM'S METHOD

The description of Sturm's method which has been given so far amounts to little more than a cook book recipe. Let us now see what makes it work.

Preliminary Theorem: Roots of a Continuous Function

First we must digress to discuss a theorem which is fundamental to the entire procedure. After it is understood this theorem should seem intuitively obvious, though a rigorous proof, which will not be given here, is a little more difficult. Let $a < b$ be any two real numbers and $f(x)$ be any continuous function [6] of x. Then this theorem

[6] Roughly speaking a continuous function is one whose graph has no breaks (gaps) though it may have kinks (sharp corners).

states that if $f(a)$ and $f(b)$ are of opposite sign there is at least one real number c between a and b such that $f(c) = 0$, i.e., $f(x)$ has at least one real root c between a and b.

A graphic translation should convince the reader of the plausibility of this theorem. Thus in Figure 33a we have plotted the graphs of (43a) and its associated Sturm polynomials. We note that at $x = B$, $f(x)$ is positive (point Q) and its graph lies above the horizontal axis while at $x = C$ $f(x)$ is negative (point R below the x-axis). Then how can $f(x)$ get from Q above the x-axis to R below it? Since $f(x)$ is continuous its graph can have no jumps and so to get to the other side it must cross the x-axis at least once, that is, there must be at least one point T between $f(B)$ and $f(C)$ at which $f(T) = 0$. In fact between points Q and R there is exactly one such point. But between points P and S which also lie on opposite sides of the x-axis we note that $f(x)$ crosses the x-axis three times.[7]

Before ending this digression let us note that it will be convenient to assume that $f(x)$ has no multiple roots. This means that no value of x can be a root of both $f(x)$ and of its derivative.[8] In fact in this case no two consecutive polynomials such as f_4 and f_5 from among Sturm's functions can share a real root.[9]

[7] The reader will notice that there must generally be an odd number of real roots between any two points on $f(x)$ which lie on opposite sides of the x-axis, since simply going back and forth over the x-axis (an even number of crossings) done no matter how many times always gets us back to the side on which we started. There is a slight complication in the case of multiple roots at which the graph of $f(x)$ can be tangent to the x-axis but since such a point of tangency always represents several roots it can be shown that the rule which states that there is an odd number of real roots between two points on opposite sides of the horizontal axis still works out.

[8] *Proof.* By the factor theorem of algebra, if r is a single root of $f(x)$ we can write $f(x) = g(x)(x - r)$ where $g(x)$ is some polynomial which does not have r as a root, i.e., for which $g(r) \neq 0$ [for otherwise if r were a root of $g(x)$ we would have $g(x) = G(x)(x - r)$ for some other polynomial $G(x)$ so that $f(x) = g(x)(x - r) = G(x)(x - r)^2$ and x would be a double root of $f(x)$ contrary to hypothesis]. Now differentiate $f(x) = g(x)(x - r)$ to obtain $f_1(x) = \frac{dg}{dx}(x - r) + g(x)$. Setting $x = r$, $f_1(r) = \frac{dg(r)}{dx}(r - r) + g(r) = g(r) \neq 0$ so that r is not a root of $f_1(x)$.

[9] *Proof* by *reductio ad absurdum* (i.e., by assuming that the theorem to be proved is false and proving that this assumption is self-contradictory): Assume that, contrary to the theorem, there exists a real number s such that, say

How Sturm's Functions Record a Root

We can proceed to see now why Sturm's functions can act as a bookkeeping device whose variations in sign ,$V(A)$ and $V(B)$, record the number of real roots of $f(x)$ in the interval between A and B. First we note $V(x)$ can only change at a root of one of Sturm's polynomials since (by our preliminary theorem, above) in an interval which contains no root of any of these functions none of them can change in sign so that $V(x)$ will not change in this interval either. We now proceed to prove Sturm's theorem in two stages: First we show that $V(x)$ is decreased by exactly one unit by a root of $f(x)$. Then we prove that no root of any of the other Sturm functions will affect $V(x)$. Sturm's theorem will then follow at once for from these two results we note that in any interval $V(x)$ must decrease by exactly the number of roots of $f(x)$ in that interval.

A Root of f(x) Decreases V(x) by One Unit

In Figure 33a there are three roots of $f(x)$, M, T, and W. Just to the left of each of these points $f(x)$ and $f_1(x)$ are of opposite sign [e.g., to the left of M, $f(x)$ is negative and $f_1(x)$ is positive] while just to the right of each of these points the signs of $f(x)$ and $f_1(x)$ are always the same. Thus whenever we pass a root of $f(x)$ the sign of $f(x)$ changes in a way which decreases $V(x)$ by one unit. Let us see why this must always hold true.

Since $f(x)$ and $f_1(x)$ cannot have a root in common, then at any root $x = r$ of $f(x)$, its derivative, $f_1(r)$ must either be positive or

---

$f_3(s) = f_4(s) = 0$ so that s is a real root of f_3 and f_4. These Sturm polynomials were derived from equations (44) which state that

$$f(x) = g_1(x)f_1(x) - f_2(x) \qquad \text{(i)}$$

$$f_1(x) = g_2(x)f_2(x) - f_3(x) \qquad \text{(ii)}$$

$$f_2(x) = g_3(x)f_3(x) - f_4(x) \qquad \text{(iii)}$$

Substituting s for x in (iii) we obtain $f_2(s) = g_3(s) \cdot 0 - 0 = 0$ so that s must also be a root of f_2. Similarly, repeating this procedure for (ii) and then for (i) we find that s must be a root of both $f(x)$ and $f_1(x)$ which in the previous footnote we showed to be impossible if $f(x)$ has no multiple roots. Hence in this case $f_3(x)$ and $f_4(x)$ cannot have any root s in common.

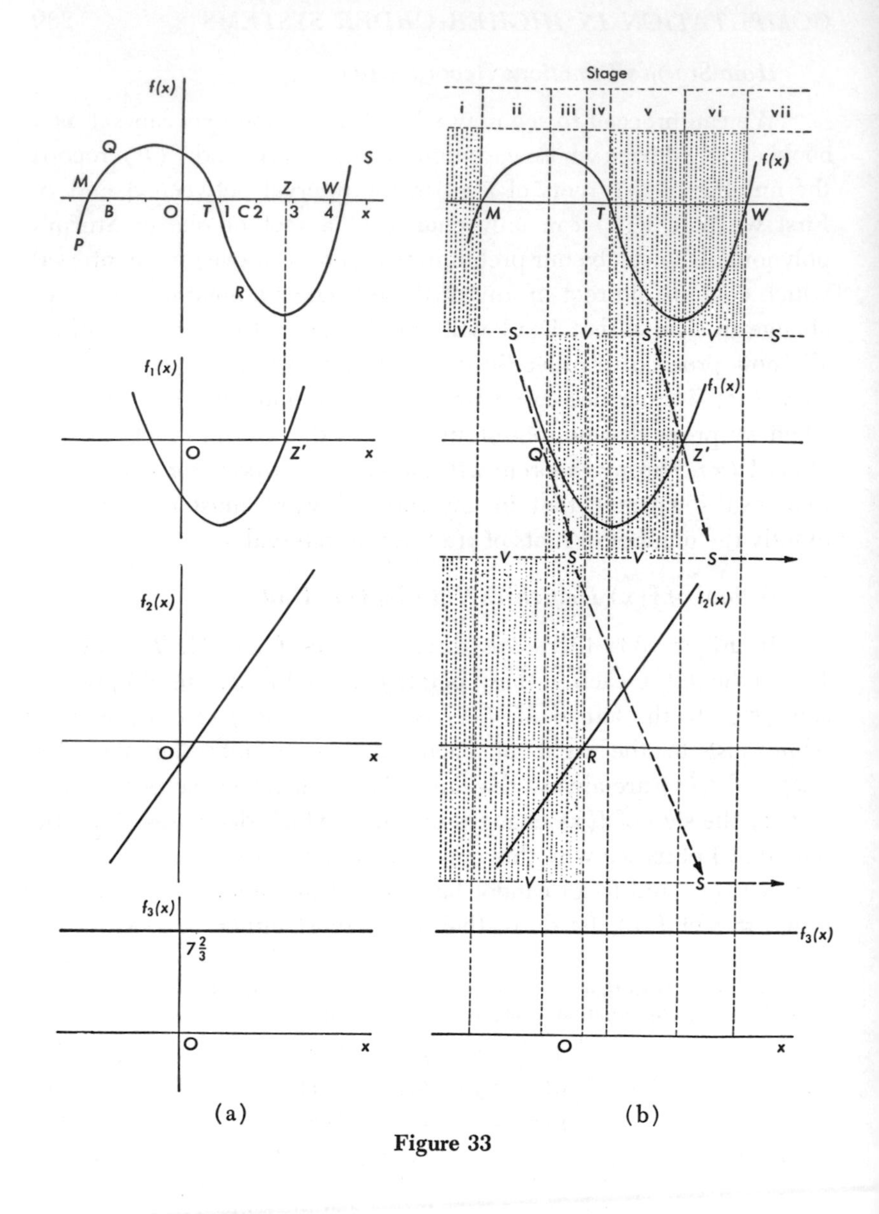
f(x)
Q
M
S
Z
W
B
O
T
1
C
2
3
4
x
P
R
f₁(x)
O
Z′
x
f₂(x)
O
x
f₃(x)
7 2/3
O
x
Stage
i
ii
iii
iv
v
vi
vii
f(x)
M
T
W
V
S
V
S
V
S
f₁(x)
Q
Z′
V
S
V
S
f₂(x)
R
V
S
f₃(x)
O
x

(a) (b)

Figure 33

negative (never zero) so that the graph of $f(x)$ will be going uphill or downhill whenever it crosses the x axis (and it can never be tangent to that axis). Suppose, e.g. $f(x)$ is going downhill and crosses the x axis at the real root $x = T$. Since $f(x)$ is going downhill, its derivative, $f_1(x)$, must be negative, and $f(x)$ goes from positive to negative. Thus to the left of the point T $f(x)$ and $f_1(x)$ must be of opposite sign [$f(x)$ positive, $f_1(x)$ negative] while to the right of point T they must be of the same sign. The reader should show that where $f(x)$ is going uphill when it crosses the x axis (point W) a similar result holds. Thus whenever $f(x)$ passes a root its sign changes in a way which decreases $V(x)$ by *exactly one unit, as Sturm's theorem requires.*

***No root of* $\mathbf{f_1(x), f_2(x), \cdots, f_n(x)}$ *affects* $\mathbf{V(x)}$**

We turn now to the second part of the proof to show that no change in V can be produced by a root of one of the Sturm functions other than $f(x)$.

Suppose that in the interval which we are considering at least one of Sturm's functions other than $f(x)$, say, $f_5(x)$, has a root $x = s$. We have seen (footnote 9 above) that no two consecutive Sturm functions can share a root so that $f_4(s) \neq 0$ and $f_6(s) \neq 0$. But by equations (44) we have

$$f_4(x) = g_5(x)f_5(x) - f_6(x) \qquad \text{so that since } f_5(s) = 0$$

$$f_4(s) = g_5(s) \cdot 0 - f_6(s) = -f_6(s)$$

and hence at a root of $f_5(x)$, $x = s$, the values of the adjacent Sturm polynomials f_4 and f_6 must be equal and opposite in sign. Hence, no matter how f_5 changes it must be equal in sign to either f_4 or f_6 and opposite in sign from the other so that f_4, f_5, and f_6 must involve exactly one variation in sign, and the number of their variations in sign will not change as x passes the root of f_5. This result is illustrated by the situation shown in the following table.

x	f_4	f_5	f_6	V (of f_4, f_5, and f_6)
$s - \Delta s$	+	+	−	1
$s + \Delta s$	+	−	−	1

Here f_5 starts out with the same sign as f_4 and after it passes its root, s, it takes on the sign of f_6. The reader should note that if instead f_5 goes from $-$ to $+$ as it passes its root V must still remain unaffected.

To summarize a) every time we pass a real root of $f(x)$ going from left to right there is a unit decrease in the number of variations of sign as between the values of $f(x)$ and $f_1(x)$; b) if none of the other Sturm polynomials have a root they can produce no change in V; c) even if one of the other polynomials passes a root it cannot change V because the polynomials on either side of it are constructed in a way which guarantees that they will be of opposite sign. Thus we have proved Sturm's theorem.

The Role of $f_1, f_2, \cdots, f_n$

What then is the need for the remaining Sturm functions f_1, $f_2, \cdots, f_n$? It may well seem that because they never affect $V(x)$ they serve no purpose at all. But these functions are needed as passive recorders of past changes in the number of variations in sign between $f(x)$ and $f_1(x)$, i.e., of roots which lie to the left of the value of x under examination. We can think of $f(x)$ and $f_1(x)$ being used to make a bookkeeping entry each time we pass a root of $f(x)$. However, this space must be kept free to record the passing of the other roots of $f(x)$ so the information is transmitted (by changes in their sign) to $f_2, f_3, \cdots, f_n$ where it is recorded and stored.

ILLUSTRATION

Let us see how this works out in the case of (44a). In Figure 33b we have reproduced Figure 33a and shaded those portions of each graph where the Sturm polynomial in question has a negative value. Thus where an unshaded region lies directly above a shaded region (or vice versa) two consecutive Sturm polynomials are of opposite sign, i.e., they contribute one variation in sign. At each such boundary a V has been written in.

Stage i: At the extreme left no two consecutive polynomials are of the same sign and there are three variations in sign.

Stage ii: As we move to the right, $f(x)$ passes its first root, M, and changes sign. At this point $f(x)$ becomes positive and hence it assumes the same sign as $f_1(x)$ so that one variation in sign disappears. The V (variation) is replaced by an S (same sign) to indicate that one root of $f(x)$ has been passed.

Stage iii: Presently as we move further to the right we come to a root, Q of $f_1(x)$[10] and the value of this expression changes from positive to negative. Since at this point $f(x)$ and $f_2(x)$ are of opposite sign, a V reappears between $f(x)$ and $f_1(x)$ and the S which formerly occupied this position may be considered to move down (arrow) to the border line between the graph of $f_1(x)$ and that of $f_2(x)$. The return of the V to the space between $f(x)$ and $f_1(x)$ is important since it permits the recording of the next root of $f(x)$ by making it possible for this V to be changed once again into an S.

Stage iv: Next we come to a root, R, of $f_2(x)$ where $f_1(x)$ and $f_2(x)$ resume opposite signs so that the S now moves down to the border line between the $f_2(x)$ and $f_3(x)$ graphs. Note the analogy between the method by which information is recorded by the Sturm polynomials and that employed by an abacus or an adding machine. In the latter, for example, when the digit column has been filled up (the total reaches ten), the digit column is cleared out and the information is moved to the tens column by there inserting a "one." Similarly, the Sturm's polynomials record a root of $f(x)$ by inserting an S between $f(x)$ and $f_1(x)$. This space is then "cleared" by returning a V to that point and then moving the S between $f_1(x)$ and $f_2(x)$, etc.

Stage v: We now come to a second root, T of $f(x)$ and a second S appears, which again lies initially between $f(x)$ and $f_1(x)$. The reader should be able to complete the description of the remaining stages vi and vii for himself.

[10] Note that between any two roots of $f(x)$ its derivative must always have at least one root as this requires. For as the graph of $f(x)$ passes one root it must be moving away from the x-axis, and to get back to the axis it must at some point reverse its direction, i.e., the derivative must switch from positive to negative or vice versa.

5. MULTIPLE AND COMPLEX ROOTS

So far we have dealt only with real simple (non-multiple) roots. We shall indicate briefly the complications introduced by the presence of multiple or complex roots.

Multiple Roots

It is easy to show that where $f(x)$ has multiple roots then:

a. All of $f(x)$, $f_1(x)$, $\cdots$, $f_n(x)$ will contain a common factor.[11]

b. At least one of the steps in the sequence of long divisions which yield these functions will involve a zero remainder (say, f_5 will divide f_4 exactly) so that the next Sturm polynomial (f_6) will be equal to zero.[12]

c. The roots of the last nonzero f (say, f_5) will be the multiple roots of $f(x)$.[13]

Though there are more efficient procedures [14] this discussion shows how we can isolate the real roots of an equation with real multiple roots. First we construct Sturm's functions. Then we divide the

[11] *Proof.* $f(x)$ and its derivative must contain a common factor since if $f(x)$ has the root of multiplicity m, $x = r$, then $f(x) = F(x)(x - r)^m$ for some polynomial $F(x)$. Then $f_1(x)$, the derivative of $f(x)$, $= F(x)m(x - r)^{m-1} + F'(x)(x - r)^m$, so that $(x - r)^{m-1}$ is a factor of both $f(x)$ and $f_1(x)$. But since by (44) $f(x) = g_1(x)f_1(x) - f_2(x)$, then $f_2(x) = g_1(x)f_1(x) - f(x)$ also has $(x - r)^{m-'}$ as a factor. Now since by (44) $f_1 = g_2f_2 - f_3$ we can show similarly that f_3 has the factor $(x - r)^{m-1}$, etc.

[12] *Proof.* The last Sturm function, $f_n(x)$, is a constant as we have seen. If it is not equal to zero it cannot have $(x - r)$ as a factor. But the previous footnote shows that in the multiple roots case $(x - r)$ is a factor of every one of $f_1, \cdots, f_n$ including f_n, so that $f_n = 0$.

[13] *Proof.* Since, e.g., $f_6 = 0$, we have by (44) $f_4(x) = g_5(x)f_5(x)$ so that $f_5(x)$ is a factor of $f_4(x)$. Similarly, since $f_3(x) = g_4(x)f_4(x) - f_5(x) = g_4(x)g_5(x) f_5(x) - f_5(x)$, $f_5(x)$ is a factor of $f_3(x)$. Continuing in this way we see that $f_5(x)$ is a common factor of f_2, f_1, and f. Thus we can write $f(x) = F(x)f_5(x)$ and $f_1(x) = F_1(x)f_5(x)$ for some polynomials $F(x)$ and $F_1(x)$. Hence, any root w of $f_5(x)$ must involve $f(w) = f_1(w) = 0$ so w must be a root common to $f(x)$ and $f_1(x)$ and hence, by footnote 8 above w must be a multiple root of $f(x)$. Moreover by footnote 11 above, any multiple root of $f(x)$ must be a root of $f_5(x)$ so that every multiple root of $f(x)$ must be a root of $f_5(x)$ and conversely.

[14] See, e.g., L. E. Dickson, *First Course in the Theory of Equations,* John Wiley, New York, 1922, p. 82.

original nth degree polynomial $f(x)$ by the last nonzero Sturm function, say f_5 (which is a polynomial of degree $n-5$). For every root of multiplicity m the (5th degree polynomial) quotient $f(x)/f_5(x)$ will (by the factor theorem and footnote 11 above) contain a term $\frac{(x-r)^m}{(x-r)^{m-1}} = x - r$ so that this quotient will contain all of the different roots of $f(x)$ but in $f(x)/f_5(x)$ there will be no multiple roots.

Thus we can isolate the real roots of any $f(x)$ in the following steps:

a. Construct Sturm's functions. If $f_n \neq 0$ there are no multiple roots and proceed as in Section 3 above.

b. If $f_n = 0$ there are multiple roots.. First isolate by step a. above the roots of f/f_k where $f_k(x)$ is the last nonzero Sturm function of $f(x)$.

c. Finally, isolate the roots of f_k by repeated applications of steps a. and b. above to locate the multiple roots of $f(x)$.

EXAMPLE

$$f(x) = x^3 - 6x^2 + 9x - 4.$$

Here we find by (44)

$$f_1(x) = 3x^2 - 12x + 9$$

$$f_2(x) = 2x - 2$$

$$f_3(x) = 0.$$

The multiple roots of $f(x) = 0$ must also be roots of $f_2(x) = 2x - 2 = 0$ so that by inspection $x = 1$ is shown to be a (double) root of $f(x) = 0$. We can then factor out $(x-1)^2$ from $f(x)$ to obtain $f(x) = (x-1)^2(x-4) = 0$ which tells us that 4 is the third root.

Complex Roots

A polynomial with complex roots can be transformed into two simultaneous polynomial equations in two variables with only real roots. For example, we know that $x^2 - 2x + 5 = 0$ has the roots

$1 \pm 2i$. But instead of finding these roots by the usual procedure we can do it by substituting into the equation the complex variable $x = c + di$ and solving for the real numbers c and d. Thus we obtain

$$0 = (c + di)^2 - 2(c + di) + 5 = c^2 + 2cdi + d^2i^2 - 2c - 2di + 5$$
$$= c^2 + 2cdi - d^2 - 2c - 2di + 5.$$

For this to hold the real and the imaginary terms must *each* sum up to zero so we have the two equations

$$c^2 - d^2 - 2c + 5 = 0$$
$$(2cd - 2d)i = 0, \quad \text{i.e., } 2cd - 2d = 2d(c - 1) = 0.$$

The second equation yields at once $c = 1$, and substituting this into the first equation we obtain $d = \pm 2$ which we know to be the correct solution of the equation.

The same method will work for any polynomial but the two simultaneous equations are usually not easy to solve. If, however, we can eliminate one of the variables (either c or d) between the two equations we can then isolate the roots of the remaining equation in the remaining variable with the aid of Sturm's theorem.

PROBLEMS

1. Find Sturm's functions for

   a) $x^3 - 3x^2 + 3x - 1$
   b) $x^3 - 3x^2 + 6x - 4$

2. a) Which of these equations has complex roots? How many?
   b) Which has multiple roots? How many?

6. GENERAL TEST FOR STABILITY

The reader will doubtless feel, justly, that our discussion of the qualitative examination of complex roots is not fully satisfactory. This is particularly important when we wish to find out whether fluctuations in the time path of the variable of a difference equation are damped in the long run, i.e., whether the variable ultimately converges in a *stable* manner toward either a stationary or a moving equilibrium.

It will be recalled that the time path of the variable will be stable if and only if there is *no* root of the characteristic equation (whether real or complex) whose absolute value is greater than or equal to unity. There is a test which permits us to determine directly whether or not all of the roots of a higher degree polynomial are less than unity in absolute value. Unfortunately, it is not readily reducible to the simple algebraic notation which has been used so far in this volume. Rather it is convenient to employ determinant notation whose explanation is beyond the scope of the book. Moreover, we do not attempt to indicate how the theorem is derived. But for completeness and purposes of reference we state this theorem without proof:[15]

Theorem: The roots of the polynomial equation

$$a_0x^n + a_1x^{n-1} + \cdots + a_{n-1}x + a_n = 0$$

will all be less than unity if and only if the following n determinants are positive (the dotted lines are inserted to bring out their symmetry):

$$\begin{vmatrix} a_0 & a_n \\ a_n & a_0 \end{vmatrix} \quad \begin{vmatrix} a_0 & 0 & a_n & a_{n-1} \\ a_1 & a_0 & 0 & a_n \\ a_n & 0 & a_0 & a_1 \\ a_{n-1} & a_n & 0 & a_0 \end{vmatrix} \cdots \begin{vmatrix} a_0 & 0 \ldots\ldots 0 & a_n & a_{n-1} \ldots a_1 \\ a_1 & a_0 \ldots\ldots 0 & 0 & a_n \ldots\ldots a_2 \\ \cdots & \cdots & \cdots & \cdots \\ a_{n-1} & a_{n-2} \ldots a_0 & 0 & 0 \ldots\ldots a_n \\ a_n & 0 \ldots\ldots 0 & a_0 & a_1 \ldots\ldots a_{n-1} \\ a_{n-1} & a_n \ldots\ldots 0 & 0 & a_0 \ldots\ldots a_{n-2} \\ \cdots & \cdots & \cdots & \cdots \\ a_1 & a_2 \ldots a_n & 0 & 0 \ldots\ldots a_0 \end{vmatrix} \tag{45}$$

EXAMPLE

Consider the general second degree polynomial equation $x^2 + bx + c = 0$. Since this is of second degree, the first two determinants in (45) must be positive for stability. In the notation of the

[15] For a list of references see John S. Chipman, *The Theory of Inter-Sectoral Money Flows and Income Formation,* Johns Hopkins Press, Baltimore, 1951, pp. 118–121.

preceding theorem, we have here $a_0 = 1$, $a_1 = b$, $a_2 = c$. Thus stability requires that the first determinant in (45), $\begin{vmatrix} 1 & c \\ c & 1 \end{vmatrix} = 1 - c_2 > 0$, i.e., that $1 > c > -1$. Reference to Figure 32 in the preceding chapter shows that this is in line with our previous results. But the figure clearly shows also that such values of c do not guarantee stability. Even with $c = 0$ a very large value of b can produce instability. And the preceding theorem shows that the equation will be stable if and only if, in addition to the first determinant, the second determinant in (45) is also positive, i.e., if and only if

$$\begin{vmatrix} 1 & 0 & c & b \\ b & 1 & 0 & c \\ c & 0 & 1 & b \\ b & c & 0 & 1 \end{vmatrix} > 0.$$

By the standard rules for the manipulation of determinants this last determinant equals (subtracting c times the second row from the last row)

$$\begin{vmatrix} 1 & 0 & c & b \\ b & 1 & 0 & c \\ c & 0 & 1 & b \\ b - bc & 0 & 0 & 1 - c^2 \end{vmatrix} = \text{(by expansion in terms of the second column)} \begin{vmatrix} 1 & c & b \\ c & 1 & b \\ b - bc & 0 & 1 - c^2 \end{vmatrix}$$

$$= \text{(subtracting } c \text{ times the second row from the first row)} \begin{vmatrix} 1 - c^2 & 0 & b - bc \\ c & 1 & b \\ b - bc & 0 & 1 - c^2 \end{vmatrix}$$

$$= \begin{vmatrix} 1 - c^2 & b - bc \\ b - bc & 1 - c^2 \end{vmatrix} = (1 - c^2)^2 - b^2(1 - c)^2.$$

Since this is required to be positive we must have

$$b^2 < \left(\frac{1 - c^2}{1 - c}\right)^2 = \left(\frac{(1 - c)(1 + c)}{1 - c}\right)^2 = (1 + c)^2,$$

i.e., b must lie between the lines $b = 1 + c$ and $b = -1 - c$. This together with the previously derived condition $c^2 < 1$ gives us the shaded triangular stable area in the center of Figure 32.

7. NUMERICAL APPROXIMATION OF THE ROOTS

As we have already stated, this chapter does not aim to describe in detail the most efficient methods known for the numerical computation of the roots of a characteristic equation. These are rather technical and tedious and their study would be unrewarding to the reader who does not plan to apply them at once to concrete numerical problems. Anyone who does have such a computational problem is referred to the standard sources.[16]

However, to provide some insight into their method of approach we will describe in rough outline one of the standard techniques for the numerical approximation of the roots of a polynomial. Perhaps the outstanding virtue of the method which we have chosen for our illustration is that it is so easily described in intuitive terms.

Newton's Method: Graphic Discussion

This method, which is ascribed to Isaac Newton employs a very simple principle—one approximates a curve by its straight line

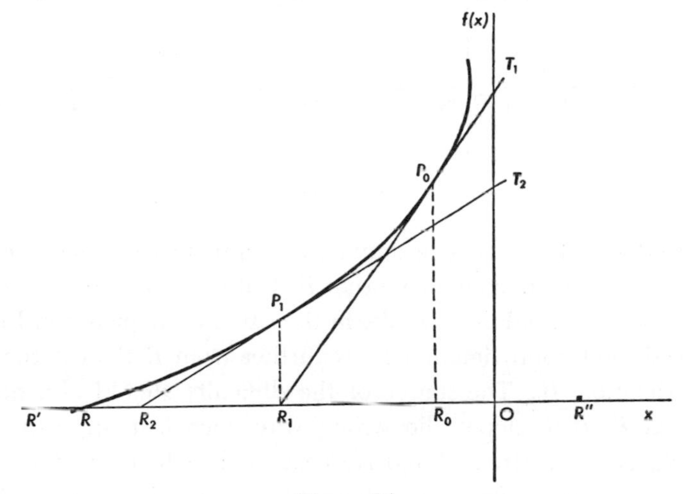

Figure 34

[16] See especially R. A. Frazer, W. J. Duncan, and A. R. Collar, *Elementary Matrices and Some Applications to Dynamics and Differential Equations,* The Macmillan Company, New York, 1946, Chapter IV, especially Part III.

tangent. In Figure 34 we have the graph of a polynomial $f(x)$. Suppose we have found (say by Sturm's theorem) that a root, R, lies between points R' and R''. We take as our first approximation to the root R some value of x, call it R_0, which lies in this interval, and draw the tangent R_1T_1 to point P_0 directly above R_0 on the graph of $f(x)$. Now we take as the second approximation to R, the point R_1 where the tangent line cuts the x-axis (the root of the equation of the tangent). Repeat this procedure by drawing the tangent R_2T_2 to point P_1 above R_1, and take as our third approximation to R the point R_2 where the second tangent line R_2T_2 cuts the x-axis, etc.

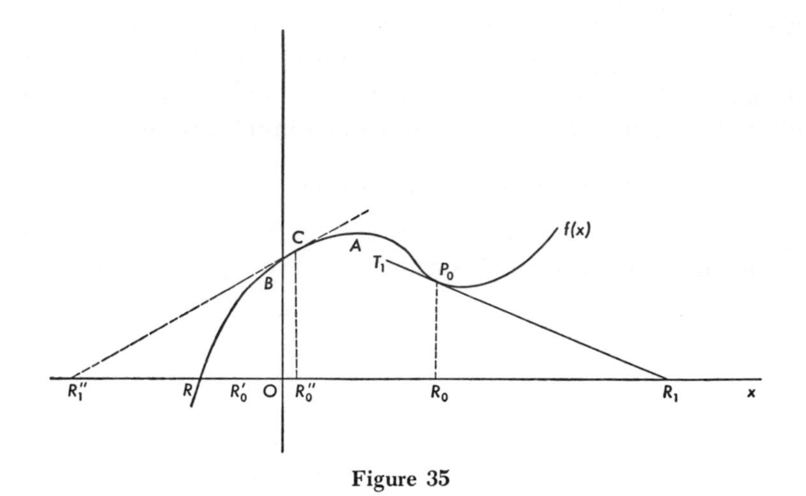

Figure 35

Note that as this has been drawn our approximations move closer and closer to the unknown true root R. Unfortunately, this need not always be the case. For example, in the situation depicted in Figure 35 the second approximation R_1 is further from R than is the first approximation, R_0. The source of the difficulty should also be obvious—at P_0 $f(x)$ slopes the wrong way. Our first approximation point R_0 is too far from R and $f(x)$ has had a chance to turn back down toward the x-axis. No such problem would have arisen if our first trial point had been one which, like R'_0, lies much closer to R. We see then why numerical approximation methods require that we begin with our roots fairly well located by Sturm's method or some other technique.[17]

EXAMPLE

In Section 3 we found that the equation $x^3 - 3x^2 - 6x + 4 = 0$ has one real root between zero and plus one.[18]

For simplicity of calculation let us use as our initial approximation $R_0 = 0$. We proceed as follows

Step (i). Computation of the slope of the tangent: The slope of the tangent to $f(x)$ at the initial approximation $x = R_0 = 0$ (line R_1T_1 in figure 34) is $\frac{dy}{dx}$ (at $x = R_0$) $= 3R_0^2 - 6R_0 - 6 = 3 \cdot 0^2 - 6 \cdot 0 - 6 = -6$. Thus the equation of this tangent must be of the (linear) form $y = -6x + k$ where k is a constant.

Step (ii). Evaluation of k: The tangent line R_1T_1 must go through the point P_0 on $f(x)$ where $x = R_0 = 0$. But the ordinate of

[17] Specifically we require that our initial point be so close to the true root that neither the first nor the second derivatives of $f(x)$ have a root between R and R_0. The reason we do not want to have a root of $\frac{df(x)}{dx}$ in the interval is that a point like A at which the graph turns back toward the x-axis must be one where $\frac{df(x)}{dx} = 0$. Similarly, at $\frac{d^2f(x)}{dx^2} = 0$ we have a point of inflection (e.g., point B in Fig. 35) and at points like C which lie further from R than is point B $f(x)$ must be moving toward R but only very slowly, so that the next approximation point R_1'' may be further from R than was the first approximation R_0'' below point C. Successive application of Sturm's method to $f(x)$, to $\frac{df(x)}{dx}$ and to $\frac{d^2f(x)}{dx^2}$ permits us to choose an interval containing R which meets these two requirements, i.e., one which contains no root of either the first or the second derivative.

[18] Moreover, $\frac{df}{dx} = 3x^2 - 6x - 6$ and $\frac{d^2f}{dx^2} = 6x - 6$. Obviously, the latter has no roots *inside* this interval (since its only root is $x = 1$). Further, writing $F(x) = \frac{df}{dx}$, Sturm's functions for $F(x)$ are $F_1(x) = 6x - 6$ and $F_2 = +9$ (the reader should check this). We have $F(0) = -6$, $F_1(0) = -6$, $F_2(0) = +9$, $F(1) = -9$, $F_1(1) = 0$, $F_2(1) = +9$ so that $V(0) = V(1) = 1$ and hence $\frac{df}{dx} = F$ can have no roots in the interval between 0 and +1 as (according to the preceding footnote) Newton's method requires.

this point is $y(R_0) = y(0) = 0^3 - 3 \cdot 0^2 - 6 \cdot 0 + 4 = 4$. Hence, at this point $y = 4$, and since the tangent must go through that point we have from the equation of the tangent, $-6R_0 + k = y = 4$, i.e., $-6 \cdot 0 + k = 4$ so that $k = 4$. We see then that the equation of R_1T_1 *is* $y = -6x + 4$.

Step (iii). Determination of the next approximation, R_1: As we have seen, Newton's method takes as the next approximation to the value of the root of $f(x)$, the abscissa R_1 of the point where the tangent line R_1T_1 intersects the horizontal axis. This is, of course, the point on the tangent where $y = 0$. Hence, R_1 is found by setting $y = 0$ and $x = R_1$ in the equation of the tangent to obtain $0 = -6R_1 + 4$ so that $x = R_1 = 2/3$ is our second approximation to the root of $f(x) = 0$.

Step (iv). Repeat steps (i)–(iii) with $x = R_1 = 2/3$ substituted for the first approximation root $R_0 = 0$, etc.

Comments: Iterative Methods

One of the most important features of the computational method which has just been described is its repetitive nature. Essentially it consists of a sequence of trial and error steps and the details of each step are completely determined by the outcome of the preceding trial. Such a systematic sequence of trials and successive approximations to the answer which is sought for is called an iterative method of solution.

At first glance iterative methods may seem a clumsy way to solve mathematical problems. Often they can do no more than approximate the answer and they involve the computer groping his way toward his result rather than proceeding to it directly. But in fact, particularly in large scale computing problems involving equations of high degree or many variables or equations, iterative techniques can be more efficient than are direct methods of solution even where direct methods are available. Increased use of high speed electronic computers has tended to favor iterative methods because they are essentially repetitive. The instructions in an iterative process usually involve several steps and then the direction—"repeat the computation using the results of the preceding step instead of the original data." This is particularly well suited to automatic machine computation where the translation of the instructions into machine language (programming) often contributes a very substantial proportion of the total computing time and costs.

It must be emphasized that a good iterative procedure will either, after a reasonable number of steps, arrive precisely at the desired answer or it should at least be capable of approximating the answer to any desired degree of accuracy. We should be able to find out that, say, by step 12 (the twelfth iteration) we have arrived to within .001 of the correct answer. It can be shown that Newton's method and many other iterative procedures possess this important feature.

PROBLEMS

1. Using the second iteration in Newton's method compute the next approximation to the root of the equation $x^3 - 3x^2 - 6x + 4$ which was used to illustrate the method in the text above.
2. Using the first aproximation $x_0 = 0$ compute the next Newton's method approximation to the root of the equation $x^2 - 2.5x + 1$ which lies in the interval between 0 and +1.

   Show that the Newton's method requirements on the first and second derivatives (see footnote 17 above) are met in this interval.

   What is the precise value of the root?

Chapter Thirteen

FIRST-ORDER NONLINEAR DIFFERENCE EQUATION MODELS[1]

1. WHY NONLINEAR MODELS?

Up to this point all of our difference equation models have been linear, that is, the variable $y(t)$ always appeared in terms which have the simple form $ay(t - w)$ where a and w are constants. Never have we used a $y^3(t)$ or a $\sin y(t)$ or any more complex expression. We have seen that this relatively restricted class of equations can produce a large variety of time paths of the variable—it can yield cycles of many sorts: explosive time paths, stable time paths, etc.

But nevertheless it has become increasingly clear to economists that linear models are often unsatisfactory. The most obvious reason is that the facts of the economy do not always meet the requirements of a linear relationship—the graphs of economic relationships are not always well approximated by straight lines, so that a linear model may not usually be able to represent an economic problem very satisfactorily.

But, worse still, for many purposes a linear construct not only poses the wrong problem—it is sometimes incapable of giving the

[1] This chapter and parts of Chapters Fifteen and Sixteen are based on work done for Prof. Paul F. Lazarsfeld's Panel Project at Columbia University in 1953–1954. An earlier version of this chapter appeared as "Analyse Graphique de Modèles de Cycles Non Linéaires de Premier Ordre" in Centre National de la Recherche Scientifique, *Les Modèles Dynamiques en Économétrie,* Paris, 1956.

complex types and some
which, ordinarily, a linear
point of view of business
a crucial weakness in the
ribed.

ation model can yield cycles
nt amplitude. By definition
xplosive cycles must doubt-
ist soon bring the entire
we want to study the long
her damped nor explosive
(as we shall see presently)
rably. This means that the
able in much of trade cycle
stant amplitude.

ill occur if and only if the
is of largest absolute value
is complex and of unit absolute value. In fact the purist can argue that even if the largest root in the equation is of absolute value 1.0001 its time path must *ultimately* explode and if the modulus of that root is 0.9998 the amplitude of the cycle must for all practical purposes disappear in the very long run, though these problems may take a very long time to show up.

Unfortunately, when we apply our analysis to empirical data we cannot ordinarily find the precise values of the roots of the equation because our statistics never permit us to be that certain of the values of the coefficients. Moreover, we can presume that *precisely* unit modulus complex roots are in most cases quite improbable. For example, the second-order polynomial $x^2 + bx + c = 0$ will have such roots if and only if [2] $c = 1$ exactly and $b^2 < 4$. Now it is difficult

[2] For we have seen in Chapter Eleven, Section 3 that c is the absolute value of a complex root, so that we must have $c = 1$, and for complex roots we must have $b^2 - 4c < 0$, i.e., $b^2 < 4c = 4$.

to believe in the abstract that when we fit such an equation to empirical data we will often obtain a value of c which, of all the infinite number of possibilities, is just equal to unity.[3] Thus we may well suspect that it is exceedingly difficult to construct out of the empirical data or out of plausible assumptions a *linear* cycle model which yields cycles that neither explode nor fade away.

This has led theorists to turn to non-linear cycle models in which, as we shall see, cycles can go on indefinitely with unchanged amplitude or in which the amplitude may approach asymptotically some plausible limit (the amplitude of the "limit cycle"—see below).

The Role of Initial Conditions

There is another reason for which nonlinear models have proved attractive to some economists. In a linear model the time path of the variable can, as we have seen, be determined for a very long time by initial conditions. Economically this might mean for example that the date of the most recent cyclical downturn (the recent time path of national income) is still very heavily influenced by some decision taken by Alexander Hamilton when he was Secretary of the Treasury if the same equation system were still applicable. In a nonlinear model, on the other hand, initial conditions can be shorn of their influence. It is easy to construct models in which the amplitude of the cycle at any point is largely independent of initial conditions.

It is really not always clear whether in this respect the advantage lies with the linear or the nonlinear models. The view that initial conditions should be confined to a negligible influence may well be considered excessively deterministic since it denies that the fortuitous events of any period can influence substantially the future history of the economy.

[3] Strictly speaking this argument is fallacious—any parameter like c always ends up taking *some one* of the infinite number of its conceivable values. And unless we have investigated carefully we cannot preclude in any particular case the possibility that, say, some institutional arrangement, e.g., some tax law, will dictate a unit value for c.

Methods of Nonlinear Analysis

Unfortunately, the mathematics of nonlinear analysis is not nearly so well developed as is that of the linear case. Analytic work has proceeded along two partly independent lines, one devoted primarily to quantitative, the other to qualitative investigation. Numerical analysis usually is based on a sequence of successive linear approximations to the nonlinear equations and employs iterative methods which are similar in spirit to Newton's method for the location of the roots of a polynomial which was outlined in the previous chapter. Nothing more will be said about these quantitative methods in this book.[4]

Qualitative analysis of nonlinear equations has, on the other hand, largely employed graphic techniques like those which are described in this chapter.

2. *FIRST-ORDER SYSTEMS*

Notation

The general first-order single difference equation system in the one time variable y_t can be written in the form [5]

$$y_{t+1} = f(y_t).$$

Here f represents any function however complicated in y_t which, at least for the relevant range, specifies a value for the variable in the

[4] Standard references in the entire area of nonlinear *differential* equation analysis are N. Minorsky, *Introduction to Non-Linear Mechanics,* J. W. Edwards, Ann Arbor, 1947, and A. A. Andronow and C. E. Chaikin, *Theory of Oscillations,* Princeton University Press, Princeton, 1949, Unfortunately very little seems to have been written on nonlinear difference (as opposed to differential) equation systems. But as Chapter Fifteen indicates the two types of equation are closely related and theorems in differential equations are often easily translatable into difference equation propositions. See also W. J. Baumol, "Topology of Second Order Linear Difference Equations," *Econometrica,* Vol. 21, April, 1958.

[5] Note that we have switched from the notation $y(t)$ to y_t to represent the value of variable y at time t.

next period corresponding to any value for the variable in period t. This function is, however, assumed not to be a function of time and, if applicable to the facts at all, it will ordinarily be so only for a very limited time.

Graphic Representation of the Time Path of y_t

Fortunately, it is quite easy to deal with the time path of the variable with the aid of a simple graph. In Figure 36 there is drawn a straight line making a 45° angle with both axes and a graphic representation of $f(y_t)$.

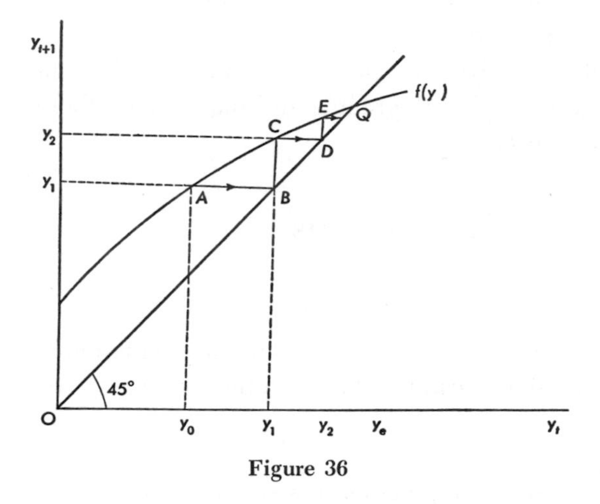

Figure 36

Suppose now that our initial condition places y_0 where it is shown along the horizontal axis by length $0y_0$. Since $y_1 = f(y_0)$ we can read off y_1 on the vertical axis by finding the point on the curve representing $f(y_t)$ above point y_0.

To find y_2 we can now repeat this procedure by measuring off y_1 on the horizontal axis in the same way that distance $0y_0$ was just used to indicate the magnitude of y_0. But y_1 can be transferred to the horizontal axis by a simple procedure which uses the 45° line. The important property of the 45° line for our purposes is that both coordinates of any point on the line are equal. Hence, if we draw a horizontal line from point y_1 on the vertical axis to where it meets the 45° line at B, and then drop a vertical line down to the other axis, the length of $0y_1$ thus obtained on this axis must be equal to the lenght $0y_1$ on the vertical axis.

We have now measured off the value of y in period 1 on the horizontal axis and can find y_2 by finding point C on the curve representing $f(y)$ which lies above y_1. We now know $0y_2$ to be the value of y in period 2. By going across from y_2 to point D on the 45° line and dropping a line down to the horizontal axis we now move this figure to that axis. Going above this point to point E gives us y_3 and so on. In sum the broken construction line $ABCDE\ldots$ traces out the time path of y_t which in this case moves in a stable manner toward equilibrium point Q.

This type of diagram is clearly very closely related to the cobweb diagrams which we used in Chapter Seven. We adopt the terminology of the analogous differential equation construction and refer to Fig. 36 as a *phase diagram* and to the graph of $f(y_t)$ as the *phase line.*

The Four Types of Time Path

In general the first-order nonlinear difference equation can generate four basic types of time path analogous with the four types of time path which can be generated by the first order *linear* difference equation with constant coefficients: [6]

Type (i) *Damped without Oscillation.* This will occur whenever the slope of the graph of $f(y_t)$ is positive and less than that of a 45° line, i.e., when

$$0 < \frac{df(y_t)}{dy_t} < 1.$$

This means that the phase line cuts the 45° line from above and the time path of y will be as in Figure 36 which is the case we have already examined. Specifically what happens here is that from wherever y_0 is located y_t will move toward Q in steps whose magnitude grows

[6] See above, Chapter Nine, Section 3. I ignore the unit root case for the reasons just discussed.

successively smaller and smaller. Thus, in the figure, CD is smaller than AB, etc. This is what is meant when the time path is said to be damped. It is easy to see intuitively why the time path of y_t will be damped whenever $\frac{df}{dy_t}$, the slope of $f(y_t)$, is less than one. For this slope is (approximately) equal to the ratio of a change in y_{t+1} such as BC to the change, AB, in y_t which brings it about. And this ratio $\frac{\text{change in } y_{t+1}}{\text{change in } y_t}$ can only be less than unity if the change in y_{t+1} is less than that in y_t. Similarly, the change, Δy_t (say, $BC = CD$ in the figure) in y_t between some other two successive periods will always lead to a smaller change, $\Delta y_{t+1} = DE$, between the next two periods. Thus the time path is damped because the successive changes in y grow smaller and smaller.

Further, in bringing y_t closer to Q these steps will never overshoot the mark, e.g., if y_0 is less than y_e the time path of y_t will, without outside intervention, never involve a value of y_t greater than the equilibrium value y_e. In the figure, for example, all the points A, C, and E are, like y_0, to the left of Q, but each is a little to the right of the preceding point. This is what is implied by the term "without oscillation." y does not get bigger and then smaller and then bigger, etc. Rather it always moves in the same direction and stays on the same side of Q. We can see intuitively why there will be no oscillation if the slope of $f(y_t) = \frac{\text{change in } y_{t+1}}{\text{change in } y_t}$ is positive. For then any change in y_{t+1} will always be of the same sign as in the change in y_t. In other words, if y rises from any one period to the next it must keep on rising. If ever, on the other hand, it falls, it must keep on falling. The time path of y_t can never reverse direction.

The linear equation $y(t+1) = ay(t) + b$ where $0 < a < 1$ with damped solution $y(t) = ka^t$ is an example of this type of difference equation. Note that its phase graph is a straight line with slope a.[7]

[7] One must not jump to the conclusion that all linear equations have straight line phase graphs. This is true of first-order equations but definitely not of equations of higher order. See Baumol, *op. cit.*

Type (ii) *Explosive without Oscillation.* This occurs whenever the slope of the phase line is greater than that of a 45° line, i.e., when

$$\frac{df(y_t)}{dy_t} > 1.$$

Here $f(y)$ has a positive slope and cuts the 45° line from below. The time path of y_t will then be unstable as shown in Figure 37 by broken construction line *ABCDE*... which moves further and further away from the equilibrium point Q and equilibrium value y_e.

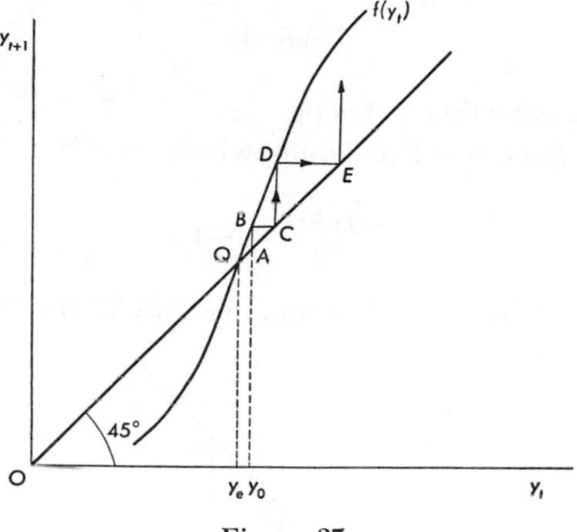

Figure 37

Type (iii) *Damped Oscillation.* Here the slope of the phase line is negative but greater than − 1, i.e.,

$$-1 < \frac{df(y_t)}{dy_t} < 0$$

and the time path of y_t is shown by the cobweb-like construction line *ABCDEF*... in Figure 38 and "dances around" equilibrium point y_e getting ever closer to it, that is, it involves stable oscillations.

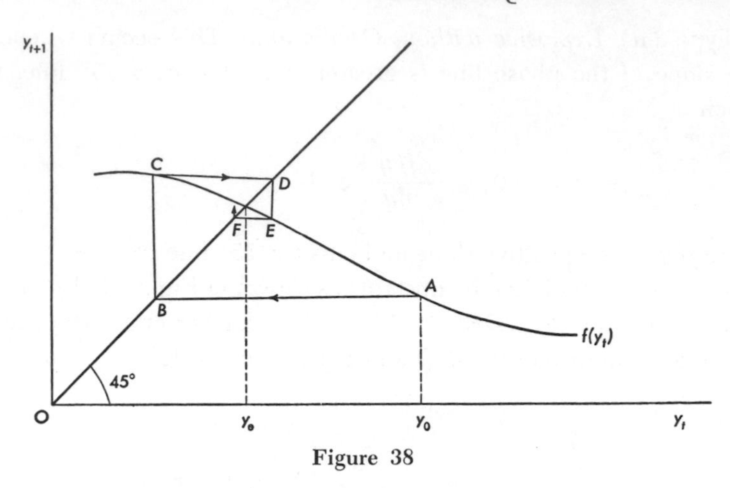

Figure 38

Finally,[8] we have time paths of
Type (iv) *Explosive Oscillation,* where

$$\frac{df(y_t)}{dy_t} < -1$$

as shown in Fig. 39 by construction line *ABCDEFGHI*. . .

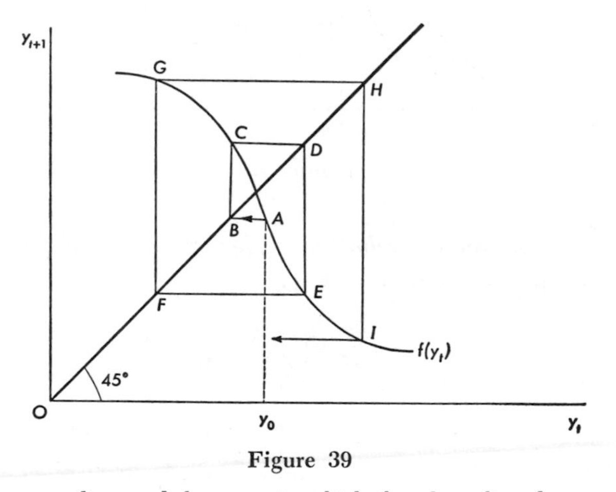

Figure 39

[8] We have not discussed the cases in which the phase line does not intersect the 45° line. The reader can readily show that if the phase line lies above the 45° line throughout its length then y_t will rise without limit, etc.

Combination of Time Paths

So far the system behaves very much like a linear system and indeed, each of the four cases just discussed could have been approximated rather satisfactorily by a linear system $y_{t+1} = ay_t + b$ where $ay_t + b$ is tangent to $f(y_t)$ at the point where the latter crosses the 45° line. For example, case 1 (damped non-oscillation) would then be represented as in Figure 40. Here income would con-

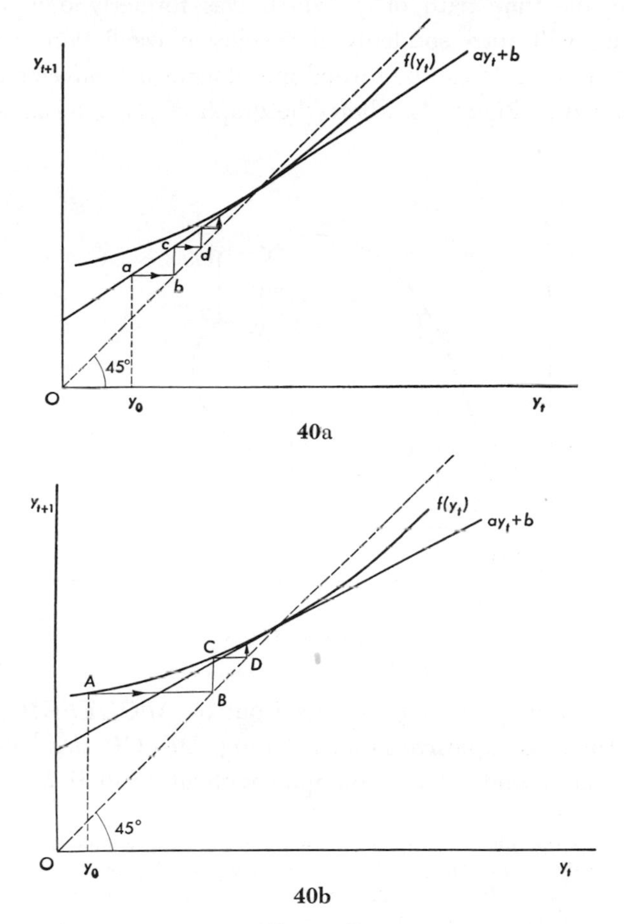

Figure 40

verge toward equilibrium relatively slowly along the time path *abcd*... (Fig. 40a) given by the linear approximation line $ay_t + b$, whereas the non-linear function would have the time path of y_t given by *ABCD*... (Fig. 40b). However, there is no great qualitative difference between the two points.

But the interesting feature of a nonlinear model is that it can easily switch over from one type of behavior to another. If the slope of $f(y_t)$ changes from small and positive to large and negative, for example, the time path of y_t which was formerly damped non-oscillating will turn suddenly to explosive oscillation. Similarly, upward movements can be turned into downward movements. This is illustrated in Figure 41 where the graph of $f(y_t)$ forms a closed loop.[9]

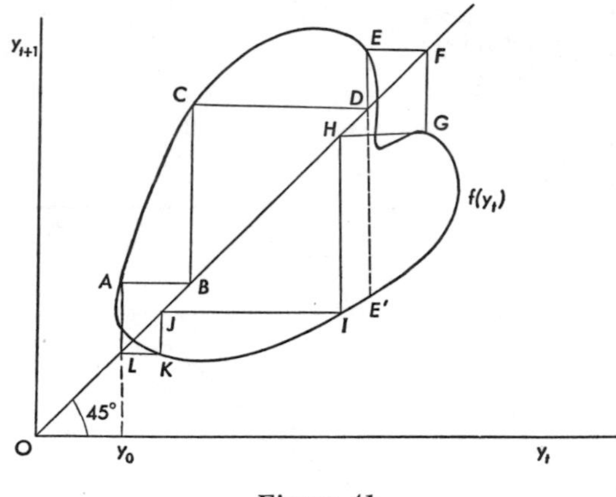

Figure 41

Here the time path of y_t is traced out by *ABCDEFGHIJKL*..., where *ABCD* is explosive non-oscillating, *DEFGH* involves explosive oscillation and *HIJK* is damped without oscillation, etc. Note

[9] We evade the difficult problem involved in deciding which value of y_{t+1} to take in a multivalued $f(y_t)$ such as that shown in Figure 41. That is, from point *D* how do we know we should go to point *E* rather than to point *E'*? But cf. Baumol, *op. cit.*, pp. 264–265.

that in this figure we finally end up with a time path which repeats itself perfectly and periodically, that is, with cycles of constant amplitude.

We have seen, then, how great a variety of time paths is really permitted by non-linear models. Presently an economic example involving a situation very much like that in Figure 41 will be described.

3. *PHASE DIAGRAM AND TIME PATH: GENERAL RULES*

We have already summarized several basic relationships between the shape of the phase line and the nature of the time path when we described which type of phase line will yield each of the four basic types of time path. In addition there are several other rules which can be helpful to the user of the phase diagram.

1. When a phase line is above the 45° line, y_{t+1} is by definition greater than y_t (what feature of the 45° line tells us this?). Hence, in such a region *y must always be increasing,* i.e., the time path will move upward and to the right. The reverse holds in regions of the phase diagram where the phase line lies below the 45° line.

2. Where the time path of the variable involves oscillations or fluctuations it must by definition involve rises in y (the phase line above the 45° line) succeeded by falls in y (the phase line below the 45° line). Thus the phase line of an oscillatory time path must cross the 45° line.

But we have seen that where the phase line has a positive slope the time path must be either of type i (stable non-oscillatory) where the 45° line is approached asymptotically *but is never crossed,* or it must be of type ii (explosive non-oscillatory) in which the time path never even approaches the 45° line. Thus if the time path is to cross the 45° line the slope of the phase line cannot be positive at the point of crossing, that is, *oscillatory motion requires that the phase line have a negative slope at the point where it crosses the 45° line.*

PROBLEMS

1. Write out the linear cobweb theorem model in the phase line equation form $P_{t+1} = f(P_t)$. [See the answer to the problem in Chapter Nine, Section 5, above.] Compare the phase diagram and the construction of the time path with the cobweb diagrams in Chapter Seven, above.
2. Write out a first-order linear equation whose time path is a special case of type ii above. Do the same for types iii and iv. Draw their phase diagrams and in each case construct a time path for the variable.

4. TWO ECONOMIC EXAMPLES

The Classical Model

Stripped to a bare caricature the classical model can be described as follows:

i) Net total production (total output minus the amount needed to pay rent and the minimum return to capital)[10] P_t, is dependent on the size of the working population, R_t. This dependence can be expressed by means of the production function

$$P_t = f(R_t). \tag{46}$$

It is usually assumed that throughout the relevant range the marginal product of labor is positive, i.e., that

$$f'(R_t) > 0. \tag{47}$$

Moreover, because of the law of diminishing returns, this function is nonlinear; in fact we have

$$f''(R_t) < 0. \tag{48}$$

ii) Total population (and hence the working population) is dependent on the level of real wages. At any time population tends to grow to a size where output per man is just large enough to provide to each worker an amount S just sufficient for a minimum customary standard of living. This can be represented by

$$P_t = R_{t+1}S \tag{49}$$

[10] By the minimum return to capital we mean the minimum payment needed to induce capitalists to continue saving.

which states that population at $t+1$ will tend to a level at which minimum customary subsistence wage payments to workers will exhaust the total net product of the preceding period. The length of our time period is thus the time it takes population to adjust to changed economic conditions, and is perhaps of the order of magnitude of 25 years.

Finally, the classical argument implies that eventually, because of the diminishing returns (48), the marginal product of labor will, if population becomes sufficiently large, fall below subsistence, i.e.,

$$f'(R_t) < S \qquad \text{for} \quad R_t > K \text{ (some constant).} \qquad (50)$$

The model can be complicated further to bring it closer to the classical analyses but for our present purpose, to illustrate nonlinear model analysis, this will suffice.

Equations (46) and (49) together yield the nonlinear first order difference equation

$$R_{t+1} = f(R_t)/S.$$

By (47) above we know that the slope of its graph will be positive. Moreover, by (50) we have

$$\frac{d\dfrac{f(R_t)}{S}}{dR_t} < 1 \qquad \text{for } R_t > K.$$

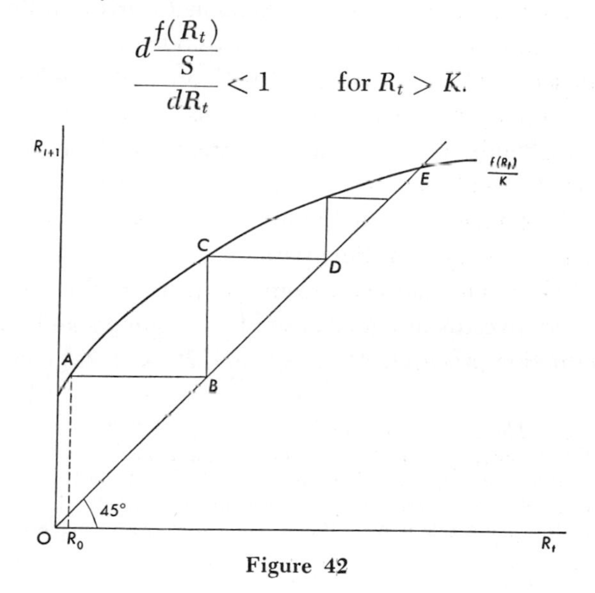

Figure 42

Thus beyond this level of population the time path of production and population will be damped without oscillation (case i, above) and the time path of population will be as shown in Figure 42.

It will head toward the point of equilibrium, *E*, the so-called classical stationary state.

The Hicks Trade Cycle Model

In a recent volume[11] Professor Hicks has constructed a nonlinear model of the trade cycle. This is interesting for our purposes because its nonlinearity takes the form of kinks (sharp corners) in an otherwise linear expression. An example of this sort of thing is given by

$$y_t = a \mid y_{t-1} \mid$$

where $\mid y_{t-1} \mid$ is the absolute value of y_{t-1} whose graph has a kink at $y_{t-1} = 0$.

The Hicks trade cycle model is designed explicitly to solve the basic problem which (as we saw in Section 1) arises in linear cycle models—the tendency of their cycles to explode or fade away. Hicks, as we shall see, deliberately starts off with an explosive linear model which is essentially the same as the Samuelson model[12] described in Section 1 of Chapter Ten. But Hicks, in effect, puts kinks in the linear relationships to bend them into a closed curve not too different from the closed loop phase line in Figure 41, and which can produce a constant amplitude cyclical time path.

In the Hicks model national income is, as usual, divided into consumption and investment (goods used by consumers and goods used in the production process). Also, as usual, Hicks takes consumption,

[11] J. R. Hicks, *The Trade Cycle,* Oxford, New York, 1950.

[12] Like the Samuelson model the Hicksian trade cycle analysis employs a second order difference equation. We have here modified the Hicksian construction to change it into a first-order analysis of the variety discussed in this chapter. For the phase diagram of the second-order Hicks model see Baumol, "Topology . . . ," *loc. cit.*

C_t, to be a fixed proportion of income in the previous period, y_{t-1}, plus a constant; thus:

$$C_t = ay_{t-1} + b \qquad a, b \text{ constants.} \quad (51)$$

However, the investment relationship will vary over the trade cycle. If we assume that there is an optimal economic-technological ratio, k, between the nation's capital stock, K_t, and national income (production) then when there is a down-turn in business activity there will be an excessive stock of capital. Equipment and inventories will not be replaced as they are used up and so net investment will be negative. This can be expressed by

$$I_t = -w \qquad \text{for} \quad K_{t-1} > ky_{t-1} \quad (52)$$

where w is a positive constant.

On the other hand when the capital stock is not in excess, as income rises investment will have to take place to keep the stock of capital at the desired proportion of income. This gives us the ordinary acceleration principle relationship [13]

$$I_t = K_t - K_{t-1} = k(y_t - y_{t-1}) \qquad \text{for } K_{t-1} \leqq ky_{t-1}. \quad (53)$$

Since, as already mentioned, income is divided into consumption and investment we have the usual identity

$$y_t \equiv I_t + C_t. \quad (54)$$

When there is excessive capital we have, substituting from (51) and (52) into (54)

$$y_t = ay_{t-1} + b - w \qquad \text{for } K_t > ky_{t-1}. \quad (55)$$

This is a first order linear difference equation which is represented by phase line RR' in Figure 43. Since its slope, a, the marginal propensity to consume, is presumably less than unity this line cuts the

[13] It may be noted that if the stock of capital is initially below the desired level this rate of investment will not fully supply the deficiency. It will only prevent the capital stock from falling further behind a rising production level.

45° line from above. On the other hand when there is no excess capital, income is no longer given by (55). Instead we have by (51), (53), and (54)

$$y_t = ay_{t-1} + k(y_t - y_{t-1}) + b \tag{56}$$

or

$$y_t = \frac{a-k}{1-k}\, y_{t-1} + \frac{b}{1-k} \tag{57}$$

where on economic or empirical grounds we expect that usually

$$k > 1 > a > 0, \tag{58}$$

so that

$$\frac{a-k}{1-k} = \frac{k-a}{k-1} > 1 \text{ and } \frac{b}{1-k} < 0. \tag{59}$$

Thus (57) is a linear phase line equation represented by UU' in Figure 43. By (59) we see that this is a case ii (explosive non-oscillatory) phase line since its slope is greater than unity.

Our nonlinear model is now complete except for the restriction that there is a maximum level of income y_e which represents the productivity of the economy when its resources are fully employed. This is another nonlinearity which states that the time path of y cannot indefinitely follow phase line UU' because y must remain inside the square $0y_eFY_e$ in Figure 43. Specifically we have

$$y_t \leqq y_e \tag{60}$$

where $y_t = y_e$ whenever our previous equations call for a level of y which is greater than the full employment ceiling, y_c.

We can now examine the time path given by this model graphically in Figure 43.

During the upswing new capital is demanded so that by (53) national income moves along the line UU', tracing out the path $ABCD$, etc. for during that period UU' corresponds to the $f(y_t)$ of our previous diagrams. Finally, at point E full employment income is attained. Now income can move no higher and it must ultimately turn down. This is because investment will no longer be undertaken when income ceases to rise [equation (53)] so that the investment

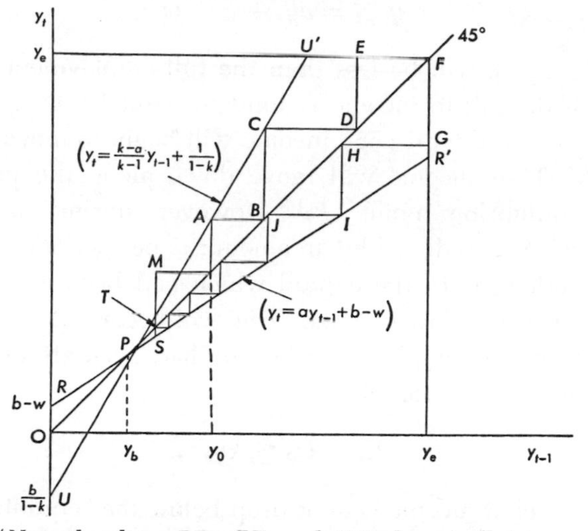

(Note that lines RR', OF, and UU' do not all intersect at the same point.)

Figure 43

component in income [equation (54)] will drop to zero.[14] By (51), (52), and (54) income in the next period will be

[14] There is a problem here about the details of the downturn mechanism. When income first reaches its full employment level, y_e, the lag in investment behind desired capital stock, as described in (53), means that capital stock will not yet have reached the level ky_e, which is appropriate for full employment output. At this point we run into a technical difficulty. Investment can no longer be given by (53) because with income unable to rise further, that relationship will call for zero investment, which is clearly wrong since the capital stock is not yet at its desired level. For similar reasons, the downswing investment function (52) will not hold here, for that relationship applies only in the case where there is excess capital. We must therefore assume that when income first reaches y_e, investment will proceed at some determinate rate representing the difference between full employment output y_e and consumption $ay_{t-1} + b$. In subsequent periods, this will be the constant and positive amount

$$v = y_e - (ay_e + b).$$

Investment at level v will continue until the accumulated capital is no longer less than the desired capital stock ky_e. At this point net investment will begin to follow (52) and in the next period income will fall to

$$y_{t+1} = ay_e + b - w < ay_e + b + v = y_e.$$

The downswing will have begun.

I am grateful to E. W. Lungren of Colorado State University for pointing out an error in my previous discussion of this matter and to my colleague S. M. Goldfeld for helping me to correct it.

$$y_{t+1} = ay_e + b - w \tag{61}$$

(point G) which will be less than the full employment income y_e. Now, with the fall in income redundant capital will appear ($k_t > ky_t$) and in accord with (55) income will begin to move downward along RR'. Thus income will move down along the path HIJ... toward "equilibrium point" P.[15] However, during this time the capital stock K_t is reduced by an amount w per period. Thus income will keep falling until the capital which had been attained at full employment is cut down to size. This will occur s periods after the period e when full employment income had been attained, where s is the smallest integer for which

$$K_e - ws \leqq ky_{e+s}.$$

Since the level of income cannot drop below the "equilibrium" level y_b this means that this downswing phase of the cycle will last at most until (approximately)

$$K_e - ws = ky_b$$

i.e., for

$$s = \frac{K_e - ky_b}{w} \text{ periods.}$$

At the end of this time capital stocks will be no larger than[16] their desired level. Investment will therefore suddenly be governed by (53) again. Income will take a sudden jump since the negative investment component will have been eliminated. Income will rise, perhaps to point M, and because income is increasing once again the time path will return to the upswing phase line UU', to begin another cycle.

Before leaving this discussion three comments are appropriate.

1. It will be noted that this nonlinear model has achieved a con-

[15] P is Hicks' lower national income equilibrium represented by line LL' in his Figure 12 (*ibid.*, p. 97).

[16] Normally the actual capital stock will then be lower than its desired level by an amount no greater than w.

stant amplitude cyclical time path. Indeed there is some presumption that after the "second go round" every cycle will, in the absence of exogenous disturbances, be a precise duplicate of the cycle which preceded it. For income will always drop from the full employment level to the level of full employment consumption given by (61) (point G) so that we can take every cycle to start out from this point. Of course, if as in the Hicks model, and has been the case historically, the full employment ceiling moves upward with the passage of time, this will no longer be true.

2. The Hicksian autonomous investment may produce an upturn more rapid than that just described. Autonomous investment will add another term $A(t)$[where $A'(t) > 0$] to the investment functions (52) and (53). According to Hicks, with the passage of time this investment will grow and shift RR' upward until some period t when the point on RR' with coordinates (y_{t+1}, y_t) lies above the 45° line and the upturn will then begin.

3. Such nonlinear cycles characterized by sudden changes in mechanism (e.g., the change from UU' to RR') are called *relaxation cycles.*

5. LIMIT CYCLES

We may generalize from the preceding discussion by noting that cycles of constant amplitude can be produced by a closed phase line, e.g., one which is circular, elliptical, heart shaped (as in Figure 41), or a quadrilateral (as in the Hicks model).

There is a second type of phase line which can produce cycles that neither explode nor disappear. Consider a phase line which has a negative slope like those in Figures 38 or 39. We know that this can produce an oscillatory time path. Now let us bend this phase line so that its slope is greater than unity in absolute value near the 45° line and its ends have slopes less than unity in absolute value (Fig. 44).

In such a case an initial point like y_o which lies in the flat region of the phase line will lead to a time path of type iii: damped oscillations whose amplitude grows smaller and smaller (construction line

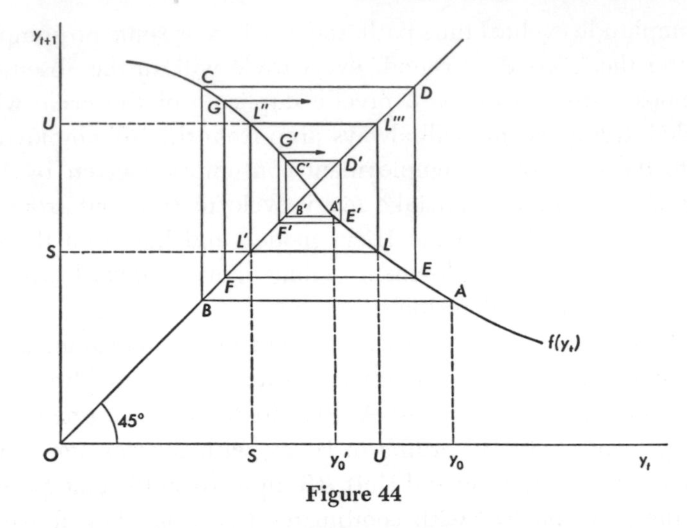

Figure 44

ABCDEFG · · ·). But an initial point like y'_0 which lies in the steep phase line region will initiate a time path of type iv, a sequence of explosive oscillations (*A′B′C′D′E′F′G′* · · ·). These two types of cycle (the growing inner cycle and the damped outer cycle) will approach a common cycle *LL′L″L‴* which is the border between them. This borderline cycle is called a stable limit cycle because any other cyclical movement near it will gradually approach closer and closer to that cycle. Furthermore, if some initial point such as *U* starts the time path along the limit cycle, then in the absence of any outside disturbances the time path will continue along *LL′L″L‴* indefinitely. In this case we may then consider the limit cycle as a stable moving equilibrium time path. It is in equilibrium because such a time path is self-sustaining. It is stable because any departure from this cycle will be followed by movement back toward the limit cycle.

It should be clear that one can construct an unstable limit cycle in which all other cycles move further and further away from the limit cycle. This will be produced by a negatively sloping phase line which is flat near the center and steep near the edges of the diagram. The reader should verify this by drawing such a graph.

One Kink Limit Cycles

It may surprise the reader to find that a stable limit cycle of the sort which has just been described can also be produced by a negatively sloping straight line phase line which has *only one kink* (Fig. 45), or by a curved phase line of similar shape. We have

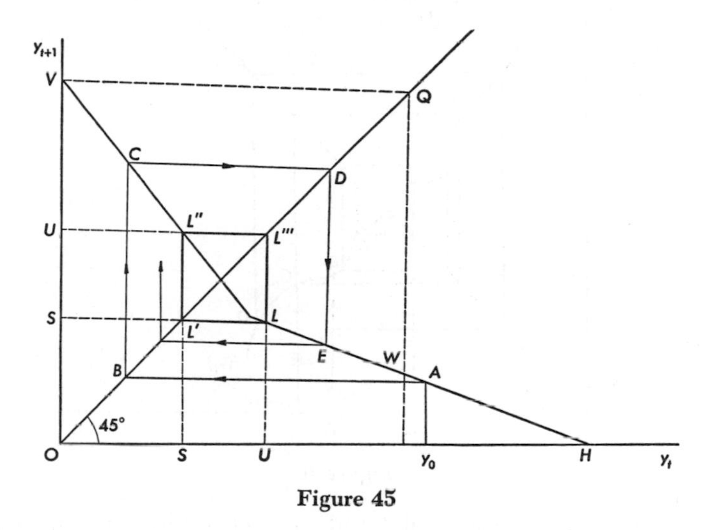

Figure 45

seen that this type of limit cycle is generated by an explosive inner cycle and a damped outer cycle, which both converge on the limit cycle as a common boundary. It is clear why, near the 45° line where the phase line is very steep, oscillations should be explosive and can produce the required explosive inner cycle. But the diagram also shows that a single flat end of the phase line can (but will not always) suffice to produce the damped outer cycle.[17]

[17] If the phase line meets the vertical axis at some point V and the horizontal axis at a point H such that $OH > OV$, a time path which passes near point H must be characterized by damped oscillation. For suppose we start off right at point H, then the time path will be given by $HOVQW \cdots$ where, since Q is on the 45° line, $VQ = OV < OH$ so that W must lie to the left of H and these oscillations must be damped.

Multiple Limit Cycles

It is also possible to construct a negatively sloping phase line which by wiggling from steep to flat stretches and then back again yields a sequence of "concentric" (nested) limit cycles, as is shown in Figure 46. A limit cycle will occur roughly each time the phase

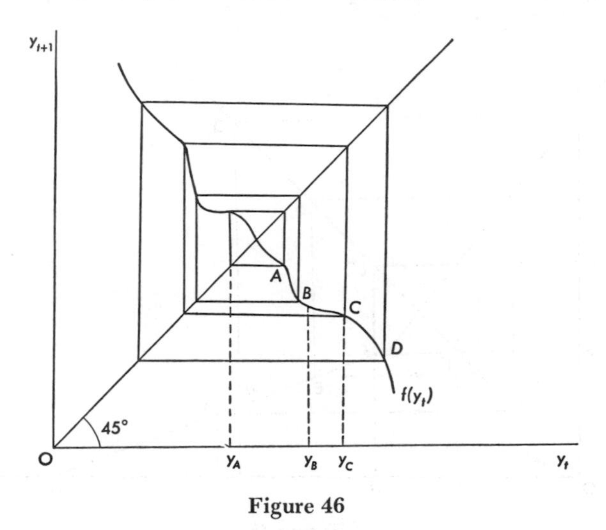

Figure 46

curve changes from steep to flat and vice versa. But as we move away from the 45° line if the curve is first steep and then flat we have seen that the limit cycle will be stable, whereas if it moves from flat to steep it will be unstable. Thus in a sequence of nested limit cycles, so long as the phase line is continuous the limit cycles will be alternatingly stable and unstable, i.e., only every other cycle will be stable.

It should also be noted that in the nested cycles case the time path which will actually be followed will be determined by initial conditions. If we start off at or near y_C the time path will move along or approach limit cycle *C*, whereas from or near y_A the pertinent limit cycle will be *A*. Thus we see that even in nonlinear models initial conditions can play an important role in the determination of the time path.

Locating the Limit Cycle

A limit cycle of the sort with which we have been dealing will involve one period oscillations between some upper value of the variable $y = U$ and some smaller value $y = S$ (Figs. 44 and 45). Thus if we can determine the magnitudes of these two numbers U and S the limit cycle will be located completely.

We can find the values of S and U with the aid of the equation of the phase line $y_{t+1} = f(y_t)$. The coordinates of the two opposite corners L and L'' (Fig. 44) of the intersection of the phase line with the square construction line which represents the limit cycle give us two equations in the unknowns S and U. At point L'' we have $y_{t+1} = U$ and $y_t = S$ so that $y_{t+1} = f(y_t)$ becomes $U = f(S)$, while at L we have $S = f(U)$. These two equations can usually be solved simultaneously to give us the values of U and S, which constitute the end points of the limit cycle.

EXAMPLE

Consider the kinked phase line whose higher segment is given by $y_{Ht+1} = 6 - 2y_t$ and whose lower segment is given by $y_{Lt+1} = 2 - \frac{1}{4}y_t$. The two segments intersect at $y_{Lt+1} = y_{Ht+1}$, i.e., at $6 - 2y_t = 2 - \frac{1}{4}y_t$ so that a simple computation yields $y_t = \frac{16}{7}$ as the abscissa of the point of intersection. Thus since point L lies to the right of this point it is on the lower segment of the phase line and so we have

$$S = f(U) = 2 - \frac{1}{4}U,$$

and similarly, for point L''

$$U = 6 - 2S.$$

These two equations readily yield $S = 1$, $U = 4$ as the values between which the variable oscillates in the limit cycle.

PROBLEMS

1. Which are the unstable limit cycles in Figure 46?
2. Toward which limit cycle will the time path converge from initial point y_b in Figure 46? Draw the time path construction line.
3. Find the *cobweb* limit cycles generated by the supply function $Q_{t+1} = P_t$ and the kinked demand curves

   a) $P_{Ht} = 15 - 3Q_t,\ P_{Lt} = 4 - \frac{1}{4}Q_t.$

   b) $P_{Ht} = 21 - 3Q_t,\ P_{Lt} = 5 - \frac{1}{5}Q_t.$

Chapter Fourteen

SIMPLE DIFFERENTIAL EQUATION SYSTEMS [1]

1. INTRODUCTORY

DEFINITIONS

An equation of the form

$$\frac{d^n y}{dt^n} + a_1 \frac{d^{n-1} y}{dt^{n-1}} + \cdots + a_{n-1} \frac{dy}{dt} + a_n y + b = 0 \qquad (62)$$

where $d^n y/dt^n$ is the nth derivative of y with respect to t, is called an nth order linear differential equation with constant coefficients (and constant term, b). If $b = 0$, we call Eq. (62) homogeneous. If we take y to be any economic variable and t to be time as before, then since dy/dt tells us how y is changing over time (it is, so to speak, the marginal change in y resulting from the passage of a small quantity of time) and since d^2y/dt^2 tells us how dy/dt is changing over

[1] The reader of this chapter should have at least a rudimentary knowledge of the differential calculus. Specifically he should know the meaning and notation of the derivative, the second derivative, etc., and should know that the derivative of $ax^r e^{xb}$ with respect to x is given by $rax^{r-1}e^{xb} + bax^r e^{xb}$ and in particular that $dae^{mx}/dx = ame^{mx}$, where the definition of e is restated below to remind those who may have forgotten. Should there be any foolhardy souls who venture here without this information they may perhaps find it helpful to think of the derivative in terms of the marginal analysis. Thus if $P = f(L)$, where L is the quantity of labor employed by a firm and P is the output of the firm, then dP/dL (the derivative of production with respect to quantity of labor employed) is the marginal product of labor. It should also be noted that one often writes y' for dy/dt, y'' for d^2y/dt^2, etc.

time, etc., it is clear that Eq. (62) tells us something about the behavior of y over time and so is of interest for economic dynamics.

An Intuitive Interpretation

The relationship among the derivatives of y and y itself given by (62) remains unchanged over time much as the relationship among $y(t)$, $y(t-1)$, etc., was taken to be unchanging over time in a linear difference equation with constant coefficients. That being the case, if we know the values of $d^{n-1}y/dt^{n-1}$, $d^{n-2}y/dt^{n-2}$, $\cdots$, dy/dt, and y at some initial moment, $t = 0$, then these together with Eq. (62) will give us the value of d^ny/dt^n at $t = 0$. It may be intuitively plausible that the value of dy/dt will determine the change in y over the next moment of time, so to speak, and thus knowing the initial value of y and the change in y over the next moment we can determine the value of y at the end of that moment. Similarly the initial values of d^2y/dt^2 and dy/dt will determine the value of dy/dt at the end of that next moment, and so on until finally we come to the initial values of d^ny/dt^n and $d^{n-1}y/dt^{n-1}$ which determine the value of $d^{n-1}y/dt^{n-1}$ at the end of that moment. Thus we will have, in effect, determined the values of y, dy/dt, d^2y/dt^2, $\cdots$, $d^{n-1}y/dt^{n-1}$ at the end of the moment after $t = 0$, but the value of d^ny/dt^n is still left undetermined. Since, however, the relationship given by Eq. (62) remains unchanging through time, we may now determine d^ny/dt^n for that moment from the values of y and its other derivatives which we have already obtained. Thus we now have as much information about the situation at the end of the moment after $t = 0$ as we did about the situation at $t = 0$, and we may now proceed similarly to calculate the same information for the "moment" after that, and then the next succeeding moment, and so on, *ad infinitum*. Thus, conceptually, the initial conditions

$$y = c_0, \quad \frac{dy}{dt} = c_1, \cdots, \quad \frac{d^{n-1}y}{dt^{n-1}} = c_{n-1} \text{ at } t = 0 \tag{63}$$

together with the differential equation (62) determine the course of y (and incidentally that of dy/dt, d^2y/dt^2, $\cdots$, d^ny/dt^n) through time just as a difference-equation system does.

Now clearly, the process that has just been outlined for determining the course of y through time from Eq. (62) and initial conditions (63) is completely impractical. Indeed, it is not even, strictly speaking, correct. The purpose of the argument was merely to indicate intuitively what can be expected from a differential equation system and not to show how we can in fact operate with it. We shall presently return to that problem.

An Economic Example

To see how a simple differential-equation system can be employed in the analysis of a problem in economic dynamics we consider a somewhat modified version of Professor Domar's (independently formulated) analysis [2] of the problem we have in this book associated with the work of Mr. Harrod and which we have already considered several times. As in Mr. Harrod's analysis [3] we take saving (investment) at time t, $S(t)$, to be proportionate to income at time t, $y(t)$; i.e.,

$$S(t) = sy(t)$$

which we write simply

$$S = sy \tag{64}$$

where s is a constant. We also say as before that investment desires are proportioned to the rate of increase of income over time, which we formerly wrote

$$I(t) = g[y(t) - y(t-1)]$$

where g is a constant. But we know that $[y(t) - y(t-1)]$ is only an average figure for the rate of increase of income over a period. The rate of increase of income at any moment is, strictly speaking,

[2] See Evsey D. Domar, "Capital Expansion, Rate of Growth and Employment," *Econometrica*, April 1946. See also, "Expansion and Employment," *American Economic Review*, March 1947; and "The Problem of Capital Accumulation," *American Economic Review*, December 1948. All of these papers are reproduced in Evsey D. Domar, *Essays in the Theory of Economic Growth* (Oxford University Press, New York, 1957).

[3] See Chapter Nine, Section 2.

given by dy/dt, so that if investment desires are to be proportioned to the rate of increase of income, we must have

$$I = g\frac{dy}{dt} \tag{65}$$

where g is a constant.

Thus if investment demands are to be satisfied, i.e., if we are to have $I = S$, then from (64) and (65) we must have

$$sy = g\frac{dy}{dt}$$

i.e.,

$$\frac{dy}{dt} - \frac{s}{g}y = 0 \tag{66}$$

which is a first-order differential equation with constant coefficient $-s/g$. This problem has thus shown itself amenable to analysis with the aid of either difference- or differential-equation systems. It is to be noted, however, that the change in technique does involve a subtle change in economic assumptions; for Eq. (65) assumes implicitly that the entrepreneur is so sensitive to changes in income that his investment demands change at once with the most momentary changes in the rate of increase of production (income). The equation which (65) replaces clearly assumes instead that investment demands are formulated only every so often (once per period) and that these are based on what has happened to production on balance during the time since the last decision was made. The premise involved in our present analysis in Eq. (65) would seem to be the less realistic of the two, but since we are at the moment more concerned with the technique than with the realism of the analysis, we shall not delve into this problem further. It suffices to note that the two analyses are not precisely equivalent.

It should also be noted that, while this problem happens to be readily amenable to both difference- and differential-equation analysis, this should not be expected to be the case for all problems in economic dynamics.

2. FIRST-ORDER HOMOGENEOUS SYSTEMS

Our task is now to find a solution of a system such as that given by Eq. (62) and initial conditions (63). As before, by a solution we mean an expression, a "formula," giving y at all points of time such that it satisfies both (62) and (63).

The Meaning of e

However, before we can give an example and proceed on our task there is a brief preliminary matter we must get out of our way. We must say a few words about the number e which will play so important a part in our analysis.

If we invest K dollars at a rate of interest, i, compounded annually at the end of one year, the principal will, by the familiar formula, be

$$P = K(1+i).$$

If instead the sum were compounded semiannually we would have

$$P = K\left(1+\frac{i}{2}\right)^2$$

and if it were compounded three times a year this would become

$$P = K\left(1+\frac{i}{3}\right)^3.$$

Proceeding in this way we can see generally that if interest were compounded n times a year we would have

$$P = K\left(1+\frac{i}{n}\right)^n \tag{67}$$

and if interest were continuously compounded, i.e., compounded every moment, we would have a principal given by the value approached by P in (67) as n approaches infinity (becomes as large as we like). Now if K, the sum originally invested, were equal to 1 (dollar) and the rate of interest were 100 per cent so that $i = 1$, (67) would become

$$P = \left(1+\frac{1}{n}\right)^n \tag{68}$$

and e is the limit approached by this P as n approaches infinity; i.e., it is the principal on 1 (dollar) compounded continuously for one year at a 100 per cent rate of interest. The value of e can be shown to be approximately 2.718. Of course money is not in practice compounded continuously,[4] but there are standard examples of things which behave very much like a sum on which continuously compounded interest is being accumulated. A snowball rolling down a hill accumulates more snow in proportion to the size it has already attained, and a colony of bacteria, under ideal conditions, increases in number in proportion to the size it has attained at any moment.

Solution of the First-order System

It is an elementary proposition of the differential calculus that an expression of the form ae^{mt} has the derivative

$$\frac{dae^{mt}}{dt} = mae^{mt}. \tag{69}$$

Now we seek a solution of the system given by

$$\frac{dy}{dt} + by = 0 \quad (70) \qquad \text{e.g.,} \frac{dy}{dt} - 5y = 0 \quad (70a)$$

$$y = c_0 \quad (\text{at } t = 0) \quad (71) \qquad y = 2 \quad (\text{at } t = 0). \quad (71a)$$

Let us pull a rabbit out of a hat and try a solution of the form

$$y = ae^{mt}.\text{[5]} \tag{72}$$

Substituting into (70) from (69) and (72) for dy/dt and y we get

$$mae^{mt} + bae^{mt} = 0 \text{ or } mae^{mt} = +5ae^{mt}$$

or $$m = -b$$

i.e., $$m = 5$$

[4] Although given any amount invested and the interest payment on it for any given period we can obviously always find a rate of interest which with continuous compounding would have yielded the same interest payment on the investment.

[5] This can be obtained directly from (70) by those familiar with the elementary technique of differential equations as follows: (70) gives $dy/y = -bdt$. This has the integral $\log_e y = -bt + c$ or (writing $c = \log_e a$) $y = ae^{-bt}$, where a is an arbitrary constant.

so that our solution becomes

$$y = ae^{-bt} \qquad (73) \qquad\qquad y = ae^{5t}. \qquad (73a)$$

Now, substituting this into (71) to see that the initial conditions are satisfied, we get

$$y = ae^{-bt} = c_0 \qquad y = ae^{5t} = 2 \qquad (\text{for } t = 0)$$

but $e^{Kt} = 1$ for $t = 0$, so that we get

$$a = c_0 \qquad a = 2$$

and we have as our solutions

$$y = c_0 e^{-bt} \qquad (74) \qquad\qquad y = 2e^{5t}. \qquad (74a)$$

Just to be certain that this solution works, we differentiate this with the aid of (69) and obtain

$$\frac{dy}{dt} = -bc_0 e^{-bt} \quad \frac{dy}{dt} = 10e^{5t}.$$

Substituting this and (74) into Eqs. (70) and (70a) for y and dy/dt gives

$$-bc_0 e^{-bt} + b(c_0 e^{-bt}) \qquad 10e^{5t} - 5(2e^{5t})$$

which is equal to zero as required. Similarly, we can see that the initial conditions are satisfied, for setting $t = 0$ in (74) we get

$$y = c_0 e^0 = c_0 \qquad y = 2e^0 = 2$$

as required. Thus (74) is a solution of our general first-order system. We shall postpone the interpretation of the results, since this is much simpler than in the case of difference-equation systems, and so we may as well do it for first and higher order systems at the same time.

PROBLEM

1. Solve:

a) $\frac{dy}{dt} + 3y = 0, y(0) = 4$

b) $\frac{dy}{dt} - 17y = 0, y(0) = 1$

c) $\frac{dy}{dt} = 0, y(0) = 5$

d) $\frac{dy}{dt} - 2y = 0, y(0) = 0$

3. HOMOGENEOUS HIGHER-ORDER SYSTEMS

As in difference equation systems the discussion in the text will be confined to the second-order case. The arguments are so completely analogous to those of difference equation systems[6] and the extension of the operations to higher-order systems so obvious that this will for the most part be left to the reader. The illustrative examples in the text will wherever possible be chosen similar to the analogous examples in the discussion on difference equations to facilitate ready comparison by the interested reader.

Consider the system given by

$$\frac{d^2y}{dt^2} + b\frac{dy}{dt} + cy = 0 \quad (75) \qquad \frac{d^2y}{dt^2} - 3\frac{dy}{dt} + 2y = 0 \quad (75a)$$

$$\frac{dy}{dt} = c_1, \quad y = c_0 \quad (\text{at } t = 0) \quad (76)$$

$$\frac{dy}{dt} = 6, \quad y = 4 \quad (\text{at } t = 0). \quad (76a)$$

We first try a solution of the form $y = e^{xt}$, and substituting this into (75) for $\frac{d^2y}{dt^2}, \frac{dy}{dt}$, and y we get

$$x^2 + bx + c = 0 \quad (77) \qquad x^2 - 3x + 2 = 0 \quad (77a)$$

which will hold for either of the two roots of the characteristic equation

[6] Indeed the formal analogy is for the most part perfect, and most of the relevant propositions can be derived in one fell swoop with the aid of a more general type of equation, called an operator equation, of which difference and differential equations are special cases. See Section 4 of Chapter Fifteen below and the appendix on difference equations in Samuelson's *Foundations of Economic Analysis* (Harvard University Press, Cambridge, Mass., 1947).

$$x_1 = \frac{-b + \sqrt{b^2 - 4c}}{2} \qquad x_1 = \frac{3 + \sqrt{9 - 8}}{2} = 2$$

$$x_2 = \frac{-b - \sqrt{b^2 - 4c}}{2} \qquad x_2 = 1$$

so that, as the reader can easily verify, we have two solutions of (75) given by

$$y = e^{x_1 t} \quad y = e^{x_2 t} \qquad (78) \qquad\qquad y = e^{2t} \quad y = e^{t}. \qquad (78a)$$

Now it is clear that for $t = 0$ these all give $y = 1$ and in general this will not satisfy the initial conditions (76). To get a solution which satisfies our two initial conditions we want a solution with two arbitrary constants (or in the nth order case a solution with n arbitrary constants) just as in the difference equation case; and similar to Proposition Six we have here:

PROPOSITION THIRTEEN: *If* y_1 and y_2 are both solutions of (75), then so is $y = fy_1 + gy_2$, where f and g are arbitrary constants.[7]

The proof of this proposition is step by step identical with that of the corresponding proposition in difference equations and is left as an exercise for the reader.

Now by Proposition Thirteen and (78)

$$y = fe^{x_1 t} + ge^{x_2 t} \qquad (79) \qquad\qquad y = fe^{2t} + ge^{t} \qquad (79a)$$

is a solution of Eq. (75), where f and g are arbitrary constants. If this solution is to satisfy the initial conditions (76) we must have, for $t = 0$,

$$y = fe^{x_1 t} + ge^{x_2 t} = fe^0 + ge^0 = f + g = c_0 = 4$$

$$\frac{dy}{dt} = x_1 fe^{x_1 t} + x_2 ge^{x_2 t} = x_1 fe^0 + x_2 ge^0 = x_1 f + x_2 g = 2f + g = c_1 = 6$$

which give

$$f + g = 4$$
$$2f + g = 6$$

or

$$f = 2 \quad g = 2$$

[7] The extension to higher order equations should be obvious.

so that the solution to the numerical problem is

$$y = 2e^{2t} + 2e^{t}.$$

PROBLEMS

1. Solve:

a) $\dfrac{d^2y}{dt^2} - 4\dfrac{dy}{dt} + 3y = 0,\ y = 2,\ \dfrac{dy}{dt} = 4 \text{ (at } t = 0)$

b) $\dfrac{d^2y}{dt^2} - 6\dfrac{dy}{dt} + 8y = 0,\ y = 8,\ \dfrac{dy}{dt} = 22 \text{ (at } t = 0)$

c) $\dfrac{d^2y}{dt^2} - 3\dfrac{dy}{dt} - 10y = 0,\ y = 8,\ \dfrac{dy}{dt} = -2 \text{ (at } t = 0)$

d) $\dfrac{d^2y}{dt^2} - 4y = 0,\ y = 8,\ \dfrac{dy}{dt} = -4 \text{ (at } t = 0)$

2. Compare these and their solution respectively with problems (a), (b), (d) and (f) of Section 2, Chapter Ten, and their solutions.

4. NONHOMOGENEOUS SYSTEMS (WITH CONSTANT TERM)

Now let us see how we can solve

$$\frac{d^2y}{dt^2} + b\frac{dy}{dt} + cy + D = 0 \tag{80}$$

$$\frac{d^2y}{dt^2} - 3\frac{dy}{dt} + 2y + 18 = 0 \tag{80a}$$

with initial conditions (76) [where (80) is obtained from (75) by adding $D = 18$ to the right hand side of the latter]. Here, analogous to Proposition Seven in the difference-equation exposition, and with identical proof, we have:

PROPOSITION FOURTEEN: If Z is any (particular) solution of the nonhomogeneous equation (80) and X is any solution of the reduced (homogeneous) equation (75) then $y = X + Z$ is a solution of (80).

We already know how to get a solution, X, for (75) with the required number of arbitrary constants. This solution is given by (79). We now seek any solution, Z, of (80).

Let us try a particular solution of the form $Z = z$, where z is a constant equilibrium level of y. Then, since $dZ/dt = 0$ and $d^2Z/dt^2 = 0$, setting $y = Z$ in (80) we get

$$\frac{d^2Z}{dt^2} + b\frac{dZ}{dt} + cZ + D = cz + D = 0 \tag{81}$$

$$\frac{d^2Z}{dt^2} - 3\frac{dZ}{dt} + 2Z + 18 = 2z + 18 = 0 \tag{81a}$$

or $$z = -\frac{D}{c} \quad (82) \qquad z = -9 \quad (82a)$$

and the solution to (80) is, by Proposition Fourteen, (79), and (82):

$$y = X + Z = fe^{x_1 t} + ge^{x_2 t} - \frac{D}{c} \tag{83}$$

$$y = fe^{2t} + ge^{t} - 9. \tag{83a}$$

If this is to satisfy the initial conditions (76) we must have, for $t = 0$,

$$y = fe^0 + ge^0 - \frac{D}{c} = f + g - \frac{D}{c} = c_0$$

$$y = fe^0 + ge^0 - 9 = f + g - 9 = 4$$

and

$$\frac{dy}{dt} = x_1 fe^0 + x_2 ge^0 = x_1 f + x_2 g = c_1$$

$$\frac{dy}{dt} = 2f + g = 6.$$

The numerical case gives

$$f + g - 9 = 4 \quad \text{or} \quad f + g = 13$$

$$2f + g = 6$$

or $$f = -7 \quad g = 20.$$

Substituting this in (83a) gives our final solution

$$y = -7e^{2t} + 20e^{t} - 9.$$

The result given by (82) for Z is applicable unless $c = 0$. In this case (81) gives the nonsense result

$$D = 18 = 0.$$

In that case we try a particular moving equilibrium solution, Z of the form $Z = zt$, z a constant, which gives $dZ/dt = z$, $d^2Z/dt^2 = 0$. Since $c = 0$ Eqs. (80) and (80a) are now [8]

$$\frac{d^2y}{dt^2} + b\frac{dy}{dt} + D = 0 \qquad (84) \qquad\qquad \frac{d^2y}{dt^2} - 3\frac{dy}{dt} + 18 = 0 \qquad (84a)$$

so that setting $y = zt$ in (81) we get

$$\frac{d^2Z}{dt^2} + b\frac{dZ}{dt} + D = bz + D = 0 \qquad (85)$$

$$-3z + 18 = 0 \qquad (85a)$$

or

$$z = -\frac{D}{b} \qquad (86) \qquad\qquad z = 6. \qquad (86a)$$

This result is applicable unless $b = 0$ (in addition to $c = 0$). Where this is the case we try a particular moving equilibrium solution, Z, of the form $Z = zt^2$, so that $d^2Z/dt^2 = 2z$. Since $b = c = 0$, Eqs. (81) and (81a) are now

$$\frac{d^2y}{dt^2} + D = 0 \qquad (87) \qquad\qquad \frac{d^2y}{dt^2} + 18 = 0 \qquad (87a)$$

so that setting $y = zt^2$ in (87) we get

$$\frac{d^2Z}{dt^2} + D = 2z + D = 0 \qquad (88) \qquad\qquad 2z + 18 = 0 \qquad (88a)$$

or

$$z = -\frac{D}{2} \qquad\qquad z = -9.$$

EXAMPLE 1

Solve:

$$\frac{d^2y}{dt^2} - 2\frac{dy}{dt} - 3y - 9 = 0$$

[8] Of course the solution of the reduced equation of Eq. (80a) is no longer given by (79a).

with initial conditions

$$\frac{dy}{dt} = 6 \qquad y = 2 \quad (\text{at } t = 0).$$

We begin by finding the solution X, of the reduced (homogeneous) equation

$$\frac{d^2y}{dt^2} - 2\frac{dy}{dt} - 3y = 0.$$

We try a solution of the form $X = e^{mt}$, and substituting we get

$$m^2e^{mt} - 2me^{mt} - 3e^{mt} = 0 \quad \text{or} \quad m^2 - 2m - 3 = 0$$

which has the roots (obtained by the usual procedure)

$$x_1 = 3 \qquad x_2 = -1.$$

These values and (79) give

$$X = fe^{3t} + ge^{-t}$$

where f and g are arbitrary constants.

We must now find a particular solution, Z, satisfying our initial equation, and since here $c = -3 \neq 0$ we try $Z = z$ (constant), which gives

$$-3z = 9 \quad \text{or} \quad z = -3.$$

The general solution of our equation is then given by

$$y = X + Z = fe^{3t} + ge^{-t} - 3.$$

To find values for f and g satisfying the initial conditions we see that for $t = 0$ we must have

$$f + g - 3 = 2$$
$$3f - g = 6$$

which gives $f = 11/4$, $g = 9/4$, so that the final solution is

$$y = \frac{11}{4}e^{3t} + \frac{9}{4}e^{-t} - 3$$

EXAMPLE 2

Solve:

$$\frac{d^2y}{dt^2} + b\frac{dy}{dt} + d = 0 \qquad \frac{d^2y}{dt^2} - 3\frac{dy}{dt} + 9 = 0.$$

The reduced equation is

$$\frac{d^2y}{dt^2} + b\frac{dy}{dt} = 0 \qquad \frac{d^2y}{dt^2} - 3\frac{dy}{dt} = 0.$$

Trying a solution of the form $X = e^{mt}$ we get

$$m^2e^{mt} + bme^{mt} = 0 \qquad m^2e^{mt} - 3me^{mt} = 0$$

or

$$m^2 + bm = 0 \qquad m^2 - 3m = 0.$$

This has the roots

$$x_1 = \frac{-b - \sqrt{b^2}}{2} = \frac{-b - b}{2} = -b \qquad x_1 = \frac{3 + \sqrt{(-3)^2}}{2} = 3.$$

$$x_2 = \frac{-b + \sqrt{b^2}}{2} = \frac{-b + b}{2} = 0 \qquad x_2 = \frac{3 - \sqrt{(-3)^2}}{2} = 0.$$

Thus the characteristic equation of a differential (or difference) equation with $c = 0$ always has at least one of its roots equal to zero.

The solution of our reduced numerical equation is now

$$X = fe^{3t} + ge^0 = fe^{3t} + g.$$

To find a particular solution, Z, of our original nonhomogeneous equation, we note that $c = 0$, $b = -3 \neq 0$, so that we want to try a solution of the form $Z = zt$, z being a constant. This gives, substituting zt for y in the equation

$$-3z = -9 \quad \text{or} \quad z = 3$$

so that our final solution is

$$y = X + Z = fe^{3t} + g + 3t$$

where the values of f and g depend on the initial conditions.

PROBLEM

1. Solve:

a) $\frac{d^2y}{dt^2} - 6\frac{dy}{dt} + 8y + 9 = 0, y = 3, \frac{dy}{dt} = 2$ (at $t = 0$)

b) $\frac{d^2y}{dt^2} - 4y - 100 = 0$

c) $\frac{d^2y}{dt^2} + 3\frac{dy}{dt} - 9 = 0$

5. MULTIPLE ROOTS

Consider the differential equation system

$$\frac{d^2y}{dt^2} - 4\frac{dy}{dt} + 4y = 0$$

$$y = 5 \quad \frac{dy}{dt} = 6$$

at $t = 0$. Proceeding as usual, we try the solution $y = e^{mt}$, which gives

$$m^2e^{mt} - 4me^{mt} + 4e^{mt} = 0 \quad \text{or} \quad m^2 - 4m + 4 = 0$$

which has the double roots $x_1 = x_2 = 2$. Here solution (79) gives

$$y = fe^{2t} + ge^{2t} = (f + g)e^{2t} = he^{2t}$$

where, since f and g are both arbitrary constants, h is an arbitrary constant. This solution thus has only one arbitrary constant and cannot in general be adapted to satisfy both our initial conditions. Thus in our present example our initial conditions require, for $t = 0$,

$$y = he^{2t} = he^0 = h = 5$$

$$\frac{dy}{dt} = 2he^{2t} = 2he^0 = 2h = 6 \quad \text{or} \quad h = 3$$

and both of these results cannot hold at the same time.

Here, analogous to Proposition Eight in the discussion of difference equations, we have:

PROPOSITION FIFTEEN: If a second-order differential equation involves double roots $x_1 = x_2$, so that $y = e^{x_1 t}$ satisfies it, then $te^{x_1 t}$ also satisfies it.

This proposition together with Proposition Thirteen, tells us that, if the characteristic equation of our differential equation has double roots, the equation will have the solution

$$y = fe^{x_1 t} + gte^{x_1 t}. \tag{89}$$

Thus the example given above has the solution

$$y = fe^{2t} + gte^{2t}.$$

It must be remembered that the derivative of gte^{2t},

$$\frac{dgte^{2t}}{dt} = ge^{2t} + 2gte^{2t} \tag{90}$$

by the usual rule for the derivative of a product.

Thus, in order that this result satisfy the initial conditions, we require, for $t = 0$,

$$y = fe^{2t} + gte^{2t} = fe^0 = f = 5$$

$$\frac{dy}{dt} = 2fe^{2t} + ge^{2t} + 2gte^{2t} = 2fe^0 + ge^0 = 2f + g = 6$$

which give $\qquad f = 5 \quad g = -4$

so that the solution becomes

$$y = 5e^{2t} - 4te^{2t}$$

PROBLEM

1. Solve:

a) $\dfrac{d^2y}{dt^2} + 6\dfrac{dy}{dt} + 9y = 0,\ y = 1,\ \dfrac{dy}{dt} = 2$ (at $t = 0$)

b) $\dfrac{d^2y}{dt^2} - 10\dfrac{dy}{dt} + 25y = 0$

c) $\dfrac{d^2y}{dt^2} - 10 = 0$

6. COMPLEX ROOTS

The characteristic equation of the differential equation may have complex (conjugate) roots. For example, to solve the equation

$$\frac{d^2y}{dt^2} - 2\frac{dy}{dt} + 5y = 0$$

we set $y = e^{mt}$ and get

$$m^2e^{mt} - 2me^{mt} + 5e^{mt} = 0 \quad \text{or} \quad m^2 - 2m + 5 = 0$$

which has the complex conjugate roots

$$x_1 = 1 + 2i \quad \text{and} \quad x_2 = 1 - 2i.$$

Then this equation has the solution

$$y = fe^{(1+2i)t} + ge^{(1-2i)t}.$$

This is a special case of the general solution in the case involving the complex roots $x_1 = c + wi$ and $x_2 = c - wi$,[9] which is

$$y = fe^{(c+wi)t} + ge^{(c-wi)t} = e^{ct}(fe^{wit} + ge^{-wit}). \tag{91}$$

As in the difference equation case we will find it useful to rewrite this solution in trigonometric form. We have the simple relation [10]

$$e^{is} = \cos(s) + i\sin(s). \tag{92}$$

[9] As we saw in regard to difference equations, complex roots always come in conjugate pairs. Cf. footnote 19, Chapter Ten, and the proximate text.

[10] This can be indicated with the aid of Maclaurin series which also indicates how we can compute values for e, $\sin x$, and $\cos x$. Suppose that there exists a polynomial in x with an infinite number of terms which is equal to e^x. Thus

$$e^x = a_0 + a_1x + a_2x^2 + \cdots + a_nx^n + \cdots \tag{i}$$

where the $a_0, a_1, \cdots$ are constants. If this is to hold for all values of x it must also hold for $x = 0$, for which we get

$$e^0 = a_0 + a_1 \cdot 0 + \cdots, \text{ i.e., } a_0 = 1.$$

If we now differentiate (i) with respect to x, we get

$$\frac{de^x}{dx} = e^x = a_1 + 2a_2x + 3a_3x^2 + \cdots. \tag{ii}$$

Since (ii) holds for all values of x, it must hold for $x = 0$, which gives $a_1 = 1$. Now differentiate (ii) with respect to x and obtain

$$e^x = 2a_2 + 3 \cdot 2a_3x + 4 \cdot 3a_4x^2 + \cdots \tag{iii}$$

which for $x = 0$ gives $2a_2 = e^0 = 1$ or $a_2 = 1/2$. Similarly, differentiating (iii) with respect to x we get

$$e^x = 3 \cdot 2a_3 + 4 \cdot 3 \cdot 2a_4 x + 5 \cdot 4 \cdot 3a_5 x^2 + \cdots . \qquad \text{(iv)}$$

With the aid of this we get $a_3 = 1/3 \cdot 2$, and so on. If we write $r(r-1)(r-2) \cdots (3)(2)(1) = r!$ (called r factorial) so that, for example $5! = 5 \cdot 4 \cdot 3 \cdot 2 \cdot 1 = 120$, we have

$$a_0 = 1, a_1 = \frac{1}{1!}, a_2 = \frac{1}{2!}, a_3 = \frac{1}{3!}, \cdots, a_n = \frac{1}{n!}$$

so that from (i) we have

$$e^x = 1 + x + \frac{x^2}{2!} + \frac{x^3}{3!} + \cdots + \frac{x^n}{n!} + \cdots . \qquad \text{(v)}$$

This enables us to compute approximate values for e^x for any specific x. In particular we have, for $x = 1$,

$$e = 1 + 1 + \frac{1}{2!} + \frac{1}{3!} + \cdots = 2.718 \text{ (approximately)}.$$

Similarly, with the aid of

$$\frac{d \sin x}{dx} = \cos x \qquad \frac{d \cos x}{dx} = -\sin x$$

we obtain

$$\cos x = b_0 + b_1 x + b_2 x^2 + \cdots = 1 + 0x - \frac{x^2}{2!} + 0x^3 + \frac{x^4}{4!} + \cdots$$

$$= 1 - \frac{x^2}{2!} + \frac{x^4}{4!} - \frac{x^6}{6!} + \cdots \qquad \text{(vi)}$$

and

$$\sin x = x - \frac{x^3}{3!} + \frac{x^5}{5!} - \frac{x^7}{7!} + \cdots . \qquad \text{(vii)}$$

Now for $x = im$, (v) gives

$$e^{im} = 1 + im + \frac{(im)^2}{2!} + \frac{(im)^3}{3!} + \cdots = 1 + im - \frac{m^2}{2!} - \frac{im^3}{3!} + \frac{m^4}{4!}$$

$$+ \frac{im^5}{5!} - \frac{m^6}{6!} - \cdots \qquad \text{(viii)}$$

since for $i = \sqrt{-1}, i^2 = -1, i^3 = i \cdot i^2 = -i, i^4 = i^2 \cdot i^2 = -1 \cdot -1 = 1$ etc. It is now obvious from (vi), (vii), and (viii) that

$$e^{im} = \cos m + i \sin m. \qquad \text{(ix)}$$

It should be noted that the argument of this footnote is not a complete proof. We have merely shown that *if* there are polynomial expressions such as (i) for e^x, $\cos x$, and $\sin x$, then these are given by (vi), (vii), and (viii), and in this case (ix) must hold. In fact there are such polynomial expressions, and so the rest follows.

This together with (91) gives

$$y = e^{ct}\{f(\cos wt + i \sin wt) + g[\cos(-wt) + i \sin(-wt)]\}$$

$$\text{i.e., } y = e^{ct}[f(\cos wt + i \sin wt) + g(\cos wt - i \sin wt)]$$

since $\qquad \cos(-x) = \cos x \qquad \sin(-x) = -\sin x$

for any angle, x. Adding we get

$$y = e^{ct}[(f + g) \cos wt + (f - g) i \sin wt]$$

or

$$y = e^{ct}[h \cos wt + j \sin wt] \tag{93}$$

where h and j are arbitrary constants.

In general, where the characteristic equation of the differential equation has the complex roots $c + wi$ and $c - wi$, so that (91) is involved in the solution, then these terms may be rewritten in the trigonometric form (93). Thus in the example given in the beginning of the section, since the conjugate complex roots $1 + 2i$ and $1 - 2i$ were involved, we can rewrite the solution as

$$y = e^{t}(h \cos 2t + j \sin 2t).$$

There is one important point involved in the numerical interpretation of these results. The formula given in footnote 10 for the derivatives of $\sin x$ and $\cos x$ is only valid strictly speaking, if we measure the angle x, not in degrees but in another unit called the radian. The radian measure of an angle is defined to be the ratio between the length of the arc, AB (Fig. 47), of the circumference of the circle cut off by a given angle, x, and the length of the radius of the circle $OA = OB$. Thus if x is sufficiently great so that AB becomes

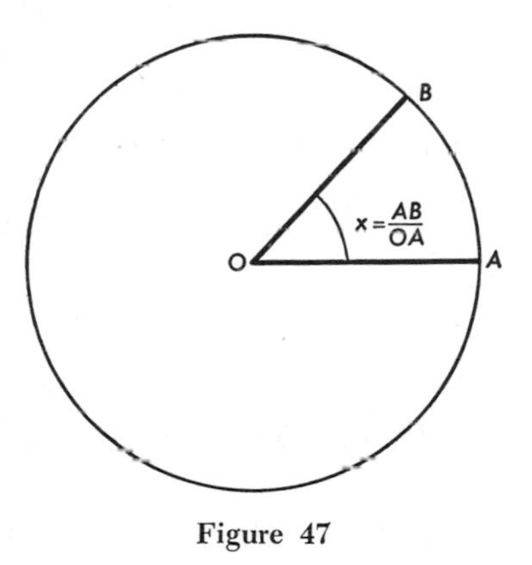

Figure 47

the entire circumference of the circle (x is 360°), the radian measure of x becomes, writing R for the length of the radius, OA,

$$\frac{AB}{R} = \frac{2\pi R}{R} = 2\pi$$

Hence 2π radians = 360°

or

$$\left.\begin{aligned} 1 \text{ radian} &= \frac{360}{2\pi} \text{ degrees} \\ 1 \text{ degree} &= \frac{2\pi}{360} \text{ radians.} \end{aligned}\right\} \tag{94}$$

In particular, 180° = π radians and 90° = $\pi/2$ radians. Thus in interpreting (93) we should not expect the expression in the brackets to repeat itself every time wt increases by 360°. Rather, since we are measuring in radians, we expect it to repeat itself every time wt changes by 2π. In getting numerical results we must also be careful to use sine and cosine tables which are given in terms of radians, not in terms of degrees. If such a table is not available, we can easily convert the angle wt into degree measure by use of Eq. (94). For rough calculation we can use the formulas

$$1 \text{ radian} = 57°, 1° = 0.017 \text{ radians.} \tag{95}$$

PROBLEM

1. Put the solution of the following into trigonometric form:

a) $\frac{d^2y}{dt^2} + 12\frac{dy}{dt} + 100y - 226 = 0$

b) $\frac{d^2y}{dt^2} - 6\frac{dy}{dt} + 13y = 0$

c) $\frac{d^2y}{dt^2} + y = 0$

7. INTERPRETATION OF THE RESULTS

The differential equation results are easier to interpret in terms of the time path of our solution than were the difference equation results. Ignoring, for the moment, cases of complex and multiple roots, our solution must consist of terms of the form ae^{mt}, where a and m are constant real numbers. This may be written $a(e^t)^m$. Now e is greater than 1. This means, as we have seen, that e^t will grow greater at an ever-increasing rate (see Section 3, Chapter Nine). Thus if m is positive the solution is unstable and $(e^t)^m$ will grow at an ever-increasing rate. If $m = 0$ then, of course, $e^{tm} = 1$ and remains constant over time. Finally, if m is negative, so that $n = -m$ is positive, then by definition $(e^t)^m = 1/(e^t)^n$, and since $(e^t)^n$ will grow at an ever-increasing rate, $1/(e^t)^n$ will get smaller and smaller with time, asymptotically approaching zero. Since a may be positive or negative, we then obtain the six kinds of time path for ae^{tm} shown in Figure 48.

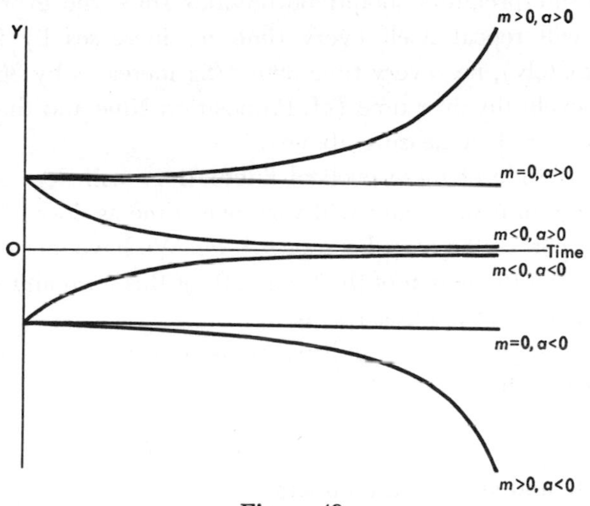

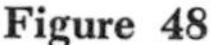
Figure 48

Several Real Roots

Suppose we have several terms in the solution, so it takes the form $y = a_1e^{m_1t} + a_2e^{m_2t} + \cdots + a_ne^{m_nt}$, where $m_1, m_2, \cdots, m_n$ are all real. Then if the largest of these is m_i eventually the solution will approximate $y = a_ie^{m_it}$ since all other terms become relatively negligible. The time path is unstable when there is at least one positive root. All terms involving a negative root are transient and approach zero, however large that root is in absolute value.[11] But "eventually" may be a long time, and we may be more interested in what happens before this. What will happen immediately, however, we can only say if all the m_i are of the same sort, i.e., all positive or all negative. Where the m_i are not all of the same sort, what will happen will depend on the relative values of $a_1, a_2, \cdots, a_n$.

Complex and Multiple Roots

Where we have a pair of complex roots there will be a term in the solution of the form

$$e^{ct}(h \cos wt + j \sin wt).$$

Here the interpretation should be obvious since the expression in brackets will repeat itself every time wt increases by $2\pi = 6.28$ (approximately), i.e., every time $360wt/2\pi$ increases by 360 and so will vary cyclically over time (cf. Proposition Nine and the remarks on our use of radian measure above).

The amplitude of these cyclical fluctuations will depend largely on the magnitude of e^{ct} and will vary over time as does e^{ct} where c is the real part of the complex root $c + wi$. We have, of course, just completed our discussion of the time path of this term and note only that stability again requires $c < 0$.

Finally, where we have multiple roots, our solution will include expressions of the form [12] at^K, $at^K e^{mt}$, and

$$at^K e^{mt}(h \cos wt + j \sin wt),$$

where a, K, and m are real numbers.

[11] Unlike difference equations, the absolute values of the roots are irrelevant. If, e.g., the roots are $+3$ and -15 the differential equation's solution approaches ae^{3t}, the term of the largest root, though that root is the smaller in absolute value. In a higher order equation with real root a and complex roots $c + wi$, $c - wi$ the real root will dominate if $a > c$ and vice versa. For e^{ct} determines the growth of (93), the term in the solution corresponding to the complex roots, since cos wt and sin wt vary between $+1$ and -1 forever.

[12] The last expression will arise in higher order systems where the characteristic equation has multiple complex roots. The solution here can be found from (93) with the aid of an obvious application of Proposition Fifteen.

Where $m \neq 0$ it can be shown $at^K e^{mt}$ has the same sort of time path as does the ordinary term ae^{mt}. Thus the only case where our result is modified is the case where there is now a term of the form at^K, which will be explosive upwards but will eventually become relatively negligible in a solution containing a term of the form ae^{mt}, where m is positive.

The effects of the addition of a constant term (or of a term of the form at^K which we have just considered) which is the particular solution required by the presence of a constant term in the original equation should be obvious. These are, respectively, the stationary or moving equilibrium values of $y(t)$, and in the stable case where the real parts of all roots are negative, $y(t)$ will approach these equilibrium values asymptotically.

Qualitative Methods

Chapter Eleven, Section 3 and most of Chapter Twelve described methods whereby the nature of the time path of the variable can at least to some extent be recognized by direct observation of the coefficients of a difference equation. After several simple modifications these same methods can be applied to differential equations.

From the point of view of qualitative analysis there are two basic differences between the difference and the differential equation cases. First, in the difference equation case of the previous chapters the critical point between stability and instability is reached when the root of largest absolute value reaches absolute value unity. In the *differential* equation case which we are now considering the critical point between stability and instability occurs when the real part of the largest root reaches zero, because any root whose real value is positive produces instability. There is a second dissimilarity in the qualitative analysis of the two types of equation. In the difference equation case we know that negative roots can produce oscillations whose duration is exactly two periods (a one period upswing followed by a one period downswing, etc.). But in the differential equation case there is no way in which such oscillations can be produced.

Taking these differences into account we can summarize in the following table the relationship between the type of root of the characteristic equation and the nature of the time path of the variable of a differential and of a difference equation:

Roots	Nature of the time path	
	Differential equations	Difference equations
complex (real part negative)	stable fluctuations	fluctuations
complex (real part positive)	unstable fluctuations	fluctuations
real and negative	stable	oscillatory
real and positive	explosive	no oscillations

Hence, for example, the theorems which were used to recognize the oscillatory second-order difference equation cases can be applied directly to find the stable nonfluctuating differential equation cases.

Only one interesting additional theorem is relevant in the differential equation case where there are complex roots. The distinction between positive and negative real parts has no particular importance in the qualitative analysis of difference-equations. But in the complex roots case it determines whether fluctuations, if they occur, will be damped (negative real part) or explosive. Fortunately there is an easy way in which we can determine by direct inspection of the general second-order linear equation (80) whether, if the roots are complex, their real part is positive or negative. For the characteristic equation is (77) whose roots are $-\frac{b}{2} \pm \frac{\sqrt{b^2 - 4c}}{2} = -\frac{b}{2} \pm i\frac{\sqrt{4c - b^2}}{2}$ in the complex roots case ($b^2 < 4c$). Hence the real part of such a complex root is $-\frac{b}{2}$ which is negative if b is positive, and positive if b is negative. Thus we have the following simple rule for the second-order case: move all the terms to the left hand side of the differential equation. Then, should the equation have complex roots, the fluctuations will be damped if the coefficient, b, of $\frac{dy}{dt}$ is positive, explosive if that coefficient is negative, and of constant amplitude if $b = 0$.

We can apply this at once to begin to revise Figure 32 of Chapter Eleven for the differential equation case. For we note now that the region of stable fluctuations is composed of the two subregions I_a and II_a, where roots are complex and b is positive, while regions I_b and II_b indicate the cases where the coefficients of the difference equation produce explosive fluctuations because the roots are complex and b is negative.

Necessary and Sufficient Conditions for Stability

As in the difference equation case there exists a test in terms of a sequence of determinants which indicates for a linear differential equation of any order, whether or not its time path is stable (whether or not all of its roots have negative real parts). Again the result (which was discovered by mathematician E. J. Routh) is stated without any attempt at explanation.[13]

Given the (characteristic) equation $a_0x^n + a_1x^{n-1} + \cdots + a_{n-1}x + a_n = 0$, consider the sequence of determinants

$$|a_1|, \quad \begin{vmatrix} a_1 & a_3 \\ a_0 & a_2 \end{vmatrix}, \quad \begin{vmatrix} a_1 & a_3 & a_5 \\ a_0 & a_2 & a_4 \\ 0 & a_1 & a_3 \end{vmatrix}, \quad \begin{vmatrix} a_1 & a_3 & a_5 & a_7 \\ a_0 & a_2 & a_4 & a_6 \\ 0 & a_1 & a_3 & a_5 \\ 0 & a_0 & a_2 & a_4 \end{vmatrix}, \ldots.$$

Then the Routh theorem states that the real parts of all of the roots will be negative if and only if the first n of these determinants are all positive, where n is the degree of the (characteristic) polynomial equation, and where we take any coefficient $a_m = 0$ for $m > n$.

[13] The proof is outlined in P. A. Samuelson, *Foundations of Economic Analysis* (Harvard University Press, Cambridge, Mass., 1947) pp. 434–435. For the derivation see E. J. Routh, *Dynamics of a System of Rigid Bodies* (paperback edition, Dover Publications, New York, 1955) Chapter VI, esp. pp. 223–231.

EXAMPLE

Consider our second order case with characteristic equation $x^2 + bx + c = 0$. Here $a_0 = 1$, $a_1 = b$, $a_2 = c$ and $a_3 = 0$ since $3 > 2 = n$, the degree of our equation. Then the first determinant condition is $|a_1| = |b| = b > 0$ so that for stability b must be positive. The second determinant condition (we only require two in the second-order case) is $\begin{vmatrix} a_1 & a_3 \\ a_0 & a_2 \end{vmatrix} = \begin{vmatrix} b & 0 \\ 1 & c \end{vmatrix} = bc > 0$. Hence stability in the second-order case requires both b and $c > 0$, i.e., stable roots occur in and only in the positive (north west) quadrant of Figure 32.

The Economic Example Again

We may now again briefly look at Professor Domar's (Harrod's) system which was given in the first section of this chapter to see what our results can tell us about it. The basic differential equation we obtained there was

$$\frac{dy}{dt} = \frac{s}{g}y \quad \text{or} \quad \frac{dy}{dt} - \frac{s}{g}y = 0$$

where s is the average and marginal propensity to save and g "the relation" of the acceleration principle.

This clearly has the solution

$$y = ae^{\frac{s}{g}t}$$

where a is a constant determined by the initial condition $y = y(0)$ (initial income), so that setting $t = 0$ in our equation we obtain

$$y = ae^0 = a = y(0)$$

and our solution becomes

$$y = y(0)e^{\frac{s}{g}t}.$$

Since economically it is clear that we will in general have income, and thus initial income, $y(0)$, positive and $m = s/g$ will also be positive for obvious reasons, then the time path of y must be of the form given by the upper line in Figure 48. The possibility of the mysterious wiggle-waggle found in a peculiar case arising in the difference equation analysis of Mr. Harrod's system in Chapter Nine has disappeared. This should not be surprising since the solution of a differential equation system, has as we have seen, fewer possible types of time path than has a difference equation system, because there is nothing which corresponds to the negative roots oscillation in the difference equation solution.[14]

PROBLEM

Complete the translation of Figure 32 to differential equations.

8. *NONHOMOGENEOUS SYSTEMS WITH VARIABLE TERMS*

Suppose, instead of the first differential equation (80) that we considered in Section 4

$$\frac{d^2y}{dt^2} + b\frac{dy}{dt} + cy + D = 0 \tag{80}$$

$$\frac{d^2y}{dt^2} - 3\frac{dy}{dt} + 2y + 18 = 0 \tag{80a}$$

we had had an equation of one of the following forms:

$$\frac{d^2y}{dt^2} + b\frac{dy}{dt} + cy + At^2 = 0 \tag{96}$$

$$\frac{d^2y}{dt^2} - 3\frac{dy}{dt} + 2y + 18t^2 = 0 \tag{96a}$$

or

$$\frac{d^2y}{dt^2} + b\frac{dy}{dt} + cy + A \sin t = 0 \tag{97}$$

$$\frac{d^2y}{dt^2} - 3\frac{dy}{dt} + 2y + 18 \sin t = 0 \tag{97a}$$

[14] Therefore periodic motion can never occur in the time path of a variable described by a first-order differential equation because fluctuation here requires complex roots which can only occur in an equation of second or higher order.

or

$$\frac{d^2y}{dt^2} + b\frac{dy}{dt} + cy + Ate^{3t} = 0 \tag{98}$$

$$\frac{d^2y}{dt^2} - 3\frac{dy}{dt} + 2y + 18te^{3t} = 0. \tag{98a}$$

Here instead of the constant term $D = 18$ in (80) we have respectively in (96), (97), and (98) the variable terms $D = At^2 = 18t^2$, $D = A \sin t = 18 \sin t$, and $D = Ate^{3t} = 18te^{3t}$. These are, of course, only three of the infinite number of possible variable terms which a differential equation may have. Such variable term systems often arise in economic analysis, and an example is given in the next section.

Now, since in the proof of Proposition Fourteen, we do not refer to the form of the term D which makes the equation nonhomogeneous, this proposition applies without change to the case where D is variable.[15] Thus the solution of (80) was given by (83) as

$$y = X + Z = fe^{x_1t} + ge^{x_2t} - \frac{D}{c} = fe^{2t} + ge^t - 9.$$

Similarly the solution of (96), (97), and (98) will be given respectively by

$$y = X + Z^* \quad y = X + Z^{**} \quad y = X + Z^{***}$$

where Z^*, Z^{**}, and Z^{***} are any (particular) solutions of any sort of (96), (97), and (98) respectively, and as before

$$X = fe^{x_1t} + ge^{x_2t} = fe^{2t} + ge^t$$

is the solution of the reduced homogeneous equation of Eqs. (80), (96), (97), and (98).

The Particular Solution

The problem is then to find any Z^*, Z^{**}, and Z^{***}. Now there are no set rules whereby these can be found in any variable term case, and a good part of the mathematical discussion of linear

[15] This was pointed out in the identical proof of Proposition Seven in Chapter Ten.

differential equations is devoted to the listing of methods for finding particular solutions in various special cases. There is one method, however, the so-called method of undetermined coefficients, which works in many cases and which we shall explain here.

The method can be employed where the variable term, D, has, apart from constant factors, only a finite number of terms of distinct forms upon successive differentiation. Since

$$\frac{dx^3}{dx} = 3x^2 \quad \frac{d3x^2}{dx} = 6x \quad \frac{d6x}{dx} = 6,$$

and all higher derivatives of x^3 are zero, then x^3 has only the three distinct forms x^2, x, and 1 on successive differentiation with respect to x, because 0 and 6 or $6x$ and x, etc., differ only by constant factors and so are considered to be of the same form. Similarly e^{mx} has, on differentiation, only the form e^{mx}; xe^{mx} has, on differentiation, terms of the two distinct forms xe^{mx} and e^{mx}; sin mx has, on differentiation the two distinct forms sin mx and cos mx; and similarly cos mx has, on differentiation, the two distinct forms sin mx and cos mx.[16]

To find a particular solution, Z, in such a case, we try Z of the form $Z = a_1D_1 + a_2D_2 + \cdots + a_nD_n$, where $D_1, \cdots, D_n$ are D and all the distinct terms arising from the successive differentiation of the variable term D and where $a_1, \cdots, a_n$ are constants to be determined. Thus if $D = At^2$, the derivatives of D are $2At$ and $2A$ so we try Z of the form

$$Z^* = a_1t^2 + a_2t + a_3.$$

The idea is roughly that on substituting this into, say,

$$\frac{d^2y}{dt^2} + b\frac{dy}{dt} + cy + At^2 = 0$$

the substitution into the term cy yields the term ca_1t^2, and by appropriate choice of a_1 we can get this, together with any other terms of similar form which are left over, to equal $-At^2$. But a_1t^2 must then

[16] An example of an expression which on successive differentiation involves an infinite number of terms distinct in form is e^{t^2}, which has the derivatives $2te^{t^2}$, $4t^2e^{t^2} + 2e^{t^2}$, etc.

also be substituted for y in d^2y/dt^2 and $b(dy/dt)$ and this unfortunately yields other terms such as $2ba_1t$ which do not add up to zero. The purpose of the terms $a_2t + a_3$ in Z is to permit these, by appropriate choice of a_2 and a_3, to cancel out such unwanted terms as $2ba_1t$ so that when Z is substituted into the difference equation the entire sum will in fact total zero as the equation requires.

EXAMPLES

The method is best explained by illustration of its application. Thus to find Z^* for (96) we try a particular solution of the form Z^* as given above.

Differentiating we obtain $dZ^*/dt = 2a_1t + a_2$, and $d^2Z^*/dt^2 = 2a_1$ so that substituting these into (96) we obtain

$$(2a_1) + (2ba_1t + ba_2) + (ca_1t^2 + ca_2t + ca_3) + At^2 = 0$$

i.e., $$(2a_1) - (6a_1t + 3a_2) + (2a_1t^2 + 2a_2t + 2a_3) + 18t^2 = 0$$

or $$(ca_1 + A)t^2 + (2ba_1 + ca_2)t + (2a_1 + ba_2 + ca_3) = 0$$

i.e., $$(2a_1 + 18)t^2 + (2a_2 - 6a_1)t + (2a_1 - 3a_2 + 2a_3) = 0.$$

We want all the expressions in parentheses in this last equation to equal zero so their sum will be zero no matter what the value of t. We must then choose a_1, a_2, and a_3 to be such that

$$(ca_1 + A) = (2a_1 + 18) = 0$$

$$(2ba_1 + ca_2) = (2a_2 - 6a_1) = 0$$

and $$(2a_1 + ba_2 + ca_3) = (2a_1 - 3a_2 + 2a_3) = 0.$$

In the numerical case the first equation gives $a_1 = -9$, the second equation gives $2a_2 = 6a_1 = -54$, or $a_2 = -27$, so that $a_3 = -31\frac{1}{2}$. Thus we obtain [17]

$$Z^* = a_1t^2 + a_2t + a_3 = -9t^2 - 27t - 31\tfrac{1}{2}$$

[17] Note that this particular solution and the two solutions which follow yield moving equilibrium rather than stationary equilibrium values of y. See above pp. 215–216

and the solution to (96a) is given by

$$y = X + Z^* = fe^{2t} + ge^t - 9t^2 - 27t - 31\tfrac{1}{2}.$$

We now find particular solutions, Z^{**} and Z^{***} for (97a) and (98a). In (97a) we note that the derivatives of the variable term $D = 18 \sin t$ involve only distinct terms of the forms $\cos t$ and $\sin t$. We thus try a solution of the form

$$Z^{**} = a_1 \sin t + a_2 \cos t.$$

This has the derivatives

$$\frac{dZ^{**}}{dt} = a_1 \cos t - a_2 \sin t$$

and

$$\frac{d^2Z^{**}}{dt^2} = -a_1 \sin t - a_2 \cos t.$$

Substituting into (97a) thus gives

$$-a_1 \sin t - a_2 \cos t - 3a_1 \cos t + 3a_2 \sin t$$
$$+ 2a_1 \sin t + 2a_2 \cos t + 18 \sin t = 0$$

or $\quad (-a_1 + 3a_2 + 2a_1 + 18) \sin t + (2a_2 - a_2 - 3a_1) \cos t = 0.$

If this is to be zero for all values of t, a_1 and a_2 must be such that

$$-a_1 + 3a_2 + 2a_1 + 18 = 3a_2 + a_1 + 18 = 0$$

$$2a_2 - a_2 - 3a_1 = a_2 - 3a_1 = 0.$$

This gives $a_1 = -9/5$, $a_2 = -27/5$ so that

$$Z^{**} = -\frac{9}{5} \sin t - \frac{27}{5} \cos t$$

and the solution of (97a) is given by

$$y = X + Z^{**} = X - \frac{9}{5} \sin t - \frac{27}{5} \cos t$$

with X as before.

Finally, to find a particular solution Z^{***} for (98a) we observe that the derivatives of the variable term $D = 18te^{3t}$ involve distinct terms of the form te^{3t} and e^{3t}. We thus try Z^{***} of the form $Z^{***} = a_1te^{3t} + a_2e^{3t}$. The derivatives of this are given by

$$\frac{dZ^{***}}{dt} = 3a_1te^{3t} + a_1e^{3t} + 3a_2e^{3t} = (a_1 + 3a_2)e^{3t} + 3a_1te^{3t}$$

and

$$\frac{d^2Z^{***}}{dt^2} = 3(a_1 + 3a_2)e^{3t} + 9a_1te^{3t} + 3a_1e^{3t} = 3(2a_1 + 3a_2)e^{3t} + 9a_1te^{3t}.$$

Substituting for $Z^{***} = y$ into (98a) we obtain

$$3(2a_1 + 3a_2)e^{3t} + 9a_1te^{3t} - 3(a_1 + 3a_2)e^{3t} - 9a_1te^{3t} + 2a_1te^{3t} + 2a_2e^{3t} + 18te^{3t} = 0$$

or collecting terms and cancelling out wherever possible gives

$$(3a_1 + 2a_2)e^{3t} + (2a_1 + 18)te^{3t} = 0$$

so that we must have

$$3a_1 + 2a_2 = 0 \qquad 2a_1 + 18 = 0$$

or

$$a_2 = \frac{27}{2} \qquad a_1 = -9$$

so that

$$Z^{***} = -9te^{3t} + \frac{27}{2}e^{3t}.$$

The method of undetermined coefficients does not always work without further modification, even where the derivatives of the variable term D involve only a finite number of terms. Where either the coefficient c of the term cy in the original differential equation is zero or where $D = at^Ke^{mt}$, where a and K are real numbers and m is one of the roots of the characteristic equation of the differential equation, then a particular solution, Z, can only be found by multiplying the Z we would have used ordinarily by a sufficiently high power of t, just as in the constant term case we were sometimes forced to use tZ or t^2Z instead of Z in our solution of the unreduced equation.

PROBLEM

1. Solve:

a) $$\frac{d^2y}{dt^2} - 2\frac{dy}{dt} + 2y - t = 0$$

b) $$\frac{d^2y}{dt^2} - 2\frac{dy}{dt} + 2y - e^t = 0$$

c) $$\frac{d^2y}{dt^2} - 2\frac{dy}{dt} + 2y - t - e^t = 0$$

d) $$\frac{d^2y}{dt^2} - 2\frac{dy}{dt} + y - t^2e^{3t} = 0$$

9. THE BURDEN OF THE DEBT

As an example of the use of differential equations we may briefly consider the problem of the effects of deficit spending upon the national debt.[18] Let us suppose that continuous full employment is maintained by deficit spending and that for any period the ratio of the deficit to national income is a constant. It follows that the rate of increase of the national debt will bear a constant proportion to national income. If we denote the national debt by D and the national income by y, we can thus write

$$\frac{dD}{dt} = ky \tag{99}$$

where k is the percentage of national income borrowed by the state.

In order to say how D will develop we have to make some assumption about the behavior of y through time. Three possible assumptions are

$$y(t) = a \text{ (national income constant)} \tag{100}$$

[18] The presentation follows that of Domar in his article, "The Burden of the Debt and the National Income," *American Economic Review*, December, 1944. Reprinted in Evsey D. Domar, *Essays in the Theory of Economic Growth* (Oxford University Press, New York, 1957).

$y(t) = a + bt$ (national income increases at a constant absolute rate) (101)

and

$$\frac{dy}{dt} = ry(t) \text{ (national income increases at a constant percentage rate).} \qquad (102)$$

Leaving cases (100) and (101) for solution by the reader, let us try to find an expression for D in the third case. To start with we need to find an expression for $y(t)$. Trying a solution of the form $y(t) = ae^{mt}$ and substituting into (102) gives

$$mae^{mt} = rae^{mt}$$

so

$$m = r$$

and

$$y(t) = ae^{rt}. \qquad (103)$$

Substitution of (103) into (99) gives

$$\frac{dD}{dt} = kae^{rt}$$

i.e.,

$$\frac{dD}{dt} - kae^{rt} = 0$$

which is a first-order nonhomogeneous differential equation with variable term $-kae^{rt}$, and this will have a solution of the form

$$D(t) = X + Z.$$

To obtain the particular solution let us try

$$Z = be^{rt}.$$

To determine b we substitute this into our differential equation, getting

$$rbe^{rt} - kae^{rt} = 0$$

i.e.,

$$e^{rt}(rb - ka) = 0$$

so we must have

$$rb - ka = 0$$

and

$$b = \frac{ka}{r}.$$

Hence

$$Z = \frac{1}{r} kae^{rt}.$$

To find X we have to solve the reduced equation

$$\frac{dD}{dt} = 0.$$

This obviously gives us

$$X = R$$

where R is some constant depending upon the initial condition. We now have

$$D(t) = R + \frac{1}{r} kae^{rt}.$$

Let us takc as our initial condition

$$D(0) = D_0.$$

Then to find R we substitute and get

$$D_0 = R + \frac{ka}{r}$$

so

$$R = D_0 - \frac{ka}{r}.$$

Our final solution is thus

$$D(t) = D_0 - \frac{ka}{r} + \frac{1}{r} kae^{rt}$$

$$= D_0 + \frac{ka}{r}(e^{rt} - 1).$$

From this and (103) we can obtain the ratio of debt to national income as

$$\frac{D(t)}{y(t)} = \frac{D_0}{ae^{rt}} + \frac{k}{r}\left(1 - \frac{1}{e^{rt}}\right).$$

We can see from this that as time passes this ratio will tend to the limit k/r.

It is of interest to compare this result with that obtained under assumptions (100) and (101). Leaving the actual derivation of the results to the reader, we get

$$\frac{D(t)}{y(t)} = \frac{D_0}{a} + kt$$

where $y(t) = a$, so that the ratio of debt to national income tends toward infinity as time passes.

Where $y(t) = a + bt$ we get the same sort of result, for

$$\frac{D(t)}{y(t)} = \frac{D_0 + kt(a + (b/2)t)}{a + bt}.$$

Thus on our assumptions, debt will in the long run remain a manageable proportion of national income only if national income is increasing at least exponentially. In a less progressive or stationary society the ratio will tend toward infinity; i.e., a perpetually unbalanced budget is apt to lead a country into difficulties. This result may be of utmost importance for fiscal employment policy.

10. FIRST-ORDER NONLINEAR SYSTEMS

The reasons which have led economists to be dissatisfied with *linear* difference equation models apply equally to the differential equation case. Moreover, the same methodological problems arise in the nonlinear differential equation analysis. The analytical technique is not well developed and we employ primarily either quantitative methods based on linear approximations or qualitative graphic techniques.

The Phase Diagram

The standard graphic technique—the phase diagram—is similar to, but not entirely the same as, that in the difference equation case. On the horizontal axis (Fig. 49) we plot the variable y, and on the vertical, the corresponding value of the time derivative, $\frac{dy}{dt}$. The general (not necessarily linear) first order differential equation may be written

$$\frac{dy}{dt} = f(y).$$

Several of the basic shapes which the graph of this relationship may take are shown in Figure 49.

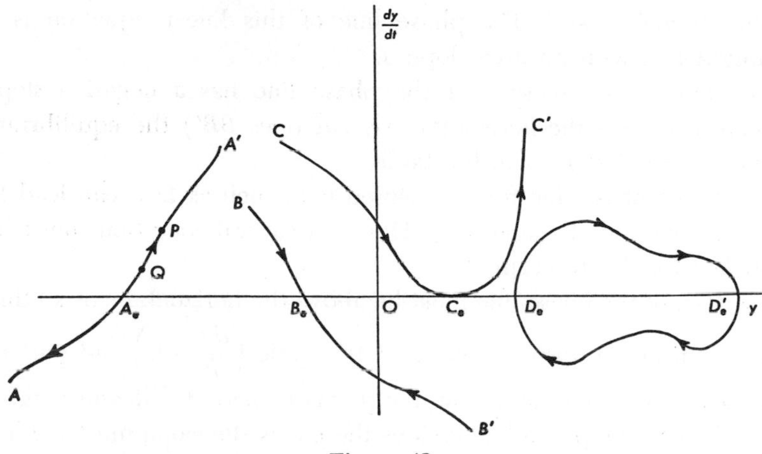

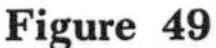
Figure 49

Phase Diagram: General Rules

i. At all points above the horizontal axis $\frac{dy}{dt}$ is positive, i.e., y is increasing so that movement along the phase line must proceed from left to right. For the same reason, below the axis the time path must go from right to left. This is shown in Figure 49 by the arrows which are used to indicate the direction of movement of the variable y.

ii. Equilibrium can only occur at points such as A_e, B_e C_e, D_e, and D_e' which lie on the horizontal axis, for only at such points is $\frac{dy}{dt} = 0$, i.e., at any other point in the diagram the system must be in motion.

iii. If the phase line has a positive slope where it crosses the horizontal axis (as does AA') then that equilibrium point must be unstable because on either side of the equilibrium point the direction of movement is away from that point (when $y > A_e$ then $\frac{dy}{dt} > 0$ so that y grows even larger and moves further away from its equilibrium value A_e, etc.). A particular case of this is the linear equation $\frac{dy}{dt} = ay + b$, $a > 0$ which as we know, has the explosive solution $y(t) = ke^{at}$. The phase line of this linear equation is a straight line with positive slope a.

iv. For similar reasons, if the phase line has a negative slope where it crosses the horizontal axis (as does BB') the equilibrium point of crossing, B_e, will be stable.

v. If the phase line forms a closed loop such as D it can lead to periodic motion (fluctuations). However several conditions must be satisfied for this to occur.

a. Part of the phase line must lie above the horizontal axis so that there can be an upswing phase of the cycle $\left(\frac{dy}{dt} > 0\right)$ and part of the phase line must lie below the y axis to permit a downswing.

b. Where the phase line crosses the y axis the slope must neither be positive and finite (since then the time path would be explosive and never cross the axis) nor must the slope be negative and finite since the time path would then converge to the equilibrium point in a stable manner and again it would never cross the axis. In other words, where it crosses the axis the phase line must be vertical (slope $= \infty$) if there is to be periodic motion.

vi. The speed with which the variable y changes is proportional to the vertical distance of the phase line from the horizontal axis, since that distance represents $\frac{dy}{dt}$. Thus, e.g., at point P, the abscissa (its horizontal coordinate), y, must be increasing twice as fast as it is at Q.

Illustration: The Goodwin Model

Very closely related to the Hicks difference equation trade cycle model which is described in Section 4 of Chapter Thirteen, are the differential equation cycle models constructed by R. M. Goodwin.[19] His article is also important in that it was so effective in bringing nonlinear techniques to the attention of the profession. Here we describe only the simplest of these constructions.

Let the desired capital stock, K_d, be proportional to the level of income, y, in accord with the acceleration principle argument.

$$K_d = ky \tag{104}$$

Further let consumption c be a linear function of income

$$c = ay + b \tag{105}$$

and as usual define income to be identically equal to the sum of consumption and net investment, I (= the rate of growth of capital $\frac{dK}{dt}$), so that

$$y = c + I = c + \frac{dK}{dt}. \tag{106}$$

Now let us assume that there are in practice three levels of investment (the nonlinear accelerator):

a) I_h which is the maximum level of investment output permitted by the economy's physical output capacity and which will be undertaken when the actual stock K is less than K_d, the desired capital stock;

b) I_l the minimum net investment level (negative) which is given by the rate of depreciation and obsolescence of capital stock. In other words I_l represents total nonreplacement of capital as it wears out, which occurs if $K > K_d$.

c) Finally, if $K = K_d$ we assume I = 0.

[19] R. M. Goodwin, "The Nonlinear Accelerator and the Persistence of Business Cycles," *Econometrica*, January, 1951.

Together these assumptions give us an equation for desired capital stock, as follows: Substituting from (105) into (106) we obtain

$$y = c + \frac{dK}{dt} = ay + b + \frac{dK}{dt},$$

so that

$$y(1-a) = b + \frac{dK}{dt} \quad \text{or} \quad y = \frac{b}{1-a} + \frac{1}{1-a}\frac{dK}{dt}.$$

Substituting this value of y into the expression for desired capital stock (104) we obtain

$$K_d = ky = \frac{kb}{1-a} + \frac{k}{1-a}\frac{dK}{dt}, \tag{107}$$

$$\text{where } \frac{dK}{dt} = I_h \text{ for } K_d > K$$

$$0 \text{ for } K_d = K$$

$$I_l \text{ for } K_d < K.$$

This is the basic equation of the Goodwin first order nonlinear differential equation model. The equation can be graphed in a phase diagram as follows (Figure 50):

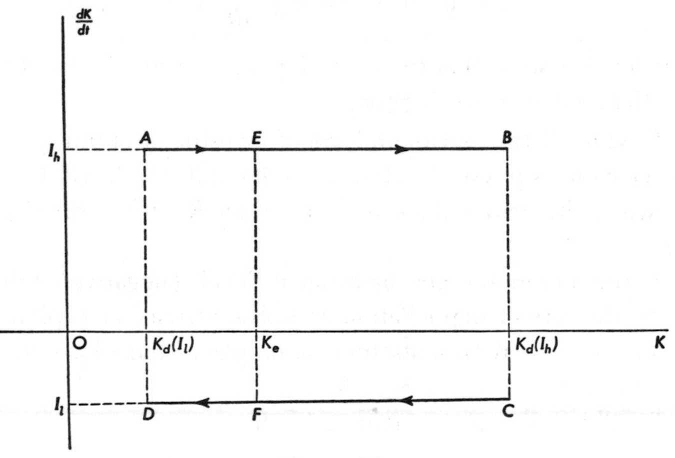

Figure 50

Suppose we start at point A. This must represent the upswing phase of the cycle since capital, K, increases at a constant rate $\frac{dK}{dt} = I_h$ and we move to the right along line AB as shown by the arrows. Meanwhile desired capital remains constant at its maximum level, which by (107) is given by

$$\frac{kb}{1-a} + \frac{k}{1-a} I_h = K_d(I_h).$$

When K reaches that desired capital level (point B) investment will fall to zero, income will drop abruptly to the level of consumption, and some capital will become redundant. As a result the rate of investment will now decrease suddenly from zero to its minimum level, I_1 (point C) and the desired capital stock will fall to its minimum level which by (107) is

$$\frac{kb}{1-a} + \frac{k}{1-a} I_l = K_d(I_l).$$

Now the capital stock, K_a will fall along line CD as shown by the arrows until it reaches its desired level at point D, and so on. The cycle $ABCD$ will be repeated again and again indefinitely.

It should be noted that the Goodwin difference equation (107) does have an equilibrium point K_e, for, setting $\frac{dK}{dt} = 0$, we obtain

$$K_e = \frac{kb}{1-a} + \frac{k}{1-a} 0 = \frac{kb}{1-a}.$$

But any time the capital stock departs by the slightest bit from this level investment will jump at once to its maximum level (point E) or fall to its minimum level (point F) so that while the cycle is stable, the equilibrium point K_e is unstable.

Note also,

i. that this cycle is of constant amplitude–it is neither damped nor explosive;

ii. its course is largely independent of initial conditions;

iii. the depression phase during which excess capital stock is depleted is presumably longer than the prosperity phase when capital stock is built up. This is because the rate of capital depletion is strictly limited by the rate of deterioration of the capital stock. It is shown on the phase diagram by the fact that the downswing segment of the cycle *CD* is closer to the horizontal axis than is the upswing segment *AB* and hence $\frac{dK}{dt}$ is greater during the latter than it is during the former, so that the horizontal stretch *AB* is traversed more quickly than is the equally long segment *CD*.

It must be reemphasized that this is the crudest and simplest of the Goodwin models, but it is perfectly adequate for illustrating the principles which have been presented in this section.

PROBLEM

Discuss the stability of the equilibrium at point C_e in Figure 49.

Part V

SIMULTANEOUS EQUATION MODELS

Chapter Fifteen

SIMULTANEOUS SYSTEMS AND SIMPLE OPERATORS

1. INTRODUCTION

The interdependence of economic phenomena and the consequent need for general equilibrium analysis should lead us to expect that there are dynamic problems for whose analysis it is appropriate to employ a number of simultaneous difference or differential equations which exhibit explicitly the interaction of several variables. This has indeed proved to be the case. Such systems have arisen in business cycle theory,[1] in multiplier analysis,[2] in dynamic input-output models [3] and in other areas of economic analysis. By and large these simultaneous equation models have employed only linear difference and differential equations because of the complexities introduced by nonlinearity. The present discussion will be confined exclusively to linear systems.

[1] See, e.g. Gerhard Tintner, "A 'Simple' Theory of Business Fluctuations," *Econometrica*, July–October, 1942.

[2] See, e.g. John S. Chipman, *The Theory of Inter-Sectoral Money Flows and Income Formation* (Johns Hopkins Press, Baltimore, 1951) and R. M. Goodwin, "The Multiplier as Matrix," *Economic Journal*, December, 1949. For a model with a small number of sectors see Ralph Turvey, "Some Notes on Multiplier Theory," *American Economic Review*, June, 1953.

[3] See Wasily Leontief, *Studies in the Structure of the American Economy* (Oxford University Press, New York, 1953), Chapter 3, and Robert Dorfman, Paul A. Samuelson, and Robert Solow, *Linear Programming and Economic Analysis* (McGraw-Hill, New York, 1957), Chapter 11. See also Chapter Sixteen, Sections 5 and 6 below.

Economic Example: The Two Sector Multiplier

As an illustration I employ the Goodwin-Chipman multi sector multiplier model.[2] In our elementary version we consider an economy which can conveniently be divided into two sectors (or countries) and assume that sector A purchases some of its own output and some of sector B's product, and vice versa. Let y_{aat} represent A's purchase of its own product during period t, y_{bat} represent its purchase of B's product, y_{abt} represent B's expenditure on A's output, etc. Then if y_{at} and y_{bt} are the respective total incomes of A and B during this period we have by summing each area's receipts

$$y_{at} = y_{aat} + y_{abt} \qquad \text{and} \qquad y_{bt} = y_{bat} + y_{bbt}. \tag{108}$$

Suppose now that A's purchases of its own and of B's products in the next period are dependent only on A's current income and that A's marginal propensities to consume are *constant.* Let c_{aa} be A's marginal propensity to consume its own products and c_{ba} its marginal propensity to purchase *B's* output, etc. Then

$$y_{aat+1} = k_{aa} + c_{aa}\, y_{at}$$

$$y_{bat+1} = k_{ba} + c_{ba}\, y_{at}$$

$$y_{abt+1} = k_{ab} + c_{ab}\, y_{bt}$$

$$y_{bbt+1} = k_{bb} + c_{bb}\, y_{bt}$$

where the k's are constants. Substituting these relationships into the preceding equations (108) we obtain

$$y_{at+1} = (k_{aa} + k_{ab}) + c_{aa}\, y_{at} + c_{ab}\, y_{bt}$$

$$y_{bt+1} = (k_{ba} + k_{bb}) + c_{ba}\, y_{at} + c_{bb}\, y_{bt}.$$

Thus we have obtained a model involving two simultaneous *linear* difference equations of a particular simple variety each of which contains the two variables y_a and y_b. They are both first-order equations since there is never more than a one period time spread between the variables appearing in either equation.

In writing our equations we have changed our notation slightly from that employed previously in that t now denotes the earliest period involved in the equation rather than the latest relevant period. It will simplify the exposition somewhat to adopt this procedure throughout this and the next chapter. For example, the first order difference equation which we would previously have designated by $y_t = 3y_{t-1} + 5$, will now be rewritten as $y_{t+1} = 3y_t + 5$. The reader should convince himself that since we are dealing with *any* two consecutive periods this is purely a matter of notation and that the two equations state precisely the same things.

Differential and Difference Equation Systems

In essentially the same way simultaneous *differential* equation models can be constructed and have occurred in the economic literature. As we have seen the methods of analysis of single difference and differential equation models are very similar, and this is also true of simultaneous equation systems for reasons which should become clearer in Section 4 below. As a result our discussion is confined largely to only one of these two types of equation system. Since most of the available literature pertains only to differential equation systems [4] we have chosen to base our exposition on the difference equation case. However, with the aid of the material in the preceding chapters, the hints which are given at various points in this chapter, and the standard differential equation literature the reader should have no difficulty translating the discussion into differential equation terms.

2. *ELEMENTARY COMPUTATIONAL METHODS* [5]

The following two equations illustrate a linear difference equation system with constant coefficients in the two time variables y_{1t} and y_{2t}.

[4] See especially R. A. Frazer, W. J. Duncan, and A. R. Collar, *Elementary Matrices and Some Applications to Dynamics and Differential Equations* (The Macmillan Company, New York, 1946), particularly Chapters V and VI. For a more recent discussion including such matters as existence and uniqueness see Earl A. Coddington, *An Introduction to Ordinary Differential Equations* (Prentice-Hall, Englewood Cliffs, N.J., 1961).

[5] This section duplicates in an elementary manner some of the material which is presented in Chapter Sixteen. It should be omitted by readers who have studied some elementary matrix algebra to whom the more systematic and deeper discussion of the next chapter will be more illuminating.

$$\left.\begin{aligned} 5y_{1t+6} - 3y_{1t+5} + 7y_{1t+1} - 2y_{2t+6} + 55y_{2t+3} + 17 &= 0 \\ 7y_{1t+6} + 2y_{1t+4} + 5y_{2t} &= 0. \end{aligned}\right\} \qquad (109)$$

The equations can be said to be of fifth order in y_{1t} since they involve values of that variable over a five period interval. Similarly, since the equations contain both y_{2t+6} and y_{2t}, we may say that the system is of sixth order in the variable y_{2t}.

This suggests that such a system will require a considerable number of initial conditions in order to determine the time path of the variables. Indeed it will apparently require 5 initial conditions for variable y_{1t} and 6 initial conditions for y_{2t}.

For example, we can have the initial conditions

$$\begin{aligned} y_{11} &= 5 & y_{20} &= 3 \\ y_{12} &= 3 & y_{21} &= 3 \\ y_{13} &= 1 & y_{22} &= 2 \\ y_{14} &= 3 & y_{23} &= 2 \\ y_{15} &= 6 & y_{24} &= 5 \\ & & y_{25} &= 7. \end{aligned}$$

Computation of Future Values of the Variables

To find the values of these two variables in the next period, period 6, we set $t = 0$ in our equations (109) and substitute in the (initial condition) values of y_{15}, y_{11}, y_{23}, y_{14}, and y_{20}. This yields

$$\begin{aligned} 5y_{16} - (3)(6) + (7)(5) - 2y_{26} + (55)(2) + 17 &= 0 \\ 7y_{16} + (2)(3) + (5)(3) &= 0 \end{aligned}$$

i.e.,

$$\begin{aligned} 5y_{16} - 2y_{26} + 144 &= 0 \\ 7y_{16} + 21 &= 0 \end{aligned}$$

which can obviously be solved to give the values of our variables in period 6:

$$y_{16} = -3,\ y_{26} = 129/2.$$

This information together with the initial conditions and the equations can then be used to compute the next period's values, y_{17} and y_{27}, in the same way and so on, so that the time paths of these variables are completely determined.

A Direct Method of Solution: Outline

The trial and error methods of the preceding chapters can also be used to solve a simultaneous system in a fairly straightforward manner. In the m variable case, by analogy with our earlier results, we try the solution

$$y_{1t} = p_1 x^t, \qquad y_{2t} = p_2 x^t, \qquad \cdots, y_{mt} = p_m x^t \tag{110}$$

where $p_1, p_2, \cdots, p_m$ are constants. We show now that it is possible to find values of $x, p_1, p_2, \cdots, p_m$ which satisfy our difference equation or rather, the system of reduced homogeneous equations obtained by dropping the constant terms. Further we shall note that as in the single equation case there are usually as many such values of x as there are initial conditions so that we will have that many distinct solutions of the form just given. As is shown later in this chapter, by multiplying these solutions by arbitrary constants and adding them together we obtain a general solution to our homogeneous system. When we have added to this a particular solution and the arbitrary constants are given values that permit the solution to satisfy the initial conditions, we will have solved our difference equation system. The analogy with the single equation analysis should be obvious enough.

EXAMPLE 1.

Solve:

$$\begin{aligned} y_{1t+1} - 6y_{1t} \quad + 8y_{2t} &= -9 \\ y_{1t} - y_{2t+1} \quad &= 0 \end{aligned}$$

with initial conditions

$$y_{10} = 19 \qquad y_{20} = 5.$$

THE CHARACTERISTIC EQUATION

The reduced equations are

$$y_{1t+1} - 6y_{1t} \qquad + 8y_{2t} = 0$$

$$y_{1t} - y_{2t+1} \qquad = 0.$$

In accord with (110) we try a solution of the form

$$y_{1t} = p_1x^t, \qquad y_{2t} = p_2x^t, \tag{111}$$

which, on substitution into our reduced equations yields

$$p_1x^{t+1} - 6p_1x^t + 8p_2x^t = 0, \qquad p_1x^t - p_2x^{t+1} = 0,$$

or dividing both sides of both these equations by x^t

$$p_1x - 6p_1 + 8p_2 = 0, \qquad p_1 - p_2x = 0.$$

These are two equations in the three unknowns x, p_1, and p_2. We can solve them for x and the ratio $p_2/p_1 = p$ by dividing both sides of both equations through by p_1 to obtain

$$x - 6 + 8p = 0 \qquad 1 - px = 0. \tag{112}$$

We see that any values of x and $p = p_2/p_1$ which satisfy these two equations (112) will provide us with a solution to our reduced (homogeneous) difference equations. To solve these equations, we note that the second equation in (112) yields $1 = px$ or $p = 1/x$, which when substituted into the first equation in (112) gives us

$$x - 6 + 8/x = 0, \qquad \text{or} \qquad x^2 - 6x + 8 = 0.$$

This polynomial equation which is obtained by elimination of p from equations (112) is called the *characteristic equation* of our two simultaneous difference equation system.

ROOTS OF THE CHARACTERISTIC EQUATION

This characteristic equation has two roots $x_1 = 4$ and $x_2 = 2$, which when substituted into the relationship $p = 1/x$ give us the two corresponding values of p, $p = \frac{1}{4}$ for $x = x_1 = 4$ and $p = \frac{1}{2}$ for $x = x_2 = 2$.

Thus going back to our trial solution (111) and for convenience arbitrarily setting $p_1 = 1$ so that $p = p_2/p_1 = p_2$, we have two pairs of solutions corresponding to the two roots of the characteristic equation

$$y_{1t}^{*} = (4)^t \qquad y_{2t}^{*} = \frac{1}{4}(4)^t$$

$$y_{1t}^{**} = (2)^t \qquad y_{2t}^{**} = \frac{1}{2}(2)^t.$$

THE GENERAL SOLUTION (REDUCED EQUATIONS)

Since we have two initial conditions we would like to end up with a solution which contains two arbitrary constants. As in the single equation case the sum of two solutions each multiplied by an arbitrary constant is also a solution [6], so we take as our general solution of the reduced equation the sum of the two solutions which correspond to the two roots of the characteristic equation multiplied by the arbitrary constants v_1 and v_2:

$$y_{1t} = v_1 y_{1t}^{*} + v_2 y_{1t}^{**} = v_1 4^t + v_2 2^t$$

$$y_{2t} = \frac{1}{4} v_1 4^t + \frac{1}{2} v_2 2^t$$

THE PARTICULAR SOLUTION

Again, as in the single equation case, to solve the nonhomogeneous system we must add a particular solution which, whenever possible, will be a constant (stationary equilibrium) solution of the form $y_{1t} = z_1$ and $y_{2t} = z_2$ where z_1 and z_2 are constants. Substituting these into our initial difference equations we obtain the ordinary simultaneous equations

$$z_1 - 6z_1 + 8z_2 = -5z_1 + 8z_2 = -9$$

$$z_1 - z_2 = 0.$$

[6] For a proof see the end of Section 1 of Chapter Sixteen.

These clearly yield $z_1 = z_2 = -3$. The general solution to our original equation system is now obtained by adding this particular solution to the general solution of the reduced equations to yield

$$\left.\begin{aligned} y_{1t} &= v_1 4^t + v_2 2^t - 3 \\ y_{2t} &= \frac{1}{4} v_1 4^t + \frac{1}{2} v_2 2^t - 3. \end{aligned}\right\} \tag{113}$$

INITIAL CONDITIONS AND ARBITRARY CONSTANTS

To complete our numerical solution we have yet only to find the values of v_1 and v_2. These we obtain with the aid of the initial conditions $y_{10} = 19$, $y_{20} = 5$, which, on setting $t = 0$ in our solution, gives us

$$v_1 + v_2 - 3 = 19$$

$$\frac{1}{4} v_1 + \frac{1}{2} v_2 - 3 = 5.$$

As the reader can readily verify this yields $v_1 = 12$, $v_2 = 10$, so that on substitution of these values (113) we obtain the solution of our two equation system.

EXAMPLE 2.

To solve our earlier sixth order two variable difference equation system (109) we can again substitute $y_{1t} = p_1 x^t$ and $y_{2t} = p_2 x^t$ into the reduced equation and divide by x^{t+1} and x^t respectively, to obtain

$$5p_1x^5 - 3p_1x^4 + 7p_1 - 2p_2x^5 + 55p_2x^2 = 0$$

$$7p_1x^6 - 2p_1x^4 + 5p_2 = 0.$$

From the second equation we obtain $p_2 = -\frac{7}{5} p_1 x^6 + \frac{2}{5} p_1 x^4$ which when substituted into the first equation yields the 11th degree polynomial equation

$$5p_1x^5 - 3p_1x^4 + 7p_1 - (2x^5 - 55x^2)\left(-\frac{7}{5} p_1x^6 + \frac{2}{5} p_1x^4\right) = 0.$$

This is the characteristic equation of the system and its solution and the solution of the two original difference equations encounters all of the difficulties involved in solving higher order polynomial equations which were discussed in Chapter Twelve.

Nature of the Time Path

The qualitative analysis of the nature of the time path of a simultaneous system must again be in terms of the role of the roots of the characteristic equation and the initial conditions in the expression for the solution [e.g., (113) in the case of example 1, above.] By analogy with the single equation case the method of interpretation should be fairly obvious—negative roots again mean oscillation, roots greater than unity mean instability, etc.

Note that as is the case in (113), because of the nature of the solution (111), the *same roots* appear in the solution expressions for every variable. That is, if -5 is a root of the characteristic equation the solution of each and every variable will involve the term $(-5)^t$ multiplied by some constant. This means that the time paths of all the variables in a linear system must ultimately take on the same qualitative character. Indeed the time paths of any two such variables y_{it} and y_{jt} will in the long run approach $pvx_m{}^t$ and $p'vx_m{}^t$ where p and p' are constants and x_m is the largest root in absolute value. Hence two such variables will tend ultimately to differ only by a constant factor of proportionality, p/p'.

PROBLEMS

Solve:

1. $y_{1t+1} - 8y_{2t} = -11$

   $y_{1t} - 2y_{2t+1} = 1$

   $y_{10} = 17 \; y_{20} = 1$

2. $y_{1t+1} - 3y_{1t} - 10y_{2t} = -12$

   $y_{1t} - y_{2t+1} = 0$

   $y_{10} = -1 \quad y_{20} = 9$

3. TRANSLATION INTO FIRST-ORDER SYSTEMS

First-Order System: Degree of the Characteristic Equation

The first example and both of the problems in the preceding section are illustrations of first-order simultaneous (two) difference equation systems. It is to be noted that all of these involved second degree characteristic equations and in general it is not difficult to show that in a first-order simultaneous equation system which is composed of n equations the characteristic equation will ordinarily be a polynomial of nth degree. In other words, in a first-order simultaneous system one does not avoid the problems which accompany a higher degree characteristic equation.

Nevertheless the analysis of first-order systems is in some ways simpler than that of higher order systems. Particularly this is so when that analysis is conducted with the aid of matrix algebra in the manner described in the next chapter. There exist simplifying theorems relevant only to the matrices which arise in first-order systems (see particularly Sections 4 and 5 of Chapter Sixteen). It is therefore often desirable to translate a higher order system into an equivalent first-order system, that is to say, into a first-order system which yields the same solution for the variables as did the original system. Fortunately, such a translation is always possible and it is also easily accomplished.

The Method of Translation

The method is best explained by illustration.

EXAMPLE 1.

Consider the second-order difference equation

$$y_{t+2} - 4y_{t+1} + 3y_t = 0.$$

We shall transform it into two simultaneous first-order equations by defining the new artificial variable

$$y_t^* \equiv y_{t+1}. \tag{114}$$

Substituting this into our second-order difference equation we obtain (since by definition $y^*_{t+1} = y_{t+2}$)

$$y^*_{t+1} = 4y^*_t - 3y_t$$

This is clearly a first-order difference equation in the two variables y_t^* and y_t. That equation together with the first-order equation (114) which defines y_t^* and which can be rewritten

$$y_t^* - y_{t+1} = 0$$

constitute a pair of two first-order simultaneous difference equations which are obviously equivalent to our original second-order equation.

Note that the trick in making this translation consists in systematic but strictly legal cheating. We reduce the order of an equation by redefining (or rather relabelling) y_{t+1} as a different variable, y_t^*, which does exactly what y_t does, but does it one period earlier.

EXAMPLE 2.

The two variable (y_t and x_t) system

$$y_{t+3} - 2y_{t+2} + 3y_{t+1} + y_t - 3x_t = 5$$

$$y_{t+2} - 4y_{t+1} + 7y_t + x_{t+1} = 1$$

can be translated into a first-order system with the aid of the two artificial variable definitions

$$\left.\begin{aligned} y_{2t} &\equiv y_{1t+1} \\ y_{1t} &\equiv y_{t+1} \end{aligned}\right\} \qquad (115)$$

which, when substituted into our original equations yield

$$y_{2t+1} = 2y_{2t} - 3y_{1t} - y_t + 3x_t + 5$$

$$x_{1t+1} = -y_{2t} + 4y_{1t} - 7y_t + 1.$$

Thus the two equations of definition (115) and these last two equations together constitute four simultaneous first-order equations which are equivalent to our original system.

PROBLEMS

1. Show that example 1 and problem 2 of Section 2 above are the respective first-order translations of problems 1b and 1c of Chapter Ten, Section 4, above. Compare and explain the relationships of the answers to the corresponding first- and second-order problems.
2. Translate into first order simultaneous systems and solve problems 1a and 1b of Section 2 and 1d of Section 4 in Chapter Ten.
3. Translate example 2 of this section into another first-order system which differs slightly from the one shown in the text.

4. DIFFERENCE, DIFFERENTIAL, AND OPERATOR EQUATIONS

The General Case: Notational Problems

The reader will doubtless have noted that even where, as in system (109) only two time variables are involved in each of two higher order equations the writing out of the equations can become rather tedious. The general two variable equation is

$$a_{10}y_{1t} + a_{11}y_{1t-1} + \cdots + a_{1n}y_{1t-n} + a_{20}y_{2t} + a_{21}y_{2t-1} + \cdots + a_{2m}y_{2t-m} + k = 0,$$

where there is no necessary relation between m and n. Writing out a complete system with an unspecified number of time variables can then be quite clumsy. For this reason as well as the great manipulative convenience which results it is useful to rewrite simultaneous linear difference equation systems in so-called "operator" notation. While seeing how this is done we shall also learn a little about operators, which are themselves very powerful weapons in the mathematician's analytic armory.

Operators: Definition

We may define an operator roughly as a symbol which represents the transformation of any item into another in any specified manner.

It is, in effect, merely an instruction to the reader to perform the indicated operation on the item involved. For example, suppose we define operator Tx to represent the instruction "subtract two from x." Then

$$T6 = 4$$
$$T^2 6 = T(T6) = T4 = 2$$

and so on. Notice that $T6$ does not represent the multiplication of the number 6 by some quantity T but that we have used multiplication notation in defining T^2. More will presently be said about such operator multiplication.

THE OPERATOR D.

Very frequently used is the operator D. This conveys the instruction "differentiate the item." Thus $Dy(x) = \frac{dy}{dx}$ and

$$D^2(2x^5) = D(D(2x^5)) = D(10x^4) = 40x^3.$$

The operator D performs essentially the same function in differential equation systems that the operator E, which we define next, plays in difference equation analysis.

THE OPERATOR E: ADDITION AND MULTIPLICATION

The operator E instructs the reader to go on to the next consecutive time period. It tells us to consider national income for 1950 instead of the national income for 1949, on which it is operating. Thus

$$Ey_{t-1} = y_t; \quad E^2y_{t-6} = Ey_{t-5} = y_{t-4}; \quad E^3y_{t+2} = y_{t+5}.$$

We see here how E, like other operators, can be multiplied (raised to a power). Also like other operators it is convenient to define addition of powers of E. An example will show how this works:

$$(E^3 + 3E^2 - 2E + 6)y_t = E^3y_t + 3E^2y_t - 2Ey_t + 6y_t$$
$$= y_{t+3} + 3y_{t+2} - 2y_{t+1} + 6y_t.$$

Rewriting a Single Difference Equation in Operator Terms

It should now be fairly obvious how a single one variable difference equation can be translated into operator terms. For example, the equation

$$y_{t+5} - 2y_{t+4} + 3y_t + 7 = 0$$

can be written

$$(E^5 - 2E^4 + 3)y_t + 7 = 0. \tag{116}$$

The expression $(E^5 - 2E^4 + 3)$ is a polynomial in the operator E. If we designate this polynomial by the symbol $P_1(E)$ our equation then may be written as $P_1(E)y_t + 7 = 0$. Indeed the general one variable single linear difference equation can also be written in this form, for if we take

$$P(E) = a_0E^n + a_1E^{n-1} + \cdots + a_{n-1}E + a_n$$

then

$$P(E)y_t + k = 0$$

is the general nth order equation

$$a_0y_{t+n} + a_1y_{t+n-1} + \cdots + a_{n-1}y_{t+1} + a_ny_t + k = 0.$$

Operator Notation for Simultaneous Difference Equations

The same device can be used to rewrite a system of simultaneous linear difference equations. In their most general form these would be written

$$\left.\begin{array}{l} P_{11}(E)y_{1t} + P_{12}(E)y_{2t} + \cdots + P_{1m}(E)y_{mt} + k_1 = 0 \\ P_{21}(E)y_{1t} + P_{22}(E)y_{2t} + \cdots + P_{2m}(E)y_{mt} + k_2 = 0 \\ \cdots\cdots\cdots\cdots\cdots\cdots\cdots\cdots\cdots\cdots \\ P_{m1}(E)y_{1t} + P_{m2}(E)y_{2t} + \cdots + P_{mm}(E)y_{mt} + k_m = 0 \end{array}\right\} \tag{117}$$

where the $P_{ij}(E)$ are all polynomials in E (though some may be constants or zero as special cases). Thus in this notation equations (109) would be written as

$$\left.\begin{aligned}(5E^6 - 3E^5 + 7E)y_{1t} + (-2E^6 + 55E^3)y_{2t} + 17 &= 0\\(7E^6 + 2E^4)y_{1t} + (5)y_{2t} &= 0\end{aligned}\right\} \quad (118)$$

Difference and Differential Equations

Differential equations too can be rewritten in operator notation with the aid of the operator D. For example,

$$\frac{d^5y(t)}{dt^5} - 2\frac{d^4y(t)}{dt^4} + 3y(t) + 7 = 0$$

can be rewritten as

$$(D^5 - 2D^4 + 3)y(t) + 7 = 0. \quad (119)$$

The similarity between this and equation (116) above is striking.

In fact this should help indicate to the reader why the analysis of difference and differential equations is so similar. For let Q represent a more general type of operator which can be interpreted either as $Q = D$ or $Q = E$ whenever we find it convenient to do so. Then equations (116) and (119) can both be rewritten as

$$(Q^5 - 2Q^4 + 3)y + 7 = 0.$$

In this way the general n^{th} order linear difference *and* differential equations with constant coefficients and constant nonhomogeneous term can be written simply as

$$(a_0Q^n + a_1Q^{n-1} + \cdots + a_{n-1}Q + a_n)y + k = 0$$

and simultaneous linear systems can be treated in the same way. Now, any theorem which can be proved for the preceding equation must necessarily hold both for single difference and differential equations. But most of the propositions which we have employed are valid for such a more general operator equation and that is why our difference equation analysis has proved so easily translatable into differential equation terms.

5. DIGRESSION: ELEMENTARY ALGEBRA OF OPERATORS

Operator Methods of Solution of Dynamic Equations

Besides simplifying notation in the way which has just been described, operators can directly be helpful in solving difference and differential equations. Indeed the operator is an exceedingly powerful instrument of computation in many areas of mathematics. Its basic advantage stems from the fact that in many cases an operator can be manipulated as an ordinary algebraic symbol. As a result the solution of a difficult difference or differential equation can sometimes be reduced to a problem in elementary algebra.

This advantage can perhaps be made clearer by analogy. The reader will recall that logarithms derive much of their utility from the fact that they can be used to transform a problem of multiplication into one of addition (the log of a product is the sum of the logs of the two items being multiplied) and to change the computation of the nth power of x into ordinary multiplication of log x by the number n. Similarly, operators can often be used to avoid integration and other difficult operations by substituting for them the addition, multiplication, and division of algebraic expressions.

Multiplication and Addition

We have already seen that operators can meaningfully be multiplied together to yield terms like E^2y_t and that such terms can be added together to form expressions like $(2E^3 + 3E^2 + 5)y_t$.

More generally, let a and b be any constants. Then we represent by $(E - a)(E - b)y_t$ the result of two consecutive operations:

(i) perform the operation $(E - b)y_t = y_t^*$

(ii) perform the second operation $(E - a)y_t^*$ on the result, y_t^*, of the first operation. Thus we have

$$(E - a)(E - b)y_t = (E - a)(y_{t+1} - by_t) = E(y_{t+1} - by_t) - a(y_{t+1} - by_t) = y_{t+2} - by_{t+1} - ay_{t+1} + aby_t = y_{t+2} - (a + b)y_{t+1} + aby_t \quad (120)$$

Suppose now that instead of adopting this two step procedure suggested by the definition of our product operator expression, we first multiply out the two operator terms $(E-a)$ and $(E-b)$ and then operate on y_t with the resulting expression. This yields

$$(E-a)(E-b)y_t = [E^2-(a+b)E+ab]y_t$$
$$= y_{t+2}-(a+b)y_{t+1}+aby_t,$$

which is exactly the result (120) that we obtained before.

This argument can readily be extended to yield the result that *any operation on a variable* y_t *which can be represented by the multiplication and/or addition of several polynomials in operators such as* D *or* E *can be obtained by first finding the products and/or sums of these polynomials and then operating on* y_t *in accord with the instructions of the resulting operator polynomial.*[7] For example, let $A(D)$, $B(D)$, and $C(D)$ be three polynomials all involving the operator D. Then if we write $P(D)$ to represent the expression $A(D)[B(D)-C(D)]$ after the indicated subtraction and multiplication have been carried out, our rule tells us that

$$A(D)[B(D)-C(D)]y = P(D)y.$$

Operator Division

We may also define division by an operator polynomial such as $P(D)$ as follows. Let $f(t)=P(D)y(t)$. Then $f(t)/P(D)\equiv y(t)$. In other words, if $f(t)$ designates the result of operating on $y(t)$ as directed by $P(D)$, then $1/P(D)$ is defined as the reverse operation which transforms $f(t)$ back into $y(t)$. The inverse polynomial in E, $P(E)$, is defined similarly.

For example, $(1/D)\dfrac{dy}{dt}=y$, $(1/E^2)y_t=y_{t-2}$, etc. Again we note that we may manipulate operator polynomials in a denominator as

[7] Indeed it is easy to show that these operators are defined in a way which makes them satisfy the axioms from which the rules of algebraic addition, subtraction, and multiplication are usually deduced. For a brief discussion see R. D. G. Allen, *Mathematical Economics* (St. Martin's Press, New York, 1956), pp. 726 and 732. For an extensive exposition of these rules see Alfred Tarski, *Introduction to Logic and to the Methodology of Deductive Sciences* (Oxford University Press, New York, 1941), Second Part.

though they were ordinary algebraic expressions. For we have seen that if, for example, $P(E) = A(E)B(E)$ where A, B, and P are three such polynomials, then

$$P(E)y_t = A(E)B(E)y_t = f_t.$$

Hence it follows by definition that both inverse operations, $f_t/P(E)$ and $f_t/A(E)B(E)$ must yield the same result y_t, i.e., that $f_t/P(E) = f_t/A(E)B(E) = y_t$.

Particular Solutions for Variable Nonhomogeneous Terms

Now let us see how operator algebra can help us solve difference or differential equations. Consider the simple nonhomogeneous linear difference equation

$$y_{t+1} - 2y_t = 5^t. \tag{121}$$

We know by Proposition Seven of Chapter Ten that the solution of this equation is the sum of some particular solution and the solution of the homogeneous (reduced) equation $y_{t+1} - 2y_t = 0$. On inspection we see that the reduced equation has the solution $y_t = 2^t$. But how can we find a particular solution?

This case illustrates a fundamental problem which arises in the solution of linear differential and difference equations with constant coefficients. In principle we know how to find the general solution of the reduced equation for *any* such equation. But when the equation contains a variable nonhomogeneous term the particular solution is not always easy to find. It may perhaps surprise the reader that it is often more difficult to find a particular solution than it is to obtain the general solution of the reduced equation. In fact no one has been able to devise a method which always produces a particular solution and there are many nonhomogeneous equations for which no particular solution is known. Much of the literature on differential equations is devoted to the discussion of devices for determining particular solutions for various classes of equation.

We have already described one such method, the method of undetermined coefficients in Chapter Fourteen, Section 8. Let us now see how operator methods can sometimes also be employed to help determine particular solutions.

PRELIMINARY THEOREM

First we establish a theorem which will also be needed later.

PROPOSITION ONE. Let k and x be any numbers, and $P(E)$ and $R(D)$ be any two polynomials in the operators E and D, respectively. Then, (i) $P(E)kx^t = kx^tP(x)$ and (ii) $R(D)ke^{xt} = ke^{xt}R(x)$.

Part i, on difference equations, states that any polynomial in E operating on kx^t yields kx^t multiplied by the same polynomial only with x substituted for E. Part ii of this proposition is the analogous result for differential equations.

PROOF OF PART I:

$$P(E)kx^t = (a_0E^n + a_1E^{n-1} + \cdots + a_{n-1}E + a_n)kx^t$$
$$= ka_0x^{t+n} + ka_1x^{t+n-1} + \cdots + ka_{n-1}x^{t+1} + ka_nx^t,$$

which on factoring out kx^t yields

$$kx^t(a_0x^n + a_1x^{n-1} + \cdots + a_{n-1}x + a_n) = kx^tP(x),$$

as the theorem requires.

The proof of Part ii of the theorem is step by step the same as that of Part i and the reader should write it out as an exercise.

Operator Methods for Finding Particular Solutions

Consider again our equation $y_{t+1} - 2y_t = 5^t$. In operator notation it is written $(E - 2)y_t = 5^t$. Let Z_t be a particular solution of this equation so that $(E - 2)Z_t = 5^t$. Then dividing through by $(E - 2)$ we may describe Z_t symbolically as $Z_t = 5^t/(E - 2)$. And if we can find out how to perform the division in question this will give us our solution. Consider first the more general equation $P(E)y_t = x^t$ where x represents some definite number. With the aid of Proposition One we can now prove that a particular solution is given by [8]

$$Z_t = \frac{x^t}{P(E)} = \frac{x^t}{P(x)}.$$

[8] Except where x is a root of $P(x) = 0$ because here, as elsewhere, we are not permitted to divide by zero. Why not?

In other words, Proposition One, Part i holds for division as well as for multiplication by $P(E)$. That is, to divide x^t by $P(E)$ we merely substitute the number x for E and perform the indicated division. An analogous result holds for Part ii of Proposition One on differential equations. The proof in the difference equation case is obtained directly by setting $kx^t = x^t/P(x)$ [that is, $k = 1/P(x)$] in Proposition One to obtain

$$P(E)Z_t = P(E)x^t/P(x) = [x^t/P(x)]\,P(x) = x^t,$$

so that $Z_t = x^t/P(x)$ is indeed a particular solution because it satisfies our equation.

ILLUSTRATIONS

Let us return to our numerical problem (121) in which we wanted to solve $Z_t = 5^t/(E-2)$. Since in this case the nonhomogeneous term, x^t, is 5^t we have $x = 5$ so that by the result we have just derived, our particular solution is obtained by substituting this number, x, for E. We obtain $Z_t = 5^t/(5-2) = 5^t/3$. Direct substitution of this value of Z_t and the corresponding value $Z_{t+1} = 5^{t+1}/3$ into our original equation (121) verifies that it is indeed a particular solution for this substitution yields $5^{t+1}/3 - 2\cdot 5^t/3 = 5\cdot 5^t/3 - 2\cdot 5^t/3 = 3\cdot 5^t/3 = 5^t$ as the equation requires.

To illustrate the corresponding differential equation procedure which the reader should be able to justify, consider the equation

$$\frac{d^2y}{dt^2} + 5\frac{dy}{dt} + 3y = (D^2 + 5D + 3)y = 2e^{3t}.$$

Since here ke^{xt} is $2e^{3t}$ so that $x = 3$, a particular solution is given by substitution of this number for D to yield

$$Z = \frac{2e^{3t}}{D^2 + 5D + 3} = \frac{2e^{3t}}{3^2 + 5\cdot 3 + 3} = \frac{2e^{3t}}{27}.$$

We have just illustrated the two most elementary cases in which particular solutions can be found by operator methods. Other cases require more difficult algebraic manipulation of the operators. But the basic technique is always the same, the reduction of a solution problem to one involving algebraic manipulation. For details the reader is referred to the appendix of R. D. G. Allen (*op. cit.*) and to the standard texts on differential equations.

PROBLEMS

1. Find particular solutions for

   a) $y_{t+3} + 6y_{t+1} - 2y_t = 2^t$

   b) $y_{t+2} - 4y_{t+1} + 5y_t = 3(4^t)$

   c) $\dfrac{dy}{dt} - 12y = e^{15t}$

2. Why doesn't the method work for

$$\frac{dy}{dt} - 15y = e^{15t}?$$

Chapter Sixteen

SIMULTANEOUS LINEAR SYSTEMS: MATRIX METHODS

1. MATRIX METHODS OF SOLUTION

From this point on the discussion requires more mathematical equipment of the reader. Those who drop out at this point can have learned how to obtain a numerical solution of a simultaneous system almost as effectively as will the readers who go on. But it is nevertheless worth explaining how the techniques of matrix algebra can be applied to our problem both because of the inherent analytic power of the matrix methods and because so much of the literature is stated in these terms and must remain at least partly incomprehensible to the reader who stops here. In particular it will be seen that matrix methods can be used in the development of a rich body of tools for qualitative analysis.

Matrix Notation for Simultaneous Systems

After translation into operator notation simultaneous systems may be rewritten further and still more compactly in matrix notation. In this form the system (118) becomes

$$\begin{bmatrix} 5E^6 - 3E^5 + 7E & -2E^6 + 55E^3 \\ 7E^6 + 2E^4 & 5 \end{bmatrix} \begin{bmatrix} y_{1t} \\ y_{2t} \end{bmatrix} + \begin{bmatrix} 17 \\ 0 \end{bmatrix} = \begin{bmatrix} 0 \\ 0 \end{bmatrix}$$

Similarly, the general system (117) may be rewritten as

$$\begin{bmatrix} P_{11}(E) & P_{12}(E) \cdots P_{1m}(E) \\ P_{21}(E) & P_{22}(E) \cdots P_{2m}(E) \\ \cdots\cdots\cdots & \cdots\cdots\cdots \\ P_{m1}(E) & P_{m2}(E) \cdots P_{mm}(E) \end{bmatrix} \begin{bmatrix} y_{1t} \\ y_{2t} \\ \cdots \\ y_{mt} \end{bmatrix} + \begin{bmatrix} k_1 \\ k_2 \\ \cdots \\ k_m \end{bmatrix} = \begin{bmatrix} 0 \\ 0 \\ \cdot \\ 0 \end{bmatrix} \quad (122)$$

which can be condensed even further to

$$P(E)y_t + k = 0 \quad (123)$$

where $P(E)$ is an $m \times m$ square matrix and y_t, k, and 0 are all m element column vectors.

It is this form which we will find most convenient to use in discussing the method of solution of the system of equations.

The Solution of Homogeneous Systems

As we have seen the form x^t, where x is some constant, plays a basic role in the solution of simultaneous difference equation systems just as e^{xt} does in the solution of differential equation systems. We shall proceed to show that there exists a column vector which multiplied by some number x raised to the tth power serves as a solution to the reduced homogeneous equation system obtained by setting $k = 0$ in (123).

The Inverse of a Matrix

It is first convenient to remind the reader of a definition and a basic theorem of matrix algebra.

Definition: The adjoint A^* of any matrix A is given by substituting for every element a_{ij} of A the *cofactor* of element a_{ji}, that is, the cofactor of the corresponding element of the transposed matrix. Thus the adjoint of

$$\begin{bmatrix} a_{11} & a_{12} & a_{13} \\ a_{21} & a_{22} & a_{23} \\ a_{31} & a_{32} & a_{33} \end{bmatrix}$$

is given by

$$\begin{bmatrix} \begin{vmatrix} a_{22} & a_{23} \\ a_{32} & a_{33} \end{vmatrix} & -\begin{vmatrix} a_{12} & a_{13} \\ a_{32} & a_{33} \end{vmatrix} & \begin{vmatrix} a_{12} & a_{13} \\ a_{22} & a_{23} \end{vmatrix} \\ -\begin{vmatrix} a_{21} & a_{23} \\ a_{31} & a_{33} \end{vmatrix} & \begin{vmatrix} a_{11} & a_{13} \\ a_{31} & a_{33} \end{vmatrix} & -\begin{vmatrix} a_{11} & a_{13} \\ a_{21} & a_{23} \end{vmatrix} \\ \begin{vmatrix} a_{21} & a_{22} \\ a_{31} & a_{32} \end{vmatrix} & -\begin{vmatrix} a_{11} & a_{12} \\ a_{31} & a_{32} \end{vmatrix} & \begin{vmatrix} a_{11} & a_{12} \\ a_{21} & a_{22} \end{vmatrix} \end{bmatrix}$$

where the arrays of items inside the vertical lines are determinants. This definition permits us to state the following well known theorem (for proof the reader can refer to any elementary text on matrix algebra):

PROPOSITION TWO: If A^* is the adjoint of matrix A, and $|A|$ is the determinant of that matrix, and if that determinant is not equal to zero, then $A^*/|A|$ is the inverse of A, i.e.,

$$A\frac{A^*}{|A|} = I$$

where I is the unit matrix which has the value 1 for every principal diagonal element and every other element of which is zero.

More generally (even if $|A| = 0$), we have

$$AA^* = I|A|.$$

The Adjoint in the Solution

Let us now return to our equation system (123), in which we have set $k = 0$. We try substituting for the column matrix y_t the product $x^tP^*(x)$ where $P^*(x)$ is the adjoint of $P(E)$ with x substituted for E everywhere.

This gives us

$$P(E)x^tP^*(x)$$

which by Proposition One of the previous chapter equals

$$x^tP(x)P^*(x)$$

and this in turn, by Proposition Two, equals

$$x^t I \mid P(x) \mid$$

where $\mid P(x) \mid$ is the determinant of the matrix $P(x)$.

Thus we have

$$P(E) x^t P^*(x) = x^t I \mid P(x) \mid. \tag{124}$$

The right hand side will be zero (i.e., it will be an $m \times m$ matrix every element of which is zero) if the determinant $\mid P(x) \mid$ is zero, i.e., if x is any root of the determinantal (characteristic) equation [1]

$$\mid P(x) \mid = 0. \tag{125}$$

In this case, since the right hand side of (124) will be an m column square matrix all of whose elements are zero, if $P_i^*(x)$ is any column of $P^*(x)$ we will have

$$P(E) x^t P_i^*(x) = 0 \tag{126}$$

where the right hand side of (126) is the column vector of m zero elements. Thus we have proved

PROPOSITION THREE: If x_j is any root of the determinantal equation (125) and $P_i^*(x)$ is any column of the adjoint of $P(x)$, then $y_t = x_j^t P_i^*(x_j)$ is a solution of the homogeneous difference equation system

$$P(E) y_t = 0. \tag{127}$$

Nonnullity and Proportionality of the Adjoint Columns

Two problems must be dealt with before we employ this solution.

i. The adjoint $P^*(x_j)$ has m columns. Which of these should be employed in the solution of Proposition Three?

[1] Usually in the mathematical literature this is called a *characteristic* equation only in the special case where the equation system (123) takes the special first order form (131) below.

ii. The second problem is somewhat more subtle. Suppose the columns of the adjoint ever consist exclusively of zero elements. In that case the solution proposed in Proposition Three is $y_t = x_j^t P_i^* (x_j) = x_j^t \cdot 0 = 0$.

Now zero is a (particular) solution to any homogeneous difference equation. For example, the equation[2] $y_{t+2} = 5y_{t+1} - 6y_t$ has the solutions $y_t^* = a(2)^t$ and $y_t^{**} = b(3)^t$ but it also has the solution $y_t^{***} = 0$, since on substituting this constant into the right hand side of the equation we obtain $y_{t+2} = 5 \cdot 0 - 6 \cdot 0 = 0$, as required. We see then that zero is always a trivial (particular) solution of a homogeneous difference equation. But suppose we try to treat it like the other solutions and multiply it by an arbitrary constant and add it to the rest of the solution to obtain the general solution. Obviously multiplication of the arbitrary constant by zero gives us zero so that this procedure leaves the general solution unaffected. In other words, the zero particular solution does not contribute anything to the general solution which describes the movement of the system when it is not in equilibrium.

Similarly, if to solve our simultaneous equation problem we insert in Proposition Three the column of an adjoint all of whose elements are zero we obtain the trivial zero solution. In such a case while the solution of Proposition Three is formally valid, it is redundant because we knew before we began our computations that zero is a solution of the homogeneous system. And again, this zero particular solution plays no role in the general solution which we seek.

Fortunately, problem i, which column of the adjoint to choose, never arises if x_j is not a multiple root of the determinantal equation. For in this case the columns of the adjoint $P^* (x_j)$ will differ only by a constant factor, i.e., they will all be proportional.

Moreover, in this case where the roots are all distinct the columns of the adjoint will never be null (never consist entirely of zeros) so

[2] In fact in deriving its characteristic equation $x^2 - 5x + 6 = 0$ from $x^{t+2} - 5x^{t+1} + 6x^t = 0$ by dividing through by x^t we have implicitly decided to ignore the t roots $x = 0$ which are solutions of the latter but not of the former.

that problem ii will not occur either.[3] However, in the multiple roots case which we do not treat here, these columns are very likely to be null, and a modified procedure must be employed.

The Various Roots and the Arbitrary Constants

It is easy to see by substitution into (127) that if the column vector representing a solution is multiplied by a constant the result will still be a solution, for if y_t^* is the original solution and a is the constant then we will have, since by the definition of a solution $P(E)y_t^* = 0$,

$$P(E)ay_t^* = P(E)y_t^*a = 0 \cdot a = 0.$$

Similarly, the sum of any two solutions can be shown to be a solution since if y_t^* and y_t^{**} are solutions then

$$P(E)(y_t^* + y_t^{**}) = P(E)y_t^* + P(E)y_t^{**} = 0 + 0 = 0.$$

Thus we have

PROPOSITION FOUR: If $x_1, \cdots, x_w$ are the roots of the determinantal equation (125) and none of them are multiple roots then

$$y_t = \sum_{j=1}^{w} V_j x_j^t P_i^*(x_j)$$

will be a solution to the difference equation system (127), where the V_j are arbitrary constants and $P_i^*(x_j)$ is any column of the adjoint $P^*(x_j)$.

It can be shown that this is the general solution, i.e., that it has the same number of arbitrary constants as there are initial conditions.[4]

[3] For proofs and the methods to be employed in the multiple roots case the reader is referred to R. A. Frazer, W. J. Duncan, and A. R. Collar, *Elementary Matrices and Some Applications to Dynamics and Differential Equations* (The Macmillan Company, New York, 1946), pp. 16–17, 23, 61–62, and 166. See also Earl A. Coddington, *An Introduction to Ordinary Differential Equations* (Prentice-Hall, Englewood Cliffs, N.J., 1961).

[4] For proof the reader is referred to Section 6.5 of E. L. Ince, *Ordinary Differential Equations* (Longmans, New York, 1927).

2. NONHOMOGENEOUS SYSTEMS

The General and the Particular Solution

We have just seen how to obtain the general solution of the homogeneous reduced equation system (127) which is obtained by setting $k = 0$ in equation (123). We now require

PROPOSITION FIVE: The general solution of (123) is given by the sum of any particular solution of (123) and the general solution of the reduced equation (127).
Proof: Let x_t be the general solution of (127) so that

$$P(E)x_t = 0$$

and let Z_t be a particular solution of (123) so that

$$P(E)Z_t = -\mathrm{k}.$$

Then substituting the proposed solution $(x_t + Z_t)$ into (123) we obtain

$$\begin{aligned} P(E)(x_t + Z_t) + k &= P(E)x_t + P(E)Z_t + k \\ &= 0 - k + k \\ &= 0. \end{aligned}$$

Thus the sum $x_t + Z_t$ satisfies (123). It should be intuitively clear that the addition of the nonhomogeneous term does not affect the number of initial conditions required to complete the system. Hence if x_t has the same number of arbitrary constants as the system has initial conditions, and if Z_t has no arbitrary constants, $x_t + Z_t$ will have the correct number of arbitrary constants.

Obtaining a Particular Solution

Since we know how to obtain the general solution of the reduced equations (127) we need merely discuss the finding of a particular solution to (123). This is simple if the k is a vector of constants. First we must observe that operator E has no effect on any constant b since b does not vary with time. Therefore

$$\begin{aligned} P(E)b &= a_1E^nb + a_2E^{n-1}b + \cdots + a_{n-1}Eb + a_nb \\ &= a_1b + a_2b \qquad\qquad + \cdots + a_{n-1}b \;\; + a_nb \\ &= P(1)b. \end{aligned}$$

That is to say, multiplication of a constant by a polynomial in E results in the product of b multiplied by the polynomial with the number 1 substituted for E throughout.

Returning to equation (123), if we substitute for the column of time variables y_t the column of constants b, we obtain

$$P(E)b + k = P(1)b + k = 0$$

i.e.,

$$\left.\begin{array}{l} P_{11}(1)b_1 + P_{12}(1)b_2 + \cdots + P_{1m}(1)b_m = -k_1 \\ \cdots\cdots\cdots\cdots\cdots\cdots\cdots\cdots\cdots\cdots \\ P_{m1}(1)b_1 + P_{m2}(1)b_2 + \cdots + P_{mm}(1)b_m = -k_m. \end{array}\right\} \quad (128)$$

Here the $P_{ij}(1)$ are obviously constants, in fact, they are the sums of the coefficients of the original polynomials. E.g., if $P_{ij}(E) = 3E^3 - 2E^2 + 6E + 5$, $P_{ij}(1) = (3 \cdot 1^3) - (2 \cdot 1^2) + (6 \cdot 1) + 5 = 12$.

Thus this is a system of m linear equations which can be solved for the unknowns $b_1, \cdots, b_m$ provided the determinant of the system is non-zero. This gives us a particular solution: the column of constants, b.[5]

3. *THE INITIAL CONDITIONS*

Let us now see how to take account of the initial conditions in the solution

$$y_t = \sum_{j=1}^{w} V_j x_j^t P_i^*(x_j) + b \qquad (129)$$

of our difference equation system.

[5] It should be noted that this method of finding the particular solution will fail when unity is a root of the determinantal equation (125). For the determinant of the system (128) is precisely the same as that on the right-hand side of (125) when x is given the value one. Thus the determinant [which is the denominator in the Cramer's rule solution of system (128)] will be zero.

For concreteness let us go back to the initial conditions of the illustrative system given in Section 2 of the preceding chapter. These may be written as

$$y_{11} = C_{11} = 5, \; y_{12} = C_{12} = 3, \; \cdots, \; y_{15} = C_{15} = 6,$$

$$y_{20} = C_{20} = 3, \; y_{21} = C_{21} = 3, \; y_{22} = C_{22} = 2, \cdots, \; y_{25} = C_{25} = 7.$$

More generally these initial conditions may be written in the form

$$y_{ij} = C_{ij} \qquad \text{for some specified values of } i, j \qquad (130)$$

where the C_{ij}'s are constants.

If in the left hand side of equations (130) we substitute the values of the y_{ij} given by setting $t = j$ in the solution (129) we obtain a set of equations of which the following is an example:

$$C_{25} = 7 = \sum_{j=1}^{w} V_j x_j{}^5 P^*_{2i}(x_j) + b_2$$

where the $P^*_{2i}(x_j)$ and b_2 are respectively the (known) second elements in the column vectors $P^*_i(x_j)$ and b. The only unknowns in this equation are therefore the w arbitrary constants V_j.

Because there are w initial conditions (130) (see above footnote 3 for a reference to the proof) there are exactly w such equations. There are thus w nonhomogeneous linear equations in the w unknowns V_j and the system can ordinarily be solved for the V_j.

EXAMPLE

Solve the equations

$$y_{1t+2} - 2y_{1t+1} + y_{1t} + y_{2t+1} + 5y_{2t} + 5 = 0$$

$$y_{1t+1} - 2y_{1t} + 2y_{2t} + 7 = 0$$

$$y_{10} = 1; \; y_{20} = 1.$$

THE NUMBER OF INITIAL CONDITIONS

Here two initial conditions suffice. To show this we indicate how they enable us to calculate the future values of the variables y_{1t} and

y_{2t} of the system. The two initial conditions given above enable us to compute from the second equation of the system

$$y_{11} = 2y_{10} - 2y_{20} - 7 = 2 - 2 - 7 = -7.$$

We can now find y_{12} and y_{21} from the equations

$$\begin{aligned} y_{12} - 2y_{11} + y_{10} + y_{21} + 5y_{20} + 5 &= 0 \\ y_{12} - 2y_{11} \qquad + 2y_{21} \qquad + 7 &= 0 \end{aligned}$$

which are obtained by setting $t = 0$ in the first equation and $t = 1$ in the second equation. These last equations together with our initial conditions and the computed value of y_{11} give us

$$\begin{aligned} y_{12} - (2)(-7) + 1 + y_{21} + (5)(1) + 5 &= 0 \\ y_{12} + 14 \qquad + 2y_{21} \qquad + 7 &= 0 \end{aligned}$$

or

$$\begin{aligned} y_{12} + y_{21} + 25 &= 0 \\ y_{12} + 2y_{21} + 21 &= 0 \end{aligned}$$

from which we can readily evaluate y_{12} and y_{21}. From these values of our variables in period two and one and the values previously obtained we can go on to compute the values of our variables for the next period, then the period after that, etc. Thus we have a sufficient number of initial conditions, since they suffice to "set the system in motion."

Solving the Reduced Equation System

The reduced equations of our system may be written in matrix-operator form as:

$$\begin{bmatrix} E^2 - 2E + 1 & E + 5 \\ E - 2 & 2 \end{bmatrix} \begin{bmatrix} y_{1t} \\ y_{2t} \end{bmatrix} = \begin{bmatrix} 0 \\ 0 \end{bmatrix}.$$

The determinantal equation is

$$|P(x)| = \begin{vmatrix} x^2 - 2x + 1 & x + 5 \\ x - 2 & 2 \end{vmatrix} = 0.$$

Expanding this determinant we have

$$2x^2 - 4x + 2 - (x+5)(x-2) = 2x^2 - 4x + 2 - x^2 - 3x + 10$$
$$= x^2 - 7x + 12 = 0.$$

This has the roots $x_1 = 3$, $x_2 = 4$.

The adjoint of the matrix $P(E)$ is

$$P^*(E) = \begin{bmatrix} 2 & -(E+5) \\ -(E-2) & E^2 - 2E + 1 \end{bmatrix}$$

so that

$$P^*(x_1) = P^*(3) = \begin{bmatrix} 2 & -8 \\ -1 & 4 \end{bmatrix}$$

and

$$P^*(x_2) = P^*(4) = \begin{bmatrix} 2 & -9 \\ -2 & 9 \end{bmatrix}.$$

It will be seen that the columns of these adjoints are proportional as is to be expected from the nonmultiplicity of the roots.

By Proposition Four we see now that the solution to the reduced equations of our system is given by

$$\begin{bmatrix} y_{1t} \\ y_{2t} \end{bmatrix} = V_1 3^t \begin{bmatrix} 2 \\ -1 \end{bmatrix} + V_2 4^t \begin{bmatrix} 2 \\ -2 \end{bmatrix}$$

where we have arbitrarily chosen to use the first columns of the adjoints. This causes no loss of generality because of the presence of the arbitrary constants V_1 and V_2, and, in fact, instead of the last column vector employed in the solution it might have been convenient to use $\begin{bmatrix} 1 \\ -1 \end{bmatrix}$.

A PARTICULAR SOLUTION

We have now to find a particular solution for our equation system which we obtain by substituting the constants b_1 and b_2 for y_{1t} and y_{2t} in the original equations. This yields

$$\begin{bmatrix} E^2 - 2E + 1 & E + 5 \\ E - 2 & 2 \end{bmatrix} \begin{bmatrix} b_1 \\ b_2 \end{bmatrix} + \begin{bmatrix} 5 \\ 7 \end{bmatrix} = \begin{bmatrix} 0 \\ 0 \end{bmatrix}$$

i.e., setting $E = 1$ since $P(E)b = bP(1)$

$$\begin{bmatrix} 0 & 6 \\ -1 & 2 \end{bmatrix} \begin{bmatrix} b_1 \\ b_2 \end{bmatrix} = - \begin{bmatrix} 5 \\ 7 \end{bmatrix}$$

that is,

$$6b_2 = -5$$

$$-b_1 + 2b_2 = -7.$$

Solving these equations we obtain $b_2 = -\frac{5}{6}$, $b_1 = \frac{32}{6}$

so that, by Proposition Five, the solution to our difference equation system is given by

$$y_{1t} = 2V_1 3^t + 2V_2 4^t + 32/6$$

$$y_{2t} = -V_1 3^t - 2V_2 4^t - 5/6.$$

The Arbitrary Constants and the Initial Conditions

Finally, to find V_1 and V_2 we take note of the initial conditions

$$y_{10} = 1 \quad \text{and} \quad y_{20} = 1.$$

Setting $t = 0$ in the first equation of our solution gives us together with the first of these initial conditions

$$1 = y_{10} = 2V_1 3^0 + 2V_2 4^0 + 32/6$$

or

$$1 = 2V_1 + 2V_2 + 32/6.$$

Similarly, setting $t = 0$ in the second equation gives us, together with the second initial condition

$$1 = -V_1 - 2V_2 - 5/6$$

and these two equations can be solved simultaneously for the values of V_1 and V_2

PROBLEMS

Re-solve the problems of Chapter Fifteen, Section 2, employing the methods of this section.

4. THEOREMS FOR QUALITATIVE ANALYSIS

It would, of course, be desirable to find methods which permit us to characterize the roots of the determinantal equation simply by looking at the simultaneous equation system as we did in the single equation case. For then we could, by inspection of the equations, draw qualitative conclusions about the nature of the time path of the variables.

A Class of Simple First-Order Systems

We shall see now that there is an important class of first-order systems—systems of the variety we encountered in the two sector multiplier analysis in Section 1 of Chapter Fifteen—for which such theorems can be developed. This indicates, incidentally, one of the reasons why it is desirable to have a method for converting higher order systems into first-order form as we learned to do in Section 3 of the preceding chapter.

The type of first-order system in question can be written

$$\left.\begin{array}{l} y_{1t+1} = a_{11}y_{1t} + a_{12}y_{2t} + \cdots + a_{1n}y_{nt} + k_1 \\ y_{2t+1} = a_{21}y_{1t} + a_{22}y_{2t} + \cdots + a_{2n}y_{nt} + k_2 \\ \dots\dots\dots\dots\dots\dots\dots\dots\dots\dots \\ y_{nt+1} = a_{n1}y_{1t} + a_{n2}y_{2t} + \cdots + a_{nn}y_{nt} + k_n \end{array}\right\}. \qquad (131)$$

It will be noted that each of these equations involves the value of only one variable in period $t+1$ and there is one equation to each of these variables. All other variables in the equations take on their values as of period t.[6]

[6] Most first-order equations can be rewritten in form (131) by treating them as n simultaneous linear equations in the variables $y_{1t+1}, y_{2t+1}, \cdots y_{nt+1}$ and solving for these variables. However, for such a system the theorems which follow do not permit qualitative conclusions to be drawn by direct inspection *until after it has been rewritten in form* (131).

The Characteristic Equation and the Roots

Subtracting the elements of column vector y_{t+1} from both sides of these equations (131) we obtain

$$
\begin{array}{llll}
a_{11}y_{1t} - y_{1t+1} + a_{12}y_{2t} & + \cdots + a_{1n}y_{nt} & & + k_1 = 0 \\
a_{21}y_{1t} \quad + a_{22}y_{2t} - y_{2t+1} & + \cdots + a_{2n}y_{nt} & & + k_2 = 0 \\
\cdots\cdots\cdots & \cdots\cdots\cdots & & \cdots \\
a_{n1}y_{1t} \quad + a_{n2}y_{2t} & + \cdots + a_{nn}y_{nt} & - y_{nt+1} & + k_n = 0.
\end{array}
$$

Hence we see that the determinantal (characteristic) equation of system (131) takes the relatively simple form

$$
|A(x)| \equiv \begin{vmatrix} a_{11} - x & a_{12} & \cdots & a_{1n} \\ a_{21} & a_{22} - x & \cdots & a_{2n} \\ \cdots & \cdots & \cdots & \cdots \\ a_{n1} & a_{n2} & \cdots & a_{nn} - x \end{vmatrix} = 0 \quad (132) \quad \text{e.g.,} \begin{vmatrix} 3-x & -2 \\ 1 & -x \end{vmatrix} = 0 \quad (132a)
$$

where the a_{ij}'s are the coefficients in our equations. The determinant on the left side of the equation which we represent by the symbol $|A(x)|$ is called the *characteristic determinant* of the system. It is to be noted that x appears only in the principal diagonal and always with the coefficient -1. The expanded form of this determinantal equation is of course a polynomial equation in x which we may write as [7]

$$x^n + R_1x^{n-1} + \cdots + R_{n-1}x + R_n = 0 \qquad (133)$$

$$x^2 - 3x + 2 = 0. \qquad (133a)$$

We now derive an important relation between R_1, R_n, and the roots of this polynomial equation:

PROPOSITION 6a: i) In the general n^{th} degree polynomial equation (133), R_1, the coefficient of x^{n-1} is equal to the sum of the roots

[7] Note that the first term of the polynomial form of (132) is $(-x)^n$ which is negative if n is an odd number. In that case we multiply both sides of (132) by -1 to get it into form (133).

multiplied by -1 and ii) R_n, the constant term in (133) is equal to the product of the roots multiplied by $(-1)^n$.

Proof: Let the roots of the characteristic equation be $x_1, x_2, \cdots, x_n$, where in the numerical case (133a) $x_1 = 2$, $x_2 = 1$. The factor theorem tells us that the general polynomial equation (133) can be rewritten as

$$(x - x_1)(x - x_2) \cdots (x - x_n) = x^n + R_1 x^{n-1} + \cdots + R_{n-1}x + R_n = 0,$$

or in the case of (133a)

$$(x - 2)(x - 1) = x^2 + R_1 x + R_2 = x^2 - 3x + 2 = 0.$$

Multiplying out the left-hand side and collecting terms we obtain

$$x^n - (x_1 + x_2 + \cdots + x_n)x^{n-1} + \cdots + (-x_1 \cdot -x_2 \cdot \cdots \cdot -x_n) = x^n + R_1 x^{n-1} + \cdots + R_n = 0$$

$$x^2 - (2 + 1)x + (-2 \cdot -1) = x^2 + R_1 x + R_2 = x^2 - 3x + 2 = 0.$$

Thus, we have

$$R_1 = -(x_1 + x_2 + \cdots + x_n) \text{ and } R_n = (-x_1 \cdot -x_2 \cdot \cdots \cdot -x_n) = (-1)^n (x_1 \cdot x_2 \cdot \cdots \cdot x_n).$$

In particular, in the numerical case (133a),

$$-3 = R_1 = -(x_1 + x_2) = -(2 + 1) \quad \text{and} \quad 2 = R_2 = -x_1 \cdot - x_2 = -2 \cdot -1 = (-1)^2(2)(1)$$

as we require.

In sum, it has been demonstrated that we can find the sum and the product of the roots of a determinantal equation such as (132) if we can evaluate the coefficients R_1 and R_n in the corresponding polynomial equation (133).

The Determinant, R_1 and R_n

We shall now show that

PROPOSITION 6b: i) R_1 in equation (133) is equal simply to minus the sum of the principal diagonal elements in the determinant $|A(0)|$ in (132) in which x is set equal to zero, i.e., $R_1 = -(a_{11} + a_{22} + \cdots + a_{nn})$, and ii) R_n in (133) is equal to the determinant $|A(0)|$ multiplied by $(-1)^n$, where n is the degree of the characteristic equation [and also the number of variables and equations in system (131)].

The expression $(a_{11} + a_{22} + \cdots + a_{nn})$, the sum of the diagonal elements, is called the *trace* of the matrix $A(0)$ whose determinant is obtained by setting $x = 0$ in (132).

To prove the proposition we first recall a theorem on determinants: Given a determinant any of whose columns (rows) is composed of elements which are the sum of two terms, that determinant can be rewritten as the sum of two other determinants in the manner represented by the following third order case: [8]

$$\begin{vmatrix} a_{11} & (a_{12}+b_{12}) & a_{13} \\ a_{21} & (a_{22}+b_{22}) & a_{23} \\ a_{31} & (a_{32}+b_{32}) & a_{33} \end{vmatrix} = \begin{vmatrix} a_{11} & a_{12} & a_{13} \\ a_{21} & a_{22} & a_{23} \\ a_{31} & a_{32} & a_{33} \end{vmatrix} + \begin{vmatrix} a_{11} & b_{12} & a_{13} \\ a_{21} & b_{22} & a_{23} \\ a_{31} & b_{32} & a_{33} \end{vmatrix}.$$

Continuing with the third-order case for expository simplicity, we may rewrite our characteristic equation $|A(x)| = 0$ as

$$\begin{vmatrix} a_{11} - x & a_{12} + 0 & a_{13} + 0 \\ a_{21} + 0 & a_{22} - x & a_{23} + 0 \\ a_{31} + 0 & a_{32} + 0 & a_{33} - x \end{vmatrix} = 0$$

so by successive application of the preceding theorem on the sums of determinants we see this can be rewritten

$$\begin{vmatrix} -x & a_{12} + 0 & a_{13} + 0 \\ 0 & a_{22} - x & a_{23} + 0 \\ 0 & a_{32} + 0 & a_{33} - x \end{vmatrix} + \begin{vmatrix} a_{11} & a_{12} + 0 & a_{13} + 0 \\ a_{21} & a_{22} - x & a_{23} + 0 \\ a_{31} & a_{32} + 0 & a_{33} - x \end{vmatrix} = 0$$

[8] *Proof.* Expanding the left hand determinant in terms of the cofactors A_{i2} of the elements of the second column we have

$(a_{12} + b_{12})A_{12} + (a_{22} + b_{22})A_{22} + (a_{32} + b_{32})A_{32} = (a_{12}A_{12} + a_{22}A_{22} + a_{32}A_{32}) + (b_{12}A_{12} + b_{22}A_{22} + b_{32}A_{32})$ where the items in the first and second brackets are, respectively, the expansion of the first and second determinants on the right. This proof is perfectly general and does not depend on the fact that our illustrative determinant is of third order.

$$= \begin{vmatrix} -x & 0 & a_{13}+0 \\ 0 & -x & a_{23}+0 \\ 0 & 0 & a_{33}-x \end{vmatrix} + \begin{vmatrix} -x & a_{12} & a_{13}+0 \\ 0 & a_{22} & a_{23}+0 \\ 0 & a_{32} & a_{33}-x \end{vmatrix} + \begin{vmatrix} a_{11} & 0 & a_{13}+0 \\ a_{21} & -x & a_{23}+0 \\ a_{31} & 0 & a_{33}-x \end{vmatrix}$$

$$+ \begin{vmatrix} a_{11} & a_{12} & a_{13}+0 \\ a_{21} & a_{22} & a_{23}+0 \\ a_{31} & a_{32} & a_{33}-x \end{vmatrix}$$

$$= \begin{vmatrix} -x & 0 & 0 \\ 0 & -x & 0 \\ 0 & 0 & -x \end{vmatrix} + \begin{vmatrix} -x & 0 & a_{13} \\ 0 & -x & a_{23} \\ 0 & 0 & a_{33} \end{vmatrix} + \begin{vmatrix} -x & a_{12} & 0 \\ 0 & a_{22} & 0 \\ 0 & a_{32} & -x \end{vmatrix}$$

$$+ \begin{vmatrix} a_{11} & 0 & 0 \\ a_{21} & -x & 0 \\ a_{31} & 0 & -x \end{vmatrix} + \begin{vmatrix} -x & a_{12} & a_{13} \\ 0 & a_{22} & a_{23} \\ 0 & a_{32} & a_{33} \end{vmatrix} + \begin{vmatrix} a_{11} & 0 & a_{13} \\ a_{21} & -x & a_{23} \\ a_{31} & 0 & a_{33} \end{vmatrix}$$

$$+ \begin{vmatrix} a_{11} & a_{12} & 0 \\ a_{21} & a_{22} & 0 \\ a_{31} & a_{32} & -x \end{vmatrix} + \begin{vmatrix} a_{11} & a_{12} & a_{13} \\ a_{21} & a_{22} & a_{23} \\ a_{31} & a_{32} & a_{33} \end{vmatrix}$$

$$= (-x)^3 + (-x)^2 a_{33} + (-x)^2 a_{22} + (-x)^2 a_{11} - x \begin{vmatrix} a_{22} & a_{23} \\ a_{32} & a_{33} \end{vmatrix}$$

$$-x \begin{vmatrix} a_{11} & a_{13} \\ a_{31} & a_{33} \end{vmatrix} - x \begin{vmatrix} a_{11} & a_{12} \\ a_{21} & a_{22} \end{vmatrix} + \begin{vmatrix} a_{11} & a_{12} & a_{13} \\ a_{21} & a_{22} & a_{23} \\ a_{31} & a_{32} & a_{33} \end{vmatrix}$$

$$= (-x)^3 + x^2(a_{11} + a_{22} + a_{33}) - x \left(\begin{vmatrix} a_{22} & a_{23} \\ a_{32} & a_{33} \end{vmatrix} + \begin{vmatrix} a_{11} & a_{13} \\ a_{31} & a_{33} \end{vmatrix} + \right.$$

$$\left. \begin{vmatrix} a_{11} & a_{12} \\ a_{21} & a_{22} \end{vmatrix} \right) + \begin{vmatrix} a_{11} & a_{12} & a_{13} \\ a_{21} & a_{22} & a_{23} \\ a_{31} & a_{32} & a_{33} \end{vmatrix} \qquad (134)$$

Multiplying through by $(-1)^3$ this equation is put into the same form as (133)

$$x^3 - x^2(a_{11} + a_{22} + a_{33}) + \cdots + (-1)^3 \begin{vmatrix} a_{11} & a_{12} & a_{13} \\ a_{21} & a_{22} & a_{23} \\ a_{31} & a_{32} & a_{33} \end{vmatrix} = 0$$

and we see at once that

$$R_1 = -(a_{11} + a_{22} + a_{33}) \quad \text{and} \quad R_3 = (-1)^3 \mid A(0) \mid$$

which is the assertion of Proposition 6b.[9]

The Roots and the Determinant

We may now compare this result with that of Proposition 6a and sum up by noting that we have proved that $-R_1$ in (133) is equal both to the trace of the matrix $A(0)$ and to the sum of the roots of the characteristic equation. Similarly, we have proved that $(-1)^n R_n$ is equal both to the determinant $\mid A(0) \mid$ and to the product of the roots of the characteristic equation. Hence we have demonstrated

PROPOSITION SIX: i) The sum of the roots of the characteristic equation of a system of first-order simultaneous difference (differential) equations of form (131) is equal to the trace of the characteristic matrix of the system (with x set equal to zero), and ii) the product of the roots is equal to the determinant of the system (with $x = 0$).

Theorems on Complex Roots

We are now almost ready to formulate several specific theorems on qualitative analysis. But first we must list several properties of the complex roots (if there are any) of the characteristic equation.

i. It will be recalled that such roots always come in conjugate pairs $c + di$ and $c - di$.

ii. The sum of such a pair of complex roots is the real number $2c$. For this sum is $c + di + c - di = 2c + di - di = 2c$.

iii. By direct multiplication we see that the product of such a pair of roots is the real number $c^2 - i^2d^2 = c^2 + d^2 \geqq 0$.

[9] For the third-order case we could of course have obtained our result directly simply by expanding our determinant $\mid A(x) \mid$, but then the argument would not have been applicable to higher order cases. As it stands the reader can generalize the argument simply by substituting n for 3 throughout and inserting dots to indicate omissions at the appropriate points.

iv. The modulus (absolute value) of such a pair of roots is, by definition, $\sqrt{c^2 + d^2}$.

v. Hence if two conjugate complex roots are less than unity in absolute value their product, $c^2 + d^2$ must be less than unity, and the *sum* of these *two* roots $2c$, must be a real number whose absolute value is less than 2, since if the absolute value of $2c \geqq 2$, then that of $c \geqq 1$ and the absolute value of the roots $\sqrt{c^2 + d^2}$ will be no less than $\sqrt{1^2 + d^2} \geqq 1$.

Three Theorems for Qualitative Analysis

At last we arrive at our theorems on qualitative analysis. For our first theorem we recall that stability requires that *each* of the roots be less than unity in absolute value. Suppose that our equation has R real roots and $2K$ complex roots which occur in conjugate pairs. Since each of the R real roots is less than unity, their sum must be less than R (in absolute value). And by observation v. on complex roots above, the modulus (absolute value) of each pair of the K pairs of conjugate complex roots must sum to less than 2 so that the sum of these $2K$ roots must be less than $2K$ and greater than $-2K$. Hence the sum of all of these $R + 2K$ roots must have an absolute value less than $R + 2K$. We have thus derived:

PROPOSITION SEVEN: If system (131) is stable, the absolute value of the trace of the matrix, which by Proposition Six part i is equal to the absolute value of the sum of the roots, must be less than n, the degree of equation (133).

Direct inspection of determinant (132) indicates that n is also the number of equations in the system.

Similarly, we have

PROPOSITION EIGHT: If system (131) is stable, the characteristic determinant with x set equal to zero (which by Proposition Six, part ii is equal to the product of the roots) must be less than unity in absolute value.

To derive this proposition we note that if one multiplies together several numbers each of which is less than unity in absolute value, then the product must also be less than unity in absolute value.

Since each real root in a stable system is less than unity in absolute value, and since by observation v. on complex roots the product of a pair of complex conjugate roots in a stable system is less than unity in absolute value it follows that by multiplying all of these roots together we must obtain a product of less than unit absolute value.

We derive yet another theorem on stability which is particularly important for the correspondence principle (Section 6 below). First we note that the highest degree term of the expanded form of the characteristic determinant (132) as shown in (134) above, is $(-x)^n$. Let us see what happens to the value of the determinant if x is assigned larger and larger values, i.e, as x approaches infinity. Eventually when x has grown sufficiently great all the other terms in (134) must become insignificant in comparison with $(-x)^n$ so that the value of the determinant must then have the same sign as does $(-x)^n$: it must be positive if n is even and negative if n is odd.

Similarly, as x is given larger and larger (in absolute value) negative values, that is, as x approaches "minus infinity" the determinant in (132) will again take on the sign of $(-x)^n$ but this time $(-x)^n$ must always be positive since x is negative so that $-x$ must be positive.

Now if the system is to be stable its characteristic equation must have no root greater than unity in absolute value so that it must have no real root between $x = +1$ and $x = +\infty$. Nor must it have a real root between $x = -1$ and $x = -\infty$. Hence (see Section 4 of Chapter Twelve) the characteristic determinant cannot change sign between $x = 1$ and $x = \infty$ or between $x = -1$ and $x = -\infty$. Thus at $x = 1$ it must have the same sign as it does at $+\infty$ [that of $(-x)^n$] and at $x = -1$ it must have the same sign as at $-\infty$ (i.e., it must be positive). In other words:

PROPOSITION NINE: If the system (131) is stable then

i) at $x = 1$ the characteristic determinant,

$$|A(1)| = \begin{vmatrix} a_{11}-1 & a_{12} & \cdots & a_{1n} \\ a_{21} & a_{22}-1 & \cdots & a_{2n} \\ \cdots & \cdots & \cdots & \cdots \\ a_{n1} & a_{n2} & \cdots & a_{nn}-1 \end{vmatrix}$$

must be positive if n is even, negative if n is odd.

ii) Similarly, when $x = -1$ the characteristic determinant

$$\begin{vmatrix} a_{11}+1 & a_{12} & \cdots & a_{1n} \\ a_{21} & a_{22}+1 & \cdots & a_{2n} \\ \cdots & \cdots & \cdots & \cdots \\ a_{n1} & a_{n2} & \cdots & a_{nn}+1 \end{vmatrix}$$ must be positive.

Insufficiency of the Stability Conditions

It must be emphasized that Propositions Seven, Eight, and Nine are only *necessary* conditions for stability. They are not *sufficient* to guarantee stability. That is, if a system *fails* to meet *any one* of the tests [if the trace is greater than n or the determinant is greater than unity in absolute value or the sign of $|A(1)|$ is not the same as that of $(-1)^n$] we can be sure the system is *unstable.* But we can never be sure of the stability of another system which passes all three tests.

For example, consider the unstable third order system whose roots are 1.2, 1.1, and 0.2. The absolute value of the trace (the sum of the roots) is $2.5 < 3 = n$, and the absolute value of the determinant (the product of the roots) is $0.264 < 1$. Finally, it can be shown that these roots require the system to satisfy the stability conditions of Proposition Nine.[10] Hence the system passes all three of our tests but it is nevertheless unstable because it has the explosive roots 1.1 and 1.2. In sum, Propositions Seven, Eight, and Nine provide tests of stability which may be compared with a sieve whose holes are too large. What passes through may not always be as pure as desired (unstable systems may sometimes pass the test). But we can be sure that everything which is caught by the sieve is an impurity (*only* unstable systems will fail to pass the tests).

Unfortunately, there is no simple (necessary and sufficient) test which will separate perfectly the stable from the unstable systems.

[10] *Proof.* Given these values of the three roots, by the factor theorem of algebra and (133) the determinant (132) must equal $|A(x)| = -x^3 + R_1x^2 - R_2x + R_3 = -(x-1.2)(x-1.1)(x-0.2)$. For $x = +1$ this equals $-(-0.2)(-0.1)(0.8)$ which is negative as part i of Proposition Nine requires. For $x = -1$, we have $|A(-1)| = -(-2.2)(-2.1)(-1.2)$ which is positive as part ii of Proposition Nine demands for stability.

The only sure test known is to compute all of the coefficients ($R_1, R_2, \cdots, R_n$) of the characteristic equation (133) and then to employ the test determinants of Chapter Twelve, Section 6, or in the differential equation case, those of Chapter Fourteen, Section 7.

A Theorem on Fluctuations

We may list one more qualitative theorem for difference equations: Since both the sum and the product of several positive numbers are positive, with the aid of Proposition Six we conclude

PROPOSITION TEN: If either the trace or the determinant of the system is negative or zero, the system must have some negative roots and/or some complex roots.

It follows that the values of the variables of such a system may very well oscillate, although even this is not certain.[11] For in such a system the root of largest absolute value may still be positive, and some initial conditions will permit this root to dominate the others from the very beginning.

Stability in Differential Equation Systems

Finally, we derive two qualitative theorems for differential equations. It will be recalled that such systems will be stable if and only if the real parts of all of the roots are negative.

Consider a first-order differential squation system of the form

$$\left.\begin{array}{l} \dfrac{dy_1}{dt} = a_{11}y_1 + a_{12}y_2 + \cdots + a_{1n}y_n + k_1 \\ \cdots\cdots\cdots\cdots\cdots\cdots\cdots\cdots\cdots\cdots \\ \dfrac{dy_n}{dt} = a_{n1}y_1 + a_{n2}y_2 + \cdots + a_{nn}y_n + k_n. \end{array}\right\} \qquad (135)$$

This system will clearly also have the characteristic equation (132) [compare system (135) with (131)]. Observation ii on complex

[11] However, we can be sure that appropriate initial conditions can make such a system oscillate at least for a time, by giving sufficiently large coefficients to the negative or complex root terms in the solutions.

roots tells us that if we add two conjugate complex roots whose real part, c, is negative, the sum $2c$ will also be negative. Therefore the sum of such complex roots must be negative, and if we add to it all the real roots (which must each be negative in the case of a stable differential equation system) we see that this grand total of all the roots must also be negative. Hence (since the sum of the roots is the trace of the characteristic matrix):

PROPOSITION ELEVEN: The sum of the roots of a stable differential equation system of type (135) must be negative, i.e., the matrix of the system must have a negative trace.

It also follows by a slightly more tedious argument that the determinant of such a system (the product of the roots) will have the same sign as $(-1)^n$, i.e., it will be negative if n is odd and positive if n is even. To see why this is so we first note again that complex roots come in pairs and (by observation iii on complex roots) the product of such a pair is always positive so that the product of all of the complex roots must always be positive. But stability requires that all of the real roots be negative. Now consider the following two cases. a) If the equation has an odd number of roots, since it has only negative and complex roots and there is always an even number of complex roots there must be an odd number of negative roots. But the product of an odd number of negative numbers is always negative so that the product of all of the roots of the equation [the determinant $|A(0)|$] will equal the positive product of the complex roots multiplied by the negative product of the odd number of negative roots. Hence $|A(0)|$ will be negative. Case b) On the other hand if the total number of roots of the characteristic equation of a stable system is even the number of negative roots must be even and their product must be positive. This proves

PROPOSITION TWELVE: The sign of the determinant of a stable differential equation system of type (135) is equal to $(-1)^n$ where n is the number of equations in the system.

This proposition can also be derived by the method employed to arrive at Proposition Nine.

PROBLEMS

1. What do Propositions Seven to Twelve tell us about the following systems?

   a) $y_{1t+1} = -2y_{1t} + y_{2t}$
   $y_{2t+1} = 1.5y_{1t} - y_{2t}$

   b) $y_{1t+1} = 0.9y_{1t} - 0.8y_{2t}$
   $y_{2t+1} = 0.8y_{1t} + 0.9y_{2t}$

   c) $y_{1t+1} = y_{1t} + \frac{1}{2}y_{2t}$
   $y_{2t+1} = \frac{1}{2}y_{1t} + y_{2t}$

   d) $\frac{dy_1}{dt} = 2y_1 + 4y_2$

   $\frac{dy_2}{dt} = y_1 + y_2.$

2. Explain why Propositions Seven to Twelve give us no certain information about

   a) $y_{1t+1} = 0.2y_{1t} + 0.3y_{2t}$
   $y_{2t+1} = 0.1y_{1t} + 0.4y_{2t}$

   b) $\frac{dy_1}{dt} = -y_1 - y_2$

   $\frac{dy_2}{dt} = y_1 - 2y_2.$

5. *FIRST-ORDER SYSTEMS WITH NONNEGATIVE COEFFICIENTS*

Solution by Matrix Multiplication

The homogeneous (reduced) system of our simple first-order system (131) may be rewritten in compact matrix notation as

$$y_{t+1} = Ay_t \quad \text{with initial conditions} \quad y_0 = C_0 \tag{136}$$

where A is an nth order square matrix and all of the other symbols represent n element column vectors.

(136) may be solved directly by matrix multiplication by noting that

$$y_1 = Ay_0, \quad y_2 = Ay_1 = A(Ay_0) = A^2y_0, \cdots, y_t = A^ty_0 \quad (137)$$

where A^t is the tth power of matrix A.

Stability in Systems with Nonnegative Coefficients

We suppose now that none of the coefficients in system (136) is negative (though some may be zero).

Let us now define $\text{norm}_j(A)$ of a matrix A as the sum of the elements in the jth column of A, and let us call *the largest of these column sums the norm(A) of matrix A*. We have the following theorem which has several important economic applications:

PROPOSITION THIRTEEN: Let all of the elements of matrix A in a system like (136) be nonnegative. Then, case a: if the norm of $A \leqq 1$ the system cannot explode (though its roots of largest absolute value can have absolute value unity); case b: if the norm of $A < 1$ the system must be stable.

Note that, unlike the preceding propositions, this provides a sufficient but not a necessary condition for stability.

The proof is rather long and we proceed in a number of steps.

i. If all of the elements of two nth order square matrices A and B are nonnegative all of the elements of the product $C = AB$ will be nonnegative since by the rule for matrix multiplication the element in the ith row and kth column of the product matrix, C, will be of the form

$$c_{ik} = \sum_{j=1}^{n} a_{ij}b_{jk}$$

which is nonnegative since it is a sum of nonnegative terms.

ii. Hence all of the elements of $A^2 = A \cdot A$ will be nonnegative; all of the elements of $A^3 = A^2 \cdot A$ will be nonnegative, etc., i.e., all of the elements of A^t in the solution (137) will be nonnegative.

iii. If the system (136) is explosive the solution (137) must tend to $+\infty$ or to $-\infty$. This means that some of the elements in the matrix A^t must increase without limit as t grows larger and larger.

iv. Similarly, if the system is stable, y_t converges toward its (zero) equilibrium value and *each* of the elements of A^t must also tend to zero. For by ii each of the elements of A^t must be nonnegative and hence the solution (137) must consist of sums of positive terms with the elements of A^t as coefficients so that the solution will tend to zero as t increases only if these elements tend to zero also.

v. If (136) is explosive, as t becomes very large a number of the elements of A^t also grow very large as we saw in iii. Some of these large elements must certainly be greater than unity, so that norm (A^t) must exceed unity since some of this matrix's column sums will be the total of such greater than unit elements plus some other nonnegative elements.

vi. On the other hand, if the norm of A^t approaches zero, *all* of the elements of A^t must approach zero, so that y_t in (137) must approach zero and the system will be stable.

vii. If the norms of two nth order square matrices A and B with nonnegative elements are both less than or equal to unity, then the norm of the product matrix $C = AB$ must be less than or equal to unity, and the norm of C will be less than or equal to the product of the norms of A and B.

We give the proof only for the second order case which is readily generalized. Here the product $AB = C$ is

$$\begin{bmatrix} a_{11} & a_{12} \\ a_{21} & a_{22} \end{bmatrix} \begin{bmatrix} b_{11} & b_{12} \\ b_{21} & b_{22} \end{bmatrix} = \begin{bmatrix} a_{11}b_{11} + a_{12}b_{21} & a_{11}b_{12} + a_{12}b_{22} \\ a_{21}b_{11} + a_{22}b_{21} & a_{21}b_{12} + a_{22}b_{22} \end{bmatrix}$$

$$= \begin{bmatrix} c_{11} & c_{12} \\ c_{21} & c_{22} \end{bmatrix}.$$

Now consider the norm of any column (e.g., the first column) of the product matrix C,

$$\begin{aligned} \text{norm}_1(C) &= c_{11} + c_{21} = a_{11}b_{11} + a_{12}b_{21} + a_{21}b_{11} + a_{22}b_{21} \\ &= (a_{11} + a_{21})b_{11} + (a_{12} + a_{22})b_{21} \\ &= \text{norm}_1(A)b_{11} + \text{norm}_2(A)b_{21} \end{aligned}$$

$$\leqq \text{norm}(A)(b_{11} + b_{21}) = \text{norm}(A)\ \text{norm}_1\ (B)$$
$$\leqq \text{norm}(A)\text{norm}(B)$$
$$\leqq 1$$ since the norms of both A and B are each less than unity.

viii. If the norm of A is less than or equal to unity, by vii the norm of $A^2 = A \cdot A$ is less than or equal to unity, that of $A^3 = A^2 \cdot A$ must be less than or equal to unity, etc. Hence if norm(A) is less than unity the norm of A^t must be less than or equal to unity and by v the system cannot be explosive.

ix. If the norm of $A = r < 1$, then by vii norm$(A^2) \leqq r^2$, norm $(A^3) \leqq$ norm$(A^2) \cdot$ norm$A \leqq r^3$, etc., so that norm$(A^t) \leqq r^t$ which approaches zero as t grows larger and larger. Therefore, by vi the system will be stable.

Proposition Thirteen now follows at once from steps viii and ix.

Application: A Dynamized Leontief System

Consider the standard two industry illustration of the Leontief system[12] in which coal is taken to be produced for use by consumers as well as for use in manufacturing by steel producers and by the coal manufacturers themselves. Similarly, steel is assumed to be used by consumers and in the production of coal mining and steel making equipment. This interdependence is the central feature of the Leontief input-output analysis.

Suppose now that raw materials are used strictly in proportion to outputs. Let S_t be the steel output in period t, C_t the coal output in period t and let D_s and D_c, respectively, be the consumer demand per period for steel and coal, all measured in dollars. Moreover, let a_{ss} be the proportion of every dollar's worth of steel output used up in the steel manufacturing process, let a_{sc} be the amount of steel used up in producing a dollar's worth of coal, etc. Then e.g., the coal

[12] Cf. Wassily Leontief, *Studies in the Structure of the American Economy* (Oxford University Press, New York, 1953), Chapter 3, and Robert Dorfman, Paul A. Samuelson, and Robert Solow, *Linear Programming and Economic Analysis* (McGraw-Hill, New York, 1957), Chapter 11.

industry's demand for steel during period t is equal to the steel demand per dollar of coal output multiplied by the number of dollars worth of coal which is produced, i.e., it is $a_{sc}C_t$. And the total demand for steel which is the sum of the steel industry, the coal industry, and the consumer demand for steel is $a_{ss}S_t + a_{sc}C_t + D_s$. There is also a similar expression for the total demand for coal.

Suppose now that there is a one period delay between the time such a demand is expressed and the time the manufacturers can meet it. Then we will have the two relationships

$$\left.\begin{aligned} S_{t+1} &= a_{ss}S_t + a_{sc}C_t + D_s \text{ (steel supply = previous period's steel demand)} \\ C_{t+1} &= a_{cs}S_t + a_{cc}C_t + D_c \text{ (coal supply = previous period's coal demand).} \end{aligned}\right\} \quad (138)$$

This is a pair of first-order linear difference equations of type (131), all of whose elements are nonnegative. The generalization to an n industry n equation dynamic input-output model should be obvious.

Now let us interpret economically the column sums of the matrix of this system. For example, the first column sum, $a_{ss} + a_{cs}$ represents the value of the raw materials (the steel and the coal) needed to produce an amount of steel which sells for one dollar. Note that labor cost is not included. If such an industry is run at a profit it follows that this column sum must be less than unity since it must cost less than a dollar to produce one dollar's worth of steel. For the same reason, if coal production is profitable, the second column sum must be less than unity. In other words the norm of the matrix must be less than unity and by Proposition Thirteen this simplified Leontief model must be stable.

This result has, incidentally, been used in computing, or rather, approximating the equilibrium values of the outputs S_t, C_t, etc. (the outputs which satisfy the technological requirements of the system). For if A is the matrix of the system, since it is stable, we know that with any initial values of the output vector Q_t (the column vector of the elements S_t, C_t) the product A^tQ_0 will provide an approximation to these equilibrium values if t is sufficiently large.

Illustration: Markov Chains [13]

Another illustration is provided by Probability Theory. For concreteness we employ a third order version of Professor Lazarsfeld's application to political problems. Suppose there are only three parties, Democrats, Republicans, and Vegetarians and that there are no undecided voters. Let D_t,R_t, and V_t, respectively, represent the number of Democrats, Republicans, and Vegetarians during period t. Let P_{dd} represent the (by assumption, fixed) probability that a man who is a Democrat during period t will remain with the party during $t+1$, let P_{rd} represent the probability that he will switch to the Republican side, etc. Then we have the first-order linear difference equations of type (131) whose coefficients are nonnegative (since they are probabilities):

$$D_{t+1} = P_{dd}D_t + P_{dr}R_t + P_{dv}V_t$$

$$R_{t+1} = P_{rd}D_t + P_{rr}R_t + P_{rv}V_t$$

$$V_{t+1} = P_{vd}D_t + P_{vr}R_t + P_{vv}V_t.$$

Such a system in which there is a sequence of trials (elections, polls), a fixed set of possible outcomes, and in which, for any outcome during one period (e.g., x was a Democrat) there is a (not necessarily fixed) conditional probability of each specific outcome during the next period (x will turn Republican) is called a Markov chain.

We now note that for such a system the norm is always equal to unity. For, e.g., the column sum $P_{dd} + P_{rd} + P_{vd}$ represents the sum of the probability that x will remain a Democrat, the probability that he will become a Republican and the probability that he will turn Vegetarian. Since we have assumed that there are no other possibilities one and only one of these outcomes is certain to occur, so that

[13] See William Feller, *An Introduction to Probability Theory and Its Applications*, Vol. I (John Wiley, New York, 1951), Chapters 15 and 16. For the application discussed here see T. W. Anderson, "Probability Models for Analyzing Time Changes and Attitudes," in P. F. Lazarsfeld, ed., *Mathematical Thinking in the Social Sciences*, pp. 17–66 (The Free Press, Glencoe, Illinois, 1955) and R. R. Bush and Frederick Mosteller, *Stochastic Models for Learning*, Chaps. 3, 5 (John Wiley, New York, 1955).

the sum of these probabilities, i.e., every column sum and hence the norm must be equal to unity.

By Proposition Thirteen we see that such a system cannot explode. However, we are led to suspect that the homogeneous Markov chain system difference equation system will not converge toward zero because its *norm is not less than unity.* In fact this turns out to be the case. A Markov chain system always has at least one unit root.[14]

PROBLEM

Apply Proposition Thirteen to problem 2a of Section 4, above.

6. A DIFFERENTIAL EQUATION CASE: THE CORRESPONDENCE PRINCIPLE

The Correspondence Principle

This section has two purposes: to illustrate the application of the materials of this chapter to differential equation systems, and to

[14] *Proof.* The determinantal equation of the system is

$$|P(x)| = \begin{vmatrix} P_{dd} - x & P_{dr} & P_{dv} \\ P_{rd} & P_{rr} - x & P_{rv} \\ P_{vd} & P_{vr} & P_{vv} - x \end{vmatrix} = 0.$$

It will be recalled that the value of a determinant is not changed by adding one or more of its rows to any other row. We can therefore, without changing the the value of the determinant add the elements of the second and third rows to the elements of the first, to obtain

$$|P(x)| = \begin{vmatrix} P_{dd} + P_{rd} + P_{vd} - x & P_{dr} + P_{rr} + P_{vr} - x & P_{dv} + P_{rv} + P_{vv} - x \\ P_{rd} & P_{rr} - x & P_{rv} \\ P_{vd} & P_{vr} & P_{vv} - x \end{vmatrix}$$

or, since the column sums of the original determinant are all equal to unity, we have $P_{dd} + P_{rd} + P_{vd} = P_{dr} + P_{rr} + P_{vr} = P_{dv} + P_{rv} + P_{vv} = 1$. Hence

$$|P(x)| = \begin{vmatrix} 1 - x & 1 - x & 1 - x \\ P_{rd} & P_{rr} - x & P_{rv} \\ P_{vd} & P_{vr} & P_{vv} - x \end{vmatrix}$$

so that for $x = 1$ we have

$$|P(1)| = \begin{vmatrix} 0 & 0 & 0 \\ P_{rd} & P_{rr} - 1 & P_{rv} \\ P_{vd} & P_{vr} & P_{vv} - 1 \end{vmatrix} = 0.$$

We have thus proved that $+1$ is a root of the characteristic equation of a Markov chain system $|P(x)| = 0$. Again the generalization to an n equation case should be obvious.

explain somewhat further Samuelson's correspondence principle [15] which was discussed briefly in the last section of Chapter Seven. It should be emphasized, however, that the correspondence principle has also been applied to difference equation systems.

The correspondence principle states that given a linear static system (or a linear approximation to a nonlinear static system) we can find out something about the comparative static behavior of the system (the effects of a change in the structure of the system on the *equilibrium* values of its variables) by assuming that it is stable.

Illustration: The Leontief System Again

To illustrate how this works we consider the input-output system which was described in the previous section, *but we drop the economic assumptions about the coefficients which permitted us to prove its stability.* Let us now ask the following comparative statics question: when the demand for coal rises, what will be the effect on the equilibrium steel output, i.e., what will be the sign of the partial derivative $\partial S/\partial D_c$? The obvious guess is of course that direct and indirect steel use in coal mining will rise when the demand for coal increases, and we may prefer to assume this directly.[16] But we may, on the other hand, prefer the roundabout route of the correspondence principle in which we assume instead that we know the full structure of the dynamic system and assume also that it is stable and see what these assumptions imply about the sign of $\partial S/\partial D_c$. Let us see how the second method works.

[15] See Paul A. Samuelson, *Foundations of Economic Analysis* (Harvard University Press, Cambridge, Mass., 1947), Chapter IX.

[16] In fact the correspondence principle can also be used the other way. We can assume that $\partial S/\partial D_c > 0$ and see what this implies about the stability of the corresponding dynamic systems. However, here Propositions Seven, Eight, Nine, Eleven, and Twelve are not directly helpful since they are necessary but not sufficient conditions for stability.

Note that our comparative statics question is not just a simple matter of the sign of a_{sc} since an increase in coal demand also affects the required steel output *indirectly* by changing the coal industry demands for other outputs which use steel.

First, we must write out the equations of the static input-output system:

$$\left.\begin{array}{ll} S = a_{ss}S + a_{sc}C + D_s & \text{i.e.,} - D_s = (a_{ss}-1)S + a_{sc}C \\ C = a_{cs}S + a_{cc}C + D_c & \quad -D_c = a_{cs}S + (a_{cc}-1)C. \end{array}\right\} \quad (139)$$

This system of two linear equations in the variables S and C may be solved by Cramer's Rule for the values of S and C in terms of D_s and D_c.[17] Thus for S we obtain, writing $|A - I|$ for the determinant of

the system, $\begin{vmatrix} a_{ss}-1 & a_{sc} \\ a_{cs} & a_{cc}-1 \end{vmatrix}$,

$$S = \frac{\begin{vmatrix} -D_s & a_{sc} \\ -D_c & a_{cc}-1 \end{vmatrix}}{|A - I|} = \frac{-(a_{cc}-1)D_s + a_{sc}D_c}{|A - I|}.$$

Differentiating this expression with respect to D_c we obtain

$$\frac{\partial S}{\partial D_c} = \frac{a_{sc}}{|A - I|}. \quad (140)$$

By assumption some steel is used in coal production so that a_{sc}, the demand for steel per dollar's worth of coal output, will be positive. Hence, to determine the sign of the derivative we require a method of finding the sign of the determinant $|A - I|$.

The Dynamic System

Here the dynamic system and the assumption of stability enter the investigation. First, for pedagogic purposes, we formulate instead of our difference equation dynamic Leontief system, (138), a differential equation model. To do this we assume that steel outputs and coal outputs rise more rapidly the larger is the unsatisfied demand for them and that the rate of increase in output is strictly propor-

[17] Here we must assume that the determinant of the system, which appears in the denominator of the (following) expression for S is not equal to zero. The premise that the system is stable is again helpful here, for by Proposition Nine, in a stable system this determinant can never be zero.

tional to the magnitude of the unsatisfied demand (is it plausible that this is usually approximately true?) Thus, using the standard notation for time derivatives $\dot{S} \equiv \frac{dS}{dt}$, $\dot{C} \equiv \frac{dC}{dt}$

$$\left.\begin{aligned} \dot{S} &= V\,(\text{Demand for steel} - \text{supply of steel}) \\ &= V(a_{ss}S + a_{sc}C + D_s - S) \\ &\text{and} \\ \dot{C} &= W(a_{cs}S + a_{cc}C + D_c - C) \end{aligned}\right\} \qquad (141)$$

where V and W are two *positive* constants. That is,

$$V(a_{ss}-1)S - \dot{S} + Va_{sc}C + VD_s = 0$$

$$Wa_{cs}S + W(a_{cc}-1)C - \dot{C} + VD_c = 0.$$

This can be rewritten in operator matrix notation with the aid of the differential operator, D, where it will be recalled that, e.g., $DS \equiv \frac{dS}{dt} \equiv \dot{S}$.

We obtain

$$\begin{bmatrix} V(a_{ss}-1) - D & Va_{sc} \\ Wa_{cs} & W(a_{cc}-1) - D \end{bmatrix} \begin{bmatrix} S \\ C \end{bmatrix} + V \begin{bmatrix} D_s \\ D_c \end{bmatrix} = \begin{bmatrix} 0 \\ 0 \end{bmatrix}.$$

The characteristic equation of the reduced equations of this system is

$$|R(x)| = \begin{vmatrix} V(a_{ss}-1) - x & Va_{sc} \\ Wa_{cs} & W(a_{cc}-1) - x \end{vmatrix} = 0.$$

For $x = 0$ we obtain

$$|R(0)| = \begin{vmatrix} V(a_{ss} - 1) & Va_{sc} \\ Wa_{cs} & W(a_{cc} - 1) \end{vmatrix} = VW \begin{vmatrix} a_{ss} - 1 & a_{sc} \\ a_{cs} & a_{cc} - 1 \end{vmatrix}$$

$$= VW\,|A - I|.$$

Here, it will be recalled, $|A - I|$ is the determinant of our static input-output system (139).

The Stability Assumption

We assume now that the dynamic differential equation system is stable. By Proposition Twelve above, since this is a second-order system, it follows that the sign of the characteristic determinant with $x = 0$ must be that of $(-1)^2 > 0$, i.e., $|R(0)|$ must be positive. But, by assumption, V and W are also positive. Therefore, $|A - I|$ must be positive as well. We may then return to our expression (140) to conclude that since both the numerator and the denominator are positive, $\partial S/\partial D_c > 0$, i.e., a rise in coal demand must lead to an increase in steel output, as we had expected all along. (Note, incidentally, that on the usual economic assumptions about its coefficients the Leontief system *must* be stable, so that this comparative statics result *necessarily* follows.)

Correspondence Principle: Summary

The correspondence principle then usually employs the following basic steps.

a. We formulate a static linear system and solve it for the (stationary equilibrium) values of the variables.

b. To examine the comparative statics question of the effects (direction) of changes in the values of the parameters (roughly, the "constants") of the system, we take the relationships obtained in step a. for the values of the dependent variables and differentiate them with respect to the values of the parameters. We then try to determine the signs of these derivatives.

c. Both the expression for the value of the variable in step a. and that for its derivative in step b. will usually contain several terms including among them the determinant of the system. About several of these terms we will usually have some information, particularly, information about their signs derived from the construction of the system. We will ordinarily not know in advance the sign of the determinant of the system. If this is the only term about which such information is lacking (sometimes, unfortunately, the signs of other terms will also not be known) we can use the correspondence principle to obtain this missing piece of information.

d. To find the sign of this determinant form the dynamic system which is related to the linear system in precisely the same ways as the dynamic differential or the difference equation Leontief systems (141) or (138) are related to the static input-output system (139), above.

e. Now apply Proposition Twelve in the differential equation case or Proposition Nine if we have employed a difference equation system. Sometimes, if more than the sign of the determinant of the system is unknown, Propositions Seven, Eight, Eleven, and Thirteen can also supply some of the required information.

PROBLEMS

1. Derive our result about the sign of $\partial S/\partial D_c$ using the correspondence principle for the dynamic Leontief *difference* equation system (138) and employing Proposition Nine.
2. Reread the results of Chapter Seven on the stability of the Walrasian and the Marshallian systems and the implication for the effects of a shift in the demand curve on the price. The Walrasian case, for example, employs the single equation excess demand (demand minus supply) curve model

   $Q = f(P) =$ (as a linear approximation) $a - bP$ ($= 0$ in equilibrium) where P is the price, Q is the quantity demanded minus the quantity supplied, a and b are constants and $-b = \dfrac{df(P)}{dP}$ is the slope of the curve $f(P) = Q$ at its equilibrium point $Q = 0$. The Walrasian dynamic assumption required for the employment of the correspondence principle is now

   $$\frac{dP}{dt} = \dot{P} = V(a - bP).$$

   Give an economic interpretation of this assumption. Derive the sign of dP/db with the aid of the correspondence principle and Proposition Twelve. Write out a linear demand equation and a linear supply equation and obtain the excess demand equation by subtracting this supply equation from the demand equation. Now interpret your results on the sign of dP/db in terms of the coefficients of your supply and demand equations.

Part VI

NEWER GROWTH MODELS

Chapter Seventeen

ON SOME RECENT GROWTH MODELS

In recent years the formal theory of economic growth has attracted a great deal of attention in the literature.[1] Much of this work has proceeded along lines other than those described in this volume, though some of its origins are to be traced to materials that have been covered in earlier chapters. No attempt will be made to offer the reader a detailed and comprehensive description of these writings.[2] Rather, the chapter seeks only to lay out the broad outlines of the discussion—to provide the reader with a very general notion of the area covered and the nature of the analysis.

Two major analytic streams encompass the bulk of the discussion. The first is associated with such names as Solow, Swan, Joan Robinson, and Phelps, who have generalized the Harrod-Domar analysis to take into account the possibility of input substitution and diminishing returns. They have thus emerged with what they describe as a neoclassical growth model, one in which the supply of inputs displaces demand as the critical element that determines the long-run growth rate. Because of diminishing returns to capital and because investment constitutes a deduction from consumption, there will,

[1] In this chapter I shall not discuss the theoretical materials relating to economic growth in the underdeveloped areas, the writings of noted economists such as W. Arthur Lewis, Ragnar Nurkse, and Harvey Leibenstein. These works are, of course, more empirical and applied in their orientation than is the bulk of the material in this book.

[2] For a far more extensive survey see Frank Hahn and R. C. O. Matthews in the bibliography.

under appropriate conditions, prove to be a level of capital per worker that maximizes consumption—and the investment level that achieves this capital-labor ratio is said to satisfy the golden rule of capital accumulation.

The second major analytic stream in growth analysis flows from the work of John von Neumann. It usually works with a general equilibrium model, one that includes many sectors of economic activity. The analysis in this area has investigated the requirements of *maximal* "balanced growth" in which the outputs of all sectors expand in exactly the same proportion. Such a maximal balanced growth path has since come to be called a "von Neumann path." The Dorfman-Samuelson-Solow conjecture which has been labeled "the turnpike theorem" also lies in this area of analysis. This conjecture, which has been shown to hold in a wide variety of cases, asserts that the maximal growth path from any initial state to any final state, in which the expansion is not necessarily proportional, will, if the time involved is sufficiently long, proceed a substantial part of the way on or near the von Neumann path, just as, if we have a long enough way to travel, it will generally pay us to make the detour to the nearest turnpike.

1. THE NEOCLASSICAL MODEL

In a noted article [3] which constitutes the basis for much of the subsequent neoclassical growth literature, Solow undertakes to show how the Harrod-Domar analysis can be extended to include more general types of production relationship. The reader will recall that the original Harrod-Domar models employ a rigid acceleration principle assumption in which, up to a point, output is strictly proportionate to the capital stock, but with the rate of growth of output limited by the rate of growth of the labor supply (the natural rate of growth). This implies that required input pro-

[3] See Robert Solow, "A Contribution to the Theory of Economic Growth," *Quarterly Journal of Economics,* Vol. LXX, February 1956.

portions are absolutely fixed by technological relations, as are input-output ratios, and that factor substitution is not possible.

These assumptions are interesting analytically for a variety of purposes, but they are hardly realistic and do not jibe with the mainstream of economic analysis. Solow therefore sets out to generalize the model to permit it to include substitution relationships and diminishing returns.

Solow begins with his predecessors' assumption that investment (dK/dt, where K is capital stock) is strictly proportioned to income Y, as a result of a fixed propensity to save, s. Thus he has the relationship [4]

$$\frac{dK}{dt} = sY. \qquad (142)$$

Output is, however, determined by a more general production function

$$Y = F(K, L), \qquad (143)$$

where L is the supply of labor, and where the production function is assumed to exhibit constant returns to scale and diminishing marginal productivity of each input by itself. Together, these equations determine the supply of capital and the level of income, provided we know the supply of labor. The latter Solow takes to be given exogenously and assumes that it is growing at a constant exponential rate

$$L = L_0 e^{nt}. \qquad (144)$$

From these conditions Solow goes on to derive his equilibrium condition which states that the volume of desired saving, $sF(K, L)$, must equal the rate of investment necessary to maintain constant the capital-labor ratio. This is so because, with constant returns to scale, if capital and labor supply rise proportionately, then output

[4] This is essentially the same requirement as the warranted growth rate condition of the Harrod-Domar model

$$k \frac{dY}{dt} = sY.$$

See Chapter Four.

and saving will also increase proportionately. Thus, in such circumstances, equilibrium balanced growth is possible. On the other hand, if the preceding condition is violated, equilibrium is not possible. If saving is greater or less than the amount of investment required to maintain the capital-labor ratio, then the ratio will rise or fall and hence that ratio cannot possibly be in equilibrium.

We must then determine an expression for the second term in the equilibrium equation—the investment rate needed to maintain the capital-labor ratio. With the volume of labor given by $L = L_0e^{nt}$, this required investment rate will obviously be achieved when $\left(\frac{dK/dt}{K}\right) = \left(\frac{dL/dt}{L}\right)$, i.e., when

$$\text{Investment} = \frac{dK}{dt} = \frac{K}{L}\frac{dL}{dt} = \frac{K}{L}\frac{dL_0e^{nt}}{dt} = n\frac{K}{L}L_0e^{nt} = n\frac{K}{L}L = nK.$$

Thus, nK is the rate of investment necessary to retain the capital-labor ration when labor is growing in accord with the exponential relationship L_0e^{nt}. The equilibrium requirement that desired saving be equal to this investment rate is therefore

$$sF(K, L) = nK. \tag{145}$$

This, in effect, is Solow's basic condition for equilibrium of the capital-labor ratio.

Solow also shows, with the aid of this relationship, that there is a simple mechanism making for stability in this equilibrium. Suppose, for example, there is a departure from equilibrium with the capital-labor ratio exceeding its equilibrium value. This would occur, for example, if the capital stock and the supply of labor were both to rise, but the former rose by a larger percentage. In that case, since the production function is linear and homogeneous, output, $f(K, L)$, would rise by a smaller percentage [5] than the capital stock, K.

[5] This assumes the operation of the "law" of diminishing returns to the expansion of one input alone; i.e., an increase in the use of labor beyond the point where it had expanded in proportion with capital stock is taken to yield less than proportionate increases in output. As we shall see in the graphic analysis of the next section, where diminishing returns do not hold, the stability analysis may break down.

Hence the equilibrium equation (145) would be replaced by the inequality

$$sF(K, L) < nK. \qquad (146)$$

But this tells us that savings will then fall short of nK, the level of investment needed to maintain the capital-labor ratio, and so K/L must decline back toward its equilibrium value. Similarly if K/L is for some reason below its equilibrium level, output and hence saving will not decline in proportion to K. Thus the inequality in (146) will be reversed, and K/L will rise toward its equilibrium value because savings will then exceed the amount needed to achieve growth in capital and labor.[6]

[6] Solow's mathematical argument is more specific than the preceding discussion indicates, and his result is derived in a more formal manner. Direct substitution of (143) into (142) obviously yields (using the standard notation $\dot{K}$ for the time derivative dK/dt, and so forth)

$$\dot{K} = sF(K, L). \qquad (147)$$

Now, writing r for the capital-labor ratio so that $r = K/L$ or $K = rL = rL_0e^{nt}$, we have by direct differentiation with respect to t

$$\dot{K} = \dot{r}L_0e^{nt} + nrL_0e^{nt}$$

or, dividing through by $L = L_0e^{nt}$,

$$\dot{K}/L = \dot{r} + nr = \dot{r} + nK/L.$$

Substitution of this expression into (147) yields

$$\dot{K}/L = sF(K, L)/L = \dot{r} + nK/L$$

or

$$\dot{r} = sF(K, L)/L - nK/L.$$

This is, essentially, Solow's basic equation. Its relationship to text equation (145) and the discussion of inequality (146) should be clear. It states that $\dot{r}$, the rate of change in the capital-labor ratio, is equal to the difference between desired saving per unit of labor, $sF(K, L)/L$, and nK/L, the investment (per unit of labor) needed to maintain constancy in the capital-labor ratio.

If saving equals required investment, nK/L, then $\dot{r}$ will be zero and the capital-labor ratio will not change. On the other hand, if saving is in excess of the required investment, $\dot{r}$ will be greater than zero, and so K/L will rise. Solow does not quite carry this mathematical argument to an explicit discussion of stability, relying for this purpose on the graphic analysis.

2. GRAPHIC ANALYSIS

The implications of the preceding analysis can be seen more clearly with the aid of a simple graphic construction, one that has appeared in various places in the literature and which also has its origins in the Solow article.[7]

In Figure 51 curve OY/L represents a curve of total output per unit of labor as a function of the quantity of capital per unit of

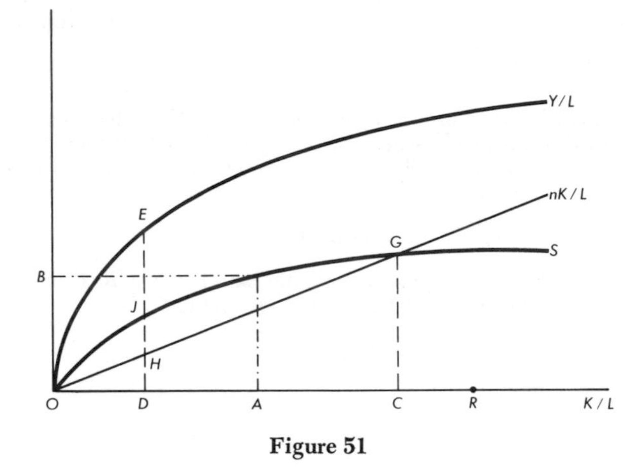

Figure 51

labor. This is a static total product curve representing the situation at a moment of time. Such a representation is made possible, despite the exponentially increasing labor force and the rising absolute quantities of capital and output, by the assumption of constant returns to scale. Since a proportionate increase in both inputs will produce a proportionate increase in output, we may prefer that

[7] As a matter of fact, there are two different lines of diagrammatic analysis that have been pursued. One starting from an average product of capital curve, is associated with the writings of John Fei, James Tobin, J. A. Hanson, and P. A. Neher, while the second has taken as its point of departure the *total* product curve and has been utilized by A. L. Marty and Harry Johnson (for references see the bibliography). Here we have, rather arbitrarily, chosen to utilize the second of these constructions.

such a diagram be magnified precisely to scale with the passage of time. But instead we have obviated the need for such magnification by standardizing the scales and representing everything on a per-unit-of-labor basis, for with constant returns to scale, when everything increases proportionately, output per unit of labor and capital per unit of labor will remain unchanged.[8]

Returning to the curve OY/L, we note that the curve exhibits a diminishing slope as we move from left to right, i.e., it shows diminishing marginal output returns to capital. For that reason, with savings (per unit of labor) proportional to output (per unit of labor), the savings curve, OS, will have the same general shape. That is, with the constant marginal propensity to save, s, the curve of total saving per unit of labor will be given by sY/L, whose slope at any point will be reduced by the fraction s from the slope at the corresponding point on the output curve.

Finally, our diagram contains the straight line OnK/L, a straight line through the origin, whose slope, n, is the growth rate of the supply of labor. That line shows for any value of the capital-labor ratio, K/L, the amount of investment required (per unit of labor) to keep the level of the capital-labor ratio from changing with the passage of time. Thus, for example, if the initial capital-labor ratio is given by OA, and then if current investment is OB, the next period's capital-labor ratio will remain at OA. If investment exceeds OB, the capital-labor ratio will rise above OA, and so forth. The reason for this has already been indicated but it may be well to explain the point in an intuitive manner. Roughly, neglecting compounding (and assuming that we are in a position to talk in terms of well-defined periods), in one period the supply of labor will grow from L to $(1+n)L$. Hence, the supply capital, *to keep pace,* must

[8] More formally, with constant returns to scale, by definition for any k we must have $F(kK, kL) = kF(K, L)$, so that if we set $k - 1/L$, this last relationship becomes $F(K/L, 1) = (1/L)F(K, L)$; i.e., output as a function of the ratio of capital to labor, $F(K/L, 1)$, is equal to output per unit of labor, $(1/L)F(K, L)$. This relationship constitutes the basis for our diagram in which, if the quantities of capital, labor, and output all rise in a way that maintains their initial ratios, the diagram will remain totally unchanged.

also rise from K to $(1 + n)K$, i.e., it must rise by nK, so that capital per unit of labor must then increase in the amount nK/L. We may then describe the line OnK/L as the balanced growth requirement line—the locus giving the investment necessary to maintain over time the current capital-labor ratio.

Having now represented the three relationships, the output curve, the savings curve, and the balanced growth requirement line, we may readily determine the equilibrium capital-labor ratio. This will be given by OC, the capital-labor ratio at which the savings curve intersects the balanced growth requirement line. Only at such a point is the supply of saving equal to the investment required for balanced growth. At some other value of K/L, say at OD, the two will not be equal. Realized investment, which is equal to DJ, the supply of savings, will exceed DH, the investment required to keep K/L at its initial level, OD.

Note that with the savings curve having the shape indicated—the shape imparted by the diminishing returns in the output function—and since the investment requirement locus is a straight line through the origin, there can be at most one intersection between the two (though in principle it is possible that there will be no intersection—that no equilibrium point will exist; the reader need merely imagine one of the two loci lying below the other throughout its length).

The relative shape of the two curves also enables us to examine the stability of the equilibrium point, OC. Note first that because of diminishing returns the savings curve must cut the investment requirement locus from above as we move from left to right. That is, to the left of point C the savings curve lies above the other, while to the right of C the savings curve is the lower of the two loci. We shall see now that this implies that the equilibrium point will be stable.[9]

As we have seen, at any point such as D, where savings, OJ,

[9] It also shows that if the savings curve cuts the investment requirements line from below—as may happen if the "law" of diminishing returns does not apply—then the intersection point will be unstable. The reader is urged to draw such a diagram and to run through the argument for himself.

exceed the investment required to maintain the capital-output ratio, in the next period that ratio will have increased—capital will have grown by more than the amount necessary to keep this ratio at its old level, *OD*. Hence we will move toward a higher value of *K/L;* i.e., from point *D* we will move to the right toward equilibrium point *C*. Similarly, from any initial point such as *R*, to the right of the equilibrium point, *C*, there will automatically be movement to the left, toward equilibrium point *C*. This will be so because savings will then fall short of the investment level required to keep the capital-labor ratio at its initial level, *R*, and therefore that ratio will subsequently decline.

This, then, is the essence of the specification of the equilibrium of the neoclassical growth model and of its stability properties. We may now profitably pause to consider some characteristics of that equilibrium. First, it will be noted that it is a *balanced growth* equilibrium—that is, the economy will be in equilibrium when inputs and outputs all grow in the same proportion. Under the assumptions of the model the system will automatically move toward balanced growth and any movement toward an increase in the capital-labor ratio (or the reverse) will tend to eliminate itself. This is so because there are diminishing savings returns to capital so that any saving in excess of that required for balanced growth will tend to eliminate itself and the reverse will happen where savings are insufficient for the purpose.

Second, we may note that in equilibrium the rate of growth of the system will be equal to *n*, the rate of growth of the labor force. Both capital and output will adjust themselves to this growth rate.

Specifically, and this is the curious feature of the result, no change in the other parameters of the system, in the level of savings or in any component of the production function, will influence the equilibrium growth rate. This is surprising because our instincts and training lead us to expect that a rise in saving (which in this model is always added to the stock of real capital) should increase the rate of growth. And so it will—in the short run when the system is not in equilibrium. But with diminishing returns to capital and a constant propensity to save, this high growth rate will be temporary, because, as we have seen, the high savings will tend to eliminate themselves.

What, then, will be the consequences of an increase in propensity to save? A glance at Figure 52 tells us the answer. An increase in the

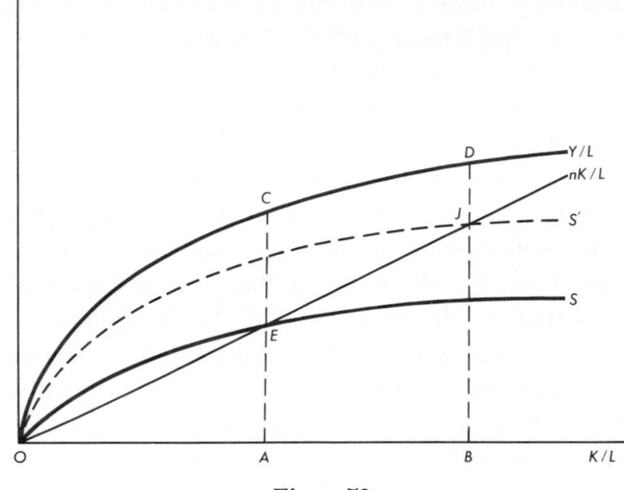

Figure 52

marginal propensity to save will cause an upward shift in the savings curve from *OS* to *OS′*. Hence the equilibrium capital-labor ratio will rise from *OA* to *OB*, since the intersection of the savings curve with the investment requirement line will change from *E* to *J*. Equilibrium output per unit of labor will increase from *AC* to *BD*. But in equilibrium, since the capital-output and capital-labor ratios will remain unchanged with the passage of time, all three of these magnitudes must fall into line with the exogenously determined growth rate of the labor force, *n*.

We may now contrast directly the shapes of the neoclassical model's output and savings curves with those of the Harrod-Domar model. In that model the acceleration principle assumption tells us that there will be no diminishing returns to capital until the point where the labor force is fully employed is reached. At that point further capital accumulation adds nothing more to output. This leads to the curve of production (per unit of labor) represented by OY/L in Figure 53. From O to P output rises linearly with an increasing

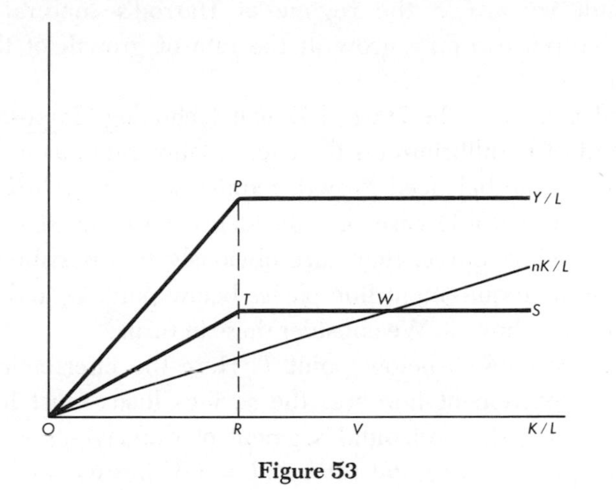

Figure 53

capital-labor ratio because unemployed labor can be put to work in the fixed proportions required to increase output according to the model's assumptions. To the right of OR labor is fully employed (we may think of there being one machine per operative) and so further additions to the capital stock will not increase output. Thus, to the right of P, the output function is horizontal. As before, since savings are equal to sY, the curve of savings per unit of labor, OS, is, in effect, a scaled down version of the production function.

Now, anywhere to the left of point R the system will possess a warranted rate of growth given by the slope of OT since that slope is equal to RT/OR = (Saving)/(Capital) [10] = (Rate of growth of

[10] Here we write (Saving)/(Capital) rather than (Saving per unit of labor)/(Output per unit of labor) because the labor appears in both numerator and denominator and hence cancels out. A similar comment applies to our interpretation of slopes and derivatives throughout the discussion, e.g., of the slope of curve OY/L as the marginal product of capital. For a rigorous justification of this interpretation see footnote 15.

capital)/(Capital). Because output can expand in proportion with capital, this is consequently also the warranted growth rate of output—the growth rate that will keep the available savings occupied. Once we get to the right of point *R*, labor becomes the bottleneck. As a result we are in the regime of Harrod's "natural rate of growth"—output can only grow at the rate of growth of the labor supply, *n*.

The inflexibility of the Harrod-Domar technology imposes a very curious sort of equilibrium on the capital-labor ratio, as we can see if we draw in the balanced growth requirement line, OnK/L. Neglecting the implausible case of coincidence with the line segment *OT* of the savings curve, there are obviously two possibilities: the case where the requirement line passes below point *T*, and the case where it passes above it. We consider these in turn.

Case i: line OnK/L below point *T*. Here the intersection point, *W*, of the requirement line and the savings locus must lie to the right of *T* along the horizontal segment of the savings locus. This yields an equilibrium capital ratio $K/L = OV$ in excess of the ratio *OR* at which labor is fully employed. With the rigid technological assumptions of the model this means that equilibrium must involve permanent excess capacity—the production and maintenance of a stock of capital part of which must remain idle because there is no labor to run it! And by the argument earlier in this section, this equilibrium will be stable, because OnK/L cuts *OS* from below.

Case ii: line OnK/L above point *T* (not shown in the diagram). In this case OnK/L will intersect the savings curve only at the origin. But with OnK/L lying above segment *OT* of the savings curve, this means that at any point between *O* and *R* the capital-labor ratio must decline—savings must fall short of the amount needed for maintenance of the capital-labor ratio. In this case the economy will move steadily toward its equilibrium point—the origin, at which the capital-labor ratio is zero.[11]

[11] In both cases, then, the equilibrium values of K/L are stable. Though it may appear to do so, this, however, does not conflict with the possible instability of the warranted growth path in the Harrod-Domar model which

Of course, these two curious equilibrium points are of no real economic significance. They merely illustrate the dangers that beset an analysis which presses too hard on a set of simplifying assumptions such as the rigid accelerator which fixes the capital-output ratio and results in the segmented linear form of the savings function, *OS*. Simplifications are always required for useful analysis, but the moral is that they must be handled with care.

3. THE GOLDEN RULE

At least one other major line of discussion has grown out of the neoclassical growth model. This is the so-called golden rule of capital accumulation, a proposition independently discovered by Phelps, Mrs. Robinson, Swan, and others (see the bibliography). The issue and its logic are very simply described. The analysis addresses itself to the following issue (which was first analyzed formally by Frank Ramsey): Suppose maximization of (equilibrium) consumption is the sole objective of the economic system; how is this goal to be achieved? First we may note that in our simple model, so long as we discuss only equilibrium situations, there is no difficulty about the formulation of the question in terms of a choice among different intertemporal consumption streams. Since in equilibrium every component of this system expands proportionately, whatever maximizes consumption in *any one* period must also maximize it in *every* period.

For an intuitive grasp of the value of K/L that will maximize consumption, let us first consider two extreme possibilities—a very high and a very low value of the capital-labor ratio. A low K/L will not normally do the job, because, given the time path of labor supply, a low level of capital stock will keep output low and hence

---

was discussed in Chapter Four. Stability of the growth *paths* is a matter of the way in which the system approaches equilibrium points *O* or *T*—whether the rate of growth of output is driven toward equality with the slope of *OT*—and has nothing to do with the long-run equilibrium value of K/L.

restrict the amount available for consumption. On the other hand, a K/L ratio that is very high will also depress consumption—first, because such a large capital-labor ratio will require a high level of investment in order for the capital stock to keep up with the growing labor supply. This large volume of investment will, of course, cut into the quantity of output available for consumption. And, second, with diminishing returns to capital, the level of output will not expand in response to the high capital stock by an amount sufficient to make up for the substantial flow of investment needed to sustain it. Thus, too low a level of K/L will reduce consumption because it restricts output, while too large a level of K/L hurts consumption by drawing too much of the economy's output into investment. Obviously, then, the golden rule value of K/L will tend to lie between these extremes. All of this can be seen in Figure 54 where consumption is represented by the vertical distance between the output curve, OY/L, and the required investment (savings) line, OnK/L, since, by definition, consumption equals income minus savings. Since the two curves approach one another at very low and very high levels of K/L, consumption levels at such points, as represented, e.g., by lengths *RT* and *WV*, will be lower than the amounts available for consumption (e.g., *BC* or *DE*) at intermediate levels of K/L.

By the standard tenets of marginal analysis, the intermediate level of K/L which maximizes consumption will obviously occur at the point where the marginal output yield of a unit of capital (the marginal product of capital) is equal to its marginal investment (savings) cost. In Figure 54 this is clearly point *A*, the capital-labor ratio at which the slope of the total income curve OY/L equals n, the slope of the (total) investment requirement line.[12] The slopes

[12] In what may be considered the "normal" Harrod-Domar model case, the golden rule requires a level of investment just consistent with the maintenance of a full employment quantity of capital (point *R* in Figure 53). To see this, draw any straight line from the origin below point *T* on our nK/L line. The maximal distance to the Y/L curve must be that below point *P*, the kinked full employment point on the output curve.

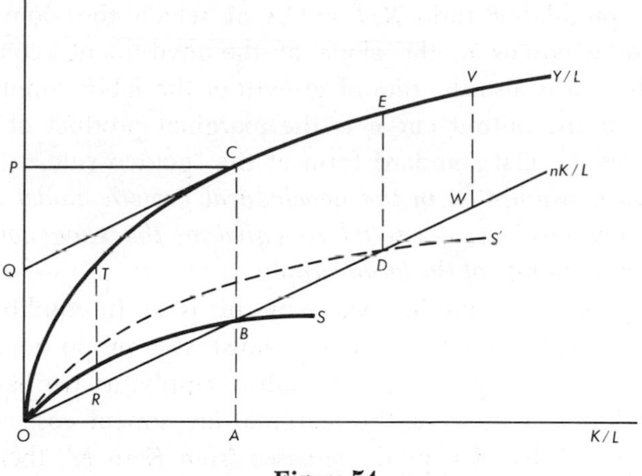

Figure 54

of these two curves equal the marginal product of capital and the marginal investment requirement, respectively.[13]

But the maximal consumption value of K/L need not be an equilibrium value. It will be an equilibrium level only if the propensity to consume is such that the savings curve is curve OS, which passes through the OnK/L linc exactly at point B, the point above the consumption-maximizing labor-output ratio, A. At this point consumption will be given by BC, the difference between output, AC, and investment-saving, AB. However, with any other propensity to save, say that which results in the savings curve OS', the equilibrium point will change to D, consumption will tend to fall to DE, and the golden rule will be honored only in the breech.

This, then, describes graphically the golden rule of capital accu-

[13] See footnote 15 for justification of this interpretation of the slopes. It should be noted that in some (nonneoclassical) models there may exist no finite solution to the golden rule problem. Suppose, for example, that the output function were to ascend everywhere more steeply than the nK/L line. Then, clearly, there would be no point of maximal distance between them. The greater the capital-labor ratio, the greater the available consumption for any finite value of K/L.

mulation. It requires that level of saving which yields as the equilibrium capital-labor ratio $K/L = OA$ at which the slope of the output curve equals n, the slope of the investment requirement curve, where n is also the rate of growth of the labor supply. Since the slope of the output curve is the marginal product of capital, we arrive at the first standard form of the "golden rule":

Maximal consumption in the neoclassical growth model requires the marginal product of capital to equal n, the exogenously determined growth rate of the labor supply.

We may see in yet another way why this is so. In equilibrium, as the capital stock grows, investment must rise proportionately to enable capital to keep up with the labor supply, as we have seen. This constitutes, as it were, the marginal investment cost of added capital. Specifically, if capital increases from K to K', then future investment must flow not at the rate nK as before but at the rate nK'; i.e., the marginal investment will be $n(K' - K)/\Delta K = n\Delta K/\Delta K = n$. This marginal investment cost of capital is required, for maximal consumption, to equal the marginal output yield of capital and that is precisely what the preceding form of the golden rule asserts.

There is a second form of the golden rule whose geometry is only a bit more complicated. This form of the rule states:

Maximal consumption requires that total savings, in equilibrium, be equal to the total earnings of capital if each unit of capital is paid its marginal product.

To prove this result, note that at OA, the optimal value of K/L, savings are given by AB (Figure 54). Now draw the line segment QC tangent to the output curve at C, where point Q lies on the vertical axis. Since when $K/L = A$ the output curve has the same slope as line OnK/L, then QC must be parallel to OB. Now draw in the horizontal line segment PC. PC is obviously equal in length to OA, and hence triangles OAB and CPQ must be congruent. It follows that $QP = AB$.

With a bit of economic interpretation we shall see that this yields our theorem, for AB is, as we have seen, the consumption maximizing volume of saving. But the slope of the output curve at $C = QP/PC$ is the marginal product of capital (MPC). Hence, MPC multiplied by the quantity of capital $= (QP/PC)(PC) = QP$. Thus, the result follows. The maximization requirement $AB = QP$ means that total saving must equal the marginal product of capital multiplied by the number of units of capital.[14]

This last form of the golden rule has one immediate corollary. It tells us that if capital is paid its marginal product and if all of capital's earnings are saved while all of wage income is spent, then the golden rule will automatically be obeyed. The propensity to save will be that which leads to golden rule savings curve OS in Figure 54 rather than to some other savings curve such as OS'; for if capital's

[14] The golden rule analysis is also easily formalized by deriving an expression for consumption which one then maximizes. Since we are dealing with balanced growth, the employment of capital must keep pace with the supply of labor so that $K = rL = rL_0e^{nt}$. Hence, investment will be given by

$$dK/dt = nrL_0e^{nt} = nK.$$

Thus, since consumption equals output, $F(K, L)$, minus investment, we have

$$C = F(K, L) - nK.$$

We wish now to transform this into a function of one variable, the capital-labor ratio $r = K/L$. We note that (as was shown in footnote 8) the linear homogeneity of the production function permits us to write

$$F(K, L)/L = F(K/L, 1) = F(r, 1)$$

and $F(r, 1)$ may be written simply as $f(r)$. Thus, dividing the consumption equation through by L, we obtain a relationship giving consumption per unit of labor as output per unit of labor minus investment per unit of labor

$$C/L = F(K, L)/L - nK/L = f(r) - nr.$$

Since the value of L is given exogenously, whatever maximizes C/L must maximize C. Hence, to find maximum C, we set the derivative of C/L with respect to r equal to zero. This yields

$$f'(r) - n = 0,$$

and that is the first form of the golden rule: to maximize consumption, $f'(r)$, the marginal product of capital must equal n, the growth rate of labor supply.

The second form of the golden rule is obtained by multiplying both sides of the preceding equation by K to yield

$$Kf'(r) = nK,$$

where nK equals investment (equals saving) as noted above. Hence the rule states that total capital, evaluated at its marginal product, must equal the total supply of saving.

payments per unit are set at its marginal product, $f'(r)$ [where, in accord with footnote 14, $f(r)$ is defined as $F(K, L)/L$], then the total income of capital will be equal to [15] $Kf'(r)$. Hence, if that is exactly the amount saved, the second form of the golden rule will then obviously be satisfied.

4. *HOW GOLDEN THE RULE?*

The name assigned to the preceding theorem is, however, quite unfortunate. It suggests that anyone who follows its admonitions is indeed doing for others what he would have them do for him. Is the golden rule in fact so effective a codification of virtue in savings behavior? The authors of the theorem have repeatedly disclaimed any intention of implying such a view. They tell us that the term "golden rule" was meant merely to emphasize the fairy tale character of the entire construct.

But aside from the oversimplification of its premises, it may not be obvious in what way the theorem fails to capture a true optimality requirement. Why should not maximization of consumption be the appropriate objective? There are two answers.

First, one might prefer some other uses of output as ends in themselves. The public in a developing country may well derive pleasure directly from a large increase in investment and may prefer it despite any resulting sacrifice in consumption. Or military or political ambitions may give priority to investment over consumption in some countries. Second, even if one does, in some sense, wish to maximize

[15] The reader may be concerned that the marginal product of capital is $\partial F/\partial K$ and not $f'(r)$. For $f'(r)$, the slope of the OY/L curve is, by definition, $\partial(F/L)/\partial r = \partial(F/L)/\partial(K/L)$.

To prove that the two derivatives are indeed the same, we note that $d(K/L)/dK = 1/L$ or $dK/d(K/L) = L$. Therefore,

$$\frac{\partial F/L}{\partial K/L} = \frac{\partial F/L}{\partial K}\,\frac{dK}{dK/L} = L\,\frac{\partial F/L}{\partial K}.$$

But (again, because L does not vary with K) $\partial(F/L)/\partial K = (1/L)\partial F/\partial K$. Substituting into the preceding equation, we obtain our required result: $\partial(F/L)/\partial(K/L) = \partial F/\partial K$; i.e., the slope of the OY/L curve is indeed the marginal product of capital.

consumption, the desired time path of this consumption remains to be specified. There is no a priori reason to prefer a time path involving a constant n per cent rate of expansion of consumption (the same as the rate of growth of the labor supply). One might perhaps want to sacrifice in the immediate future by having smaller quantities of goods made available now so that the future can be somewhat more abundantly provided than it would be by an n per cent growth rate. Thus, a golden rule path may not be optimal on either one count or the other.

One rigorous argument has, however, been mustered to bolster the policy relevance of the golden rule. It has been shown [16] that if an economy does consider consumption as its only objective, then no matter what shape of time stream of consumption the economy desires, it cannot pay to *exceed* the golden rule level of investment at some point in time *and* to maintain such excess investment for all eternity. The argument is quite simple. First we note that *under*-investment relative to the amount called for by the golden rule cannot be shown a priori to be irrational, because while it yields less future consumption, it provides more consumption today than would be made available by the golden rule path. Hence the choice between the two levels of investment is a matter of society's relative evaluation of present and future consumption. But if one over-invests *permanently*, current consumption is reduced by the initial increase in investment, and future consumption is reduced by the resulting deviation from the golden rule, with future investment taking away from that period's consumption more than the added income which today's investment yields. One now operates permanently at a point where consumption, as given by the distance between the output curve and the nK/L line (Figure 54), is below its maximum level. With over-investment, then, one pays more (in foregone present consumption) and gets less for it (in future consumption), clearly a losing proposition on both counts.

The relatively limited application of this proposition should be

[16] See E. S. Phelps, *Golden Rules of Economic Growth* (W. W. Norton, New York, 1966), p. 55ff.

recognized. It is not a very strong defense of the relevance of the golden rule, for, as we have just seen, it certainly does not preclude the superiority of any program which involves investment levels below those required by the golden rule. Moreover, over-investment for any finite period of time is not precluded, for it may be that the burst of consumption which occurs after the time of over-investment has come to an end fully justifies in the minds of the members of the community the sacrifice entailed by the long but nevertheless temporary departure from the precepts of the golden rule.

5. EXTENSIONS OF THE NEOCLASSICAL MODEL

Before leaving our discussions of the neoclassical model, it should be made clear that the literature has gone well beyond the basic construct presented in the preceding pages. It has investigated the consequences of a propensity to save that is not constant. It has examined the distinction between gross and net investment which our discussion has neglected. It has shown how technological change can be incorporated and has examined the effects of disaggregation of the economy into several sectors (several outputs each with its own production function, and so forth). It has been applied to problems of foreign trade and economic development. These matters are all beyond the scope of our discussion. We shall mention only one or two points to illustrate the techniques that have been used and then move on.

The simplest type of technological change from the point of view of the analysis is that which increases the productivity of labor and does so exponentially. In that case the consequence is merely to increase the growth rate of the effective labor supply function by changing the function from L_0e^{nt} to L_0e^{wt}, where $w > n$ and w represents the combined consequences of growth in population and growth in productivity. Once this change is effected, the remainder of the analysis proceeds without further modification.

Variations in the marginal propensity to save mean simply that the savings curve, OS, need not be a scaled down version of the output curve because savings will no longer be given by SY (s is a constant) and hence savings will no longer be proportionate to output, Y. As a result, the savings curve may cross the nK/L line several times, or it may not cross it at all. Should the savings curve cross the nK/L line from below, the point of intersection now becomes an *unstable* solution, for as the reader can check for himself, to the right of that point (where the capital-labor ratio exceeds the amount corresponding to the intersection) savings will exceed the amount of investment needed for balanced growth, and the available amount of capital will therefore increase even further relative to the labor supply. We will therefore move even more to the right of the intersection point. A similar argument clearly applies to deviations to the left of the intersection.

6. MULTISECTOR BALANCED GROWTH: THE VON NEUMANN MODEL

We turn now to the second major strand of recent growth theory: the von Neumann model. In a piece written in 1938, John von Neumann produced a multisector growth model which, while artificial in a variety of respects, still serves as a standard of ingenuity in the use of analytical tools and of a highly illuminating approach to the theory of expansion.[17]

The von Neumann model begins with a multiplicity of outputs and productive processes. It is an n-sector model in which each activity utilizes as inputs the items produced in the previous period by itself and by other sectors of the economy. In this construct there is no independent source of demand for commodities. Today's outputs are wanted only for their use as tomorrow's inputs. Presumably,

[17] The paper was presented in Princeton in 1932. It was first published as "Über ein Ökonomisches Gleichungssystem und eine Verallgemeinerung des Browerschen Fixpunktsatzes" in Karl Menger, ed., *Ergebnisse eines Mathematischen Seminars,* Vol. 8, Vienna, 1938. An English translation by George Morton appeared as "A Model of General Economic Equilibrium," *Review of Economic Studies,* Vol. XIII, 1945–1946.

human consumption, then, is to be viewed as the use of inputs for the production of labor power—much as one might treat the consumption of fodder by work horses.

In addition, it is posited that the production function is characterized by constant returns to scale, and that there are no natural resource limitations which inhibit the indefinite expansion of the economy.[18]

The object of the exercise is to investigate the possibility of balanced growth at a constant rate in such an economy. That is, it examines whether it is possible for every output in the economy to expand forever at a percentage rate *at least* equal to some fixed number, α, per period. Having posed this issue, we note the central topics studied by von Neumann's analysis—determination of whether there is a *maximal* value of α and a maximum uniform rate of expansion of the economy and an examination of the characteristics of this highest attainable growth rate.

7. OUTLINE OF THE VON NEUMANN MODEL

Before going on to discuss the answers to these questions, we pause to describe the model itself.

In the original notation, this economy contains m processes involving n commodities with no necessary relationship between the two numbers m and n. Each process uses some specified combination of the n goods as inputs and produces some specified combination of these items as outputs. More specifically, suppose the process i is

[18] von Neumann also employs one other premise which is particularly unpalatable economically, the premise that *every* commodity enters each and every production process either as an input or as an output. That is, it is assumed that there is no productive process which fails to involve, e.g., vanilla-fudge ice cream either as one of its inputs or as one of its outputs. Happily, several more recent writings have shown how one can dispense with this assumption, which, incidentally, was originally adopted to guarantee complete interdependence in the economy so that the model could not be decomposed into a number of subeconomies that are essentially independent. See, e.g., J. G. Kemeny, Oskar Morgenstern, and G. L. Thompson, "A Generalization of the von Neumann Model of an Expanding Economy," *Econometrica*, Vol. 24, April 1956.

operated at some intensity which we define as the unit level of process i. Then it will utilize a_{ij} of good j as an input and it will produce b_{ij} of commodity j as an output. Thus, if process i does not use item j as an input, we will have $a_{ij} = 0$. Similarly $b_{ij} = 0$ means that process i does not produce item j.

Now, suppose that x_i units of process i are utilized by the economy. That is, x_i is a measure of the number of units of process i that are carried out during a period. Then the total use of good j as an input to process i will be $x_i a_{ij}$ and the total output of good j by this process will be $x_i b_{ij}$. Hence the total amount of input j utilized by all processes will be $\sum_{i=1}^{m} x_i a_{ij}$ and the total output of this product will be $\sum_{i=1}^{m} x_i b_{ij}$.

If inputs and outputs are to grow by the factor α $(= 1 + k/100$, where k is the actual growth rate), any input which was $\Sigma_i a_{ij} x_i$ in period t will have expanded in magnitude to $\alpha \Sigma_i a_{ij} x_i$ one period later. But that input must, by assumption, come out of the preceding period's output supply, $\Sigma_i b_{ij} x_i$. Hence, since the inputs utilized tomorrow must not exceed the supply made available today, we obtain the first of von Neumann's requirements

$$\alpha \Sigma_i a_{ij} x_i \leqq \Sigma_i b_{ij} x_i. \tag{148}$$

In addition, von Neumann posits the obvious conditions

$$x_1 \geqq 0, x_2 \geqq 0, \cdots, x_m \geqq 0, \tag{149}$$

specifying that there is no such thing as a negative level of operation of a process. Finally, he reminds us that there is no interest in a solution in which there is nothing going on, i.e., in which $x_1 = x_2 = \cdots = x_m = 0$, so to avoid this trivial solution he requires

$$\Sigma x_i > 0. \tag{150}$$

The Dual Prices

This completes the description of what we would today (in the language of mathematical programming) call the primal problem:

the direct description of the production relationships. However, the author points out that implicit in the problem is a set of output prices, $P_1, P_2, \cdots, P_n$, and an interest factor, β ($= 1 + z/100$, where z is the percentage interest rate proper). To avoid going into details of duality theory, which a full interpretation would require, we may take our economy to represent a state of pure competition. In that case these prices will be set so that any process will yield zero profits *at most*.

Let us see how this no-profit condition can be expressed in terms of our symbols. If a unit of process i utilizes a_{ij} units of input j, each unit costing P_j dollars, the total original input cost of the unit of process i will be $\sum_{j=1}^{n} a_{ij}P_j$. But when the resources are utilized one period later, their cost, including their interest cost, will have risen from $\Sigma_j\, a_{ij}P_j$ to $\beta\, \Sigma_j\, a_{ij}P_j$. In that period, the process will produce a set of outputs whose quantities are b_{ij} and whose total market value is $\Sigma_j\, b_{ij}P_j$. Therefore, if there are to be no profits, total costs of the unit of process, $\beta\, \Sigma_j\, a_{ij}P_j$, must at least equal its total money yield $\Sigma_j\, b_{ij}P_j$. This gives us the model's second central condition

$$\beta\, \Sigma_j\, a_{ij}P_j \geqq \Sigma_j\, b_{ij}P_j. \tag{151}$$

Some processes may, under the terms of this inequality, turn out to yield only losses, and for any such uneconomic process i', we will, of course, have $x_{i'} = 0$; i.e., the process will go unutilized. We may write this requirement as

$$\text{If } \beta\, \Sigma_j\, a_{i'j}P_j > \Sigma_j\, b_{i'j}P_j, \text{ then } x_{i'} = 0. \tag{152}$$

We also have, as in the case of the x's,

$$P_1 \geqq 0, P_2 \geqq 0, \cdots, P_n \geqq 0 \tag{153}$$

and since we do not want all $P_j = 0$, we require

$$\Sigma\, P_j > 0. \tag{154}$$

This, then, is the monetary side of the von Neumann model, except for one condition formally analogous to (152) which will also complete the symmetry of the production and monetary sides of the model. [Thus, note the resemblance between conditions (148) and (151), between (149) and (153), and between (150) and (154).] The last requirement of the system states that any particular input j' will be a free good for which $P_{j'} = 0$ if there is an excess quantity of this input available; that is, if its available supply from all processes, $\Sigma_i b_{ij'}x_i$, exceeds $\alpha \Sigma_i a_{ij'}x_i$, the amount of that item which will be needed as an input in the next period. In formal terms this condition states

$$\text{If } \alpha \Sigma_i a_{ij'}x_i < \Sigma_i b_{ij'}x_i, \text{ then } P_{j'} = 0. \qquad (155)$$

8. *SOME IMPLICATIONS OF THE MODEL*

The growth rate of the availability of any specific good, j, is, of course, its total output from all sources, $\Sigma_i b_{ij}x_i$, expressed as a ratio to the total amount of j which had just been used as an input, i.e., $\Sigma_i a_{ij}x_i$. That is, we may define the growth rate of j as $\alpha_j = \Sigma_i b_{ij}x_i/\Sigma_i a_{ij}x_i$. Suppose that some good supplies grow at a rate faster than others.[19] Then the growth rate of the system as a whole, α, may be defined as the slowest of the individual good growth rates so that α equals the lowest value of the α_i, which we may write formally as

$$\alpha = \min \Sigma_i b_{ij}x_i/\Sigma_i a_{ij}x_i. \qquad (156)$$

Similarly, the real interest rate is the maximum rate of return to any process i; i.e., it is the maximal ratio for any process of the value of all its outputs to the value of all its inputs (since if capital were obtained at a lower money cost than this, it would, by defini-

[19] The reader may well feel that this is a curious sort of balanced growth. If it makes him happier, he may visualize the excess output of any good which grows faster than α to be thrown away or "wasted" on consumption rather than going back into the productive process, so that the residual growth is balanced in a tautological sense.

tion, not be paid its opportunity cost, which is, of course, its real cost to society). Thus we have

$$\beta = \max \Sigma_j b_{ij}P_j/\Sigma_j a_{ij}P_j. \tag{157}$$

von Neumann points out that (156) and (157) are not new definitions or new assumptions but follow rigorously from the earlier equations. Thus, consider, for example, (156). This can be deduced from (148), (153), (154), and (155) in the following manner. By (153) and (154) there must be at least one commodity j' for which $P_{j'} > 0$. By (155), for this item j' we must have

$$\alpha \Sigma_i a_{ij'}x_i = \Sigma_i b_{ij'}x_i. \tag{158}$$

Direct division in (158) gives us

$$\alpha = \Sigma_i b_{ij'}x_i/\Sigma_i a_{ij'}x_i.$$

Moreover, by (148), for any other value of j, $\alpha \leqq \Sigma_i b_{ij}x_i/\Sigma_i a_{ij}x_i$, and the last two expressions for α are obviously tantamount to (156). Equation (157) for β is derived in precisely the same way. Thus, von Neumann demonstrates that there is a well-defined solution for α and β, which is later also shown to be unique.

The heart of von Neumann's analysis and by far its most difficult part is the proof that there *exists* a solution to his model. He shows rigorously, using a theorem from topology, that no matter what the values of the parameters of his model, so long as it satisfies the conditions that have been described, there will always be some set of values for $x_1, \cdots, x_m, P_1, \cdots, P_n, \alpha$, and β which satisfy the requirements of maximal growth in his model. The proof, even though it has been simplified considerably since the original paper,[20] is still beyond the mathematical level of our discussion. It should only be remarked that it is considered a landmark in the history of mathematical economics, and that it represents a most ingenious applica-

[20] See, e.g., David Gale, "The Closed Linear Model of Production," in H. W. Kuhn and A. W. Tucker, eds., *Linear Inequalities and Related Systems*, Annals of Mathematics Studies 38 (Princeton University Press, Princeton, N.J., 1956). An intuitive argument for the two-commodity case is easily obtained with the aid of the geometric apparatus described in the next section.

tion of the minimax theorem, which is a basic element of game theory, and of the duality theory of mathematical programming. It may be noted also that while, as already mentioned, it is shown that the model determines the values of α and β uniquely [i.e., it is demonstrated that there is (not surprisingly) a single *maximal* growth rate, α, for the system and a single (minimal) interest rate, β], this *same* is not true of the x's and P's. There may be a number of different output combinations and prices that satisfy the requirements of the model and are compatible with maximal growth.

We turn now to what, from the point of view of economics, is perhaps the most interesting theorem to emerge from the model. This is the result that in an optimal solution we must have $\alpha = \beta$—the expansion rate of the system must equal the rate of interest.[21] An intuitive economic explanation for this result can be offered in terms of the zero profit requirement that follows from our assumption of pure competition. If outputs were capable of exceeding inputs by the proportion α, while β, the interest cost of this process, were less than α, the entire operation would clearly be profitable. Thus, as has so very often happened in the mathematically sophisticated literature of recent decades, the more powerful analysis has served in part to confirm and extend results that can be discerned from less rigorous discussions.

9. DIAGRAMMING THE VON NEUMANN SOLUTION

Koopmans [22] has provided us with a highly ingenious geometric depiction of the von Neumann analysis. A translation into diagrammatic terms involves the difficulty that even in the simplest case (a two-commodity model with a two-period horizon) four variables are

[21] Gale [*Theory of Linear Economic Models* (McGraw-Hill, New York, 1958), pp. 314–316] shows that this result depends on the assumption that the economy not be decomposable into independent subsectors (cf. footnote 18).

[22] See T. C. Koopmans, "Economic Growth at a Maximal Rate," *Quarterly Journal of Economics,* Vol. LXXVIII, August 1964, reprinted in E. Malinvaud and M. O. L. Bacharach, eds., *Activity Analysis in the Theory of Growth and Planning* (St. Martin's Press, New York, 1967).

involved. These are, of course, the two current inputs, $x_1{}^*$ and $x_2{}^*$ (which are, in the von Neumann model, the outputs of the previous period), and the two corresponding outputs, y_1 and y_2. Koopmans' objective is to provide a *three*-dimensional depiction of the production function involving the two inputs, $x_1{}^*$ and $x_2{}^*$, and the two outputs, y_1 and y_2. He accomplishes this feat of representing four variables in three dimensions by *normalizing* the input variables, i.e., by recalibrating them into more convenient units. Because in the von Neumann model the production function involves constant returns to scale and hence depends on *relative* inputs, Koopmans is able to do this by letting x_1 represent the proportion between $x_1{}^*$ and $(x_1{}^* + x_2{}^*)$ and, similarly, by defining x_2 as $x_2{}^*/(x_1{}^* + x_2{}^*)$. Since for such proportions obviously $x_1 + x_2 = 1$, we need merely know the value of one of these two variables and the other follows immediately. That is, if we are told $x_1 = 0.6$, we know at once that x_2 must equal 0.4.

We may now draw a three-dimensional diagram with one input variable, $x_1 = x_1{}^*/(x_1{}^* + x_2{}^*)$, on one axis and the other two axes representing the two output quantities, y_1 and y_2. This is done in Figure 55 in which the shaded three-dimensional surface represents the desired production function, giving all possible combinations of output y_1 and y_2 as a function of x_1, the proportion of the two inputs constituted by commodity 1. This shows, for example, if the proportion of input 1 in the input mix is $x_1 = OA$, then the next period's outputs can be given by any one of the output combinations represented by the points along locus *BC*, each of them clearly corresponding to some quantity of y_1 and some quantity of y_2.

Having thus described the range of possibilities,[23] we have two more steps to complete in our depiction of the von Neumann analy-

[23] The diagram shown here represents a smooth production function which constitutes a strictly convex set and so corresponds to the case of diminishing returns to any one input or one output (the surface approaches the x-axis and therefore represents lower returns as the proportion of x_1 in the input bundle becomes too small or too large). For some complications which arise when this condition does not hold, see Koopmans, *ibid.*

sis. First, since that analysis deals only with proportionate growth, we must determine which of the output possibilities represented in the diagram do in fact correspond to proportionate growth. Second, we must then consider the set of proportionate growth possibilities and determine which of these is *greatest,* i.e., which of these corresponds to von Neumann's maximal growth solution.

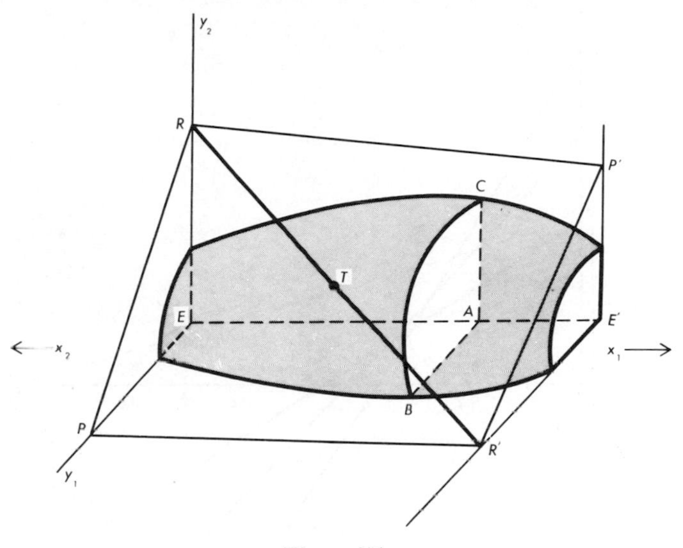

Figure 55

In Figure 56 numbers have been put on the x_1-axis, EE', which, it will be noted, run from a minimum value of $x_1 = 0$ (when the entire input bundle is composed of input 2) to a maximum value of $x_1 = 1$ (when item 1 is the only input available). This is what we read as we proceed along the axis from left to right. But if we go in the other direction, this can just as easily be interpreted as an x_2-axis, one which measures the proportion of the input bundle composed of commodity 2. Thus, the point $x_1 = 0.8$ can also be interpreted as $x_2 = 0.2$, and E_2, the leftward end of the axis, can be taken either as $x_1 = 0$ or as $x_2 = 1$.

Now from E', the right-hand end of the x-axis, draw a line $E'y'_1$ parallel to the y_1-axis. On that line measure off a point R' lying u units from point E'. It should be clear that point R' involves an output of zero units of y_2 and of u units of y_1. Since point E' represents zero units of x_2 and one unit of x_1, we see that the move from

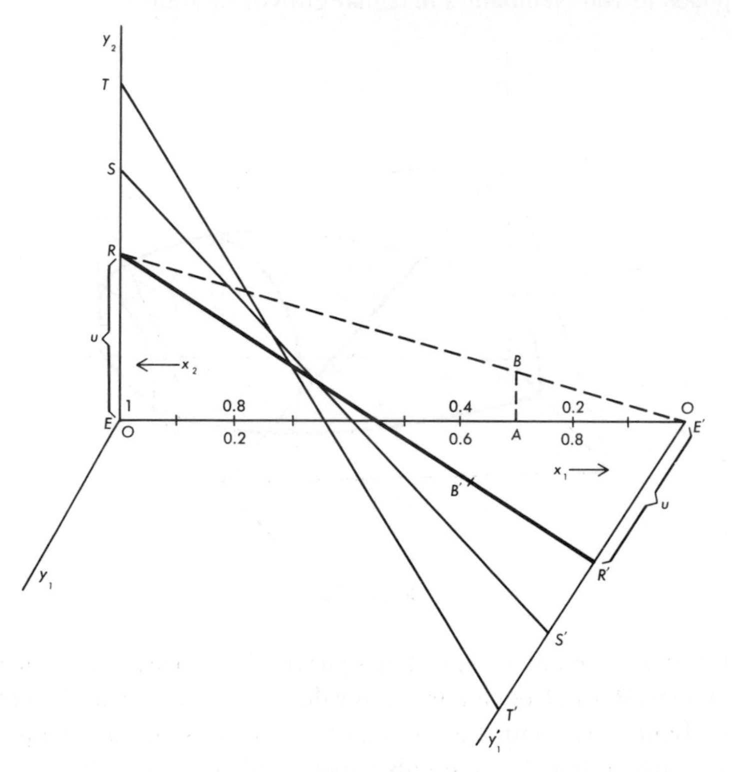

Figure 56

point E' to point R' involves proportionate growth of the two-commodity outputs: $y_1 = ux_1 = u$ and $y_2 = ux_2 = 0$. Similarly, if along the y_2-axis we measure off a point R which lies u units above E, it should be clear that this again involves proportionate growth at rate u, with $y_1 = ux_1 = 0$ and $y_2 = ux_2 = u$.

Next, let us draw a straight-line segment connecting points R and

R'. It is readily shown [24] that *every point along this line segment represents proportionate growth at rate u.*[25] For the same reasons it follows that SS' and TT' (where $ES = E'S'$ and $ET = E'T'$) are also proportionate growth loci, but they represent rates of growth greater than that on RR'. For example, RR', whose rate of growth is $ER = u$, involves a slower expansion than does SS', whose rate of growth is ES. That is, the farther from the x-axis a given proportionate growth locus lies, the more rapid the rate of growth it will represent.

Having found our proportionate growth loci, our remaining objective is to determine the *maximal* proportionate growth rate. This involves our getting onto the growth locus which lies farthest from the x-axis. Now, to find the highest of these proportionate growth loci that is *attainable* by the economy, we must return to Figure 55 to relate these loci to our shaded production surface. Obviously, a proportionate growth locus, any part of which touches or lies below this production surface, represents a feasible rate of growth—one which the economy's resources suffice to achieve. The highest attainable rate of growth is then that corresponding to the proportionate growth locus *tangent* to the production surface. In Figure 55 this is the locus RR', which is tangent to the production surface at point T.

The four coordinates of point T then represent the von Neumann growth path, the two input and output quantities that constitute maximal rate of growth. This completes the basic graphic representation of the von Neumann growth analysis. It also suggests, in this

[24] *Proof.* Consider the projection RE' of RR' on the xy_2-plane. Let B' be any point on RR' and B be the corresponding point on that projection. Call its x_2-coordinate x_{2b} and its y_2-coordinate y_{2b}. Then we have

$$\frac{y_{2b}}{u} = \frac{AB}{ER} \quad \text{and} \quad \frac{x_{2b}}{1} = \frac{AE'}{EE'}.$$

But since triangles $AE'B$ and $EE'R$ are similar, we have $AB/ER = AE'/EE'$ so that the preceding equations immediately yield $x_{2b} = uy_{2b}$.

Similarly, by projecting RR' onto the xy_1-plane, it follows that $x_{1b} = uy_{1b}$. Hence, point B' represents proportionate growth at rate u, as was to be shown.

[25] Strictly speaking, u should be called the growth *factor* with r as the growth rate, where $u = 1 + r$, for then we have $y_i = ux_i = (1 + r)x_i = x_i + rx_i$ and it is only the last of these terms that involves growth.

simple two-output case, that a maximal growth solution *always exists,* for with a bounded production possibility region there will always be a highest proportionate growth line such as RR'. Thus, in this case the geometry permits a far simpler analysis than von Neumann was forced to employ in his existence theorem.

However, there remains one element—pricing—which can usefully be added to the analysis. It will be recalled from our earlier discussion that the dual portion of the von Neumann analysis consists in the determination of an interest rate and a price for each of the outputs of the economy which just permit the economy to break even. Letting p_1 and p_2 be the respective prices of the two outputs and letting v be the interest factor, we have as the equation of an iso-profit locus

$$p_1y_1 + p_2y_2 - v(p_1x_1 + p_2x_2) = K.$$

But from the manner in which we are measuring x_1 and x_2 we have $x_2 = 1 - x_1$. Substituting this into the preceding equation, we obtain

$$p_1y_1 + p_2y_2 - v(p_1 - p_2)x_1 = K + p_2v, \qquad (159)$$

which is the equation of a plane in our diagram. Von Neumann chose as his objective the determination of values for the interest rate and the two prices at which the optimal production combination will just yield zero profits and any other output will produce a loss. To find the prices that do this, we first turn the preceding equation into a *zero* iso-profit locus by setting $K = 0$. We then determine the values of p_1, p_2, and v at which this locus is just tangent to the production surface at the optimal point T. That is, we select values of p_1, p_2, and v which, with $K = 0$, render (159) the equation for the plane $PR'P'R$ in Figure 55.

This, then, is the geometric interpretation of the von Neumann prices—they are the parameters of the equation of a zero iso-profit plane, the plane which is just tangent to the production surface at the optimal growth point. In fact, we can readily go one step farther. Solving (159) for y_2, we obtain

$$y_2 = -(p_1/p_2)y_1 + v(p_1 - p_2)x_1/p_2 + v.$$

We see now that the interest factor v is the y_2-intercept of the zero iso-profit plane, i.e., $v = y_2$ when $y_1 = x_1 = 0$. Thus, geometrically, we have $v = ER$. But, by construction, ER is equal to the growth rate u (see Figure 56). Hence this represents another of von Neumann's results: the growth rate, u, is equal to the interest factor, v.

Similarly, differentiating, we see $\partial y_2/\partial y_1 = -p_1/p_2$. That is, the price ratio is given by the absolute value of the slope of RP. In sum, the absolute value of the interest factor and the *relative* values of the prices are completely determined by the tangent hyperplane to the von Neumann point.

10. THE TURNPIKE THEOREM

The von Neumann model is clearly rather abstract, and direct application is therefore not very likely. One of its most serious limitations, from the point of view of policy, is its preoccupation with balanced growth, in which all outputs expand proportionately. Thus, for example, this model is not designed to deal with the preferences of the inhabitants of an economy who wish to consume relatively more luxury goods and comparatively fewer necessities as output expands. One step on the way toward application was taken by Professors Dorfman, Samuelson, and Solow [26] when they proposed the "turnpike theorem." This theorem states that under certain relatively mild additional assumptions, about which more will be said presently, it will be most efficient for the economy to expand along a path of which a substantial portion approximates the optimal von Neumann growth path, even if nonproportional growth is desired.

Specifically, the turnpike hypothesis asserts that if the period considered in the calculation is very long the optimal investment plan will involve an initial period when the economy alters its output proportions (usually quite rapidly) toward those called for by the von Neumann analysis; then (usually over a substantial period) the economy will expand at least approximately in accord with the

[26] Robert Dorfman, P. A. Samuelson, and R. M. Solow, *Linear Programming and Economic Analysis* (McGraw-Hill, New York, 1958).

von Neumann optimal growth path, but it will depart from that path gradually, approaching the output proportions which it is desired that the economy ultimately achieve.

A numerical example may make this remarkable proposition clearer. If in a two-commodity economy the two goods are produced in a 2 to 1 ratio, and the economy hopes ultimately to achieve a 3 to 1 ratio, but if the von Neumann solution calls for the two items to be manufactured in equal amounts, then the turnpike theorem asserts that it will pay as an intermediate step to decrease the relative output of the first good even though ultimately it is desired that its relative output become even greater than it is currently!

Graphically, we see in Figure 57 that any *proportionate* growth path requires expansion of the two outputs, y_1 and y_2, along a straight line (ray) from the origin, because only such a line satisfies the equation $y_2 = ky_1$. Thus, the ray OR_1 involves balanced growth because the output combinations indicated along it for 1960, 1961, 1962, and 1963 all involve the same ratio between y_1 and y_2.

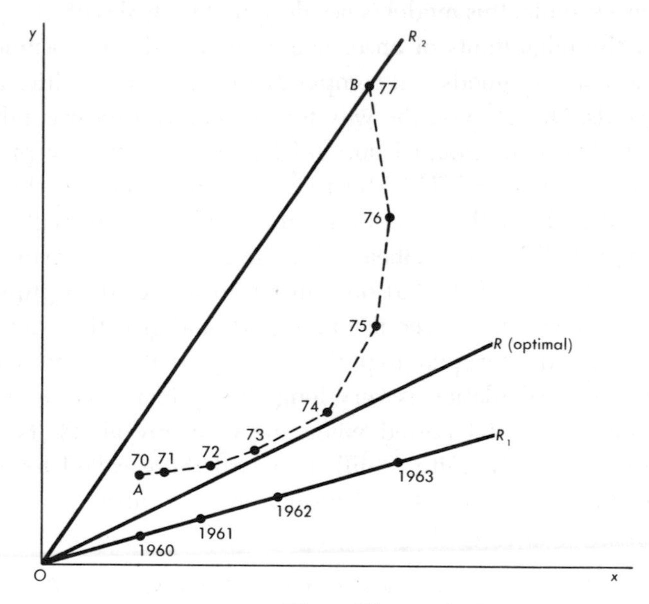

Figure 57

The von Neumann model undertakes to examine all possible proportionate growth paths, i.e., all possible rays through the origin, and to determine which of them yields the fastest expansion rate. Suppose that *OR* turns out to be the optimal (von Neumann) ray. Let us now indicate once more what is asserted by the turnpike conjecture. Suppose the economy begins its planning in 1970 when it finds itself with the output levels indicated by point *A*. Suppose, moreover, that by 1977 it hopes to achieve the proportions indicated by point *B*, i.e., that it wishes to find itself as far as possible from the origin on ray OR_2. The turnpike theorem tells us that it will *not* be optimal to proceed along a relatively straight path from *A* directly toward ray OR_2. Rather, it will pay to *detour* toward the optimal ray *OR* along a path such as that indicated by the points 70, 71, 72, · · ·, 77.

The turnpike conjecture is rendered plausible by contemplation of its title. What it suggests is the analogy with automotive routing in which, when we travel between two fairly proximate geographic points, it may pay us to proceed via whatever roads take us there most directly. But when the distance between origin and destination is substantial, it will save time to proceed via the turnpike, a route which, though it takes us out of our way, speeds up the journey because we go much of the distance on the fastest road.

11. CONDITIONS FOR THE TURNPIKE THEOREM

The graphic discussion indicates how one can deal with one matter that must be settled before one can attempt even to state rigorously the turnpike theorem. For this purpose one must decide how to define maximal *disproportionate* growth. So long as all outputs are required to increase by the same percentage, this index number problem does not arise. But if some outputs increase more than others and, perhaps, some even decline, how does one determine which of several outputs has grown most rapidly? The answer is given by the terms in which the turnpike theorem is stated, for that theorem requires society's objectives to be expressed by means of the relative outputs at some horizon date, say h years from now. If we define a target set of output quantities $h_1, h_2, \cdots, h_n$ for the relative output quantities for our horizon date, h, the objective is taken to be to maximize *absolute* outputs, with relative outputs the same as those of the h_i. That is, society's goal is to maximize that year's output of the economy's n commodities, $y_{1h}, y_{2h}, \cdots, y_{nh}$, subject to the output proportion requirements

$$y_{1h} = kh_1, y_{2h} = kh_2, \cdots, y_{nh} = kh_n. \qquad (160)$$

This clearly can be written as a single variable problem

Maximize k subject to the constraints (160).

Geometrically this is equivalent to the requirement that we move as far as possible from the origin along ray OR_2 in the preceding diagram, for it means we will have increased outputs in accord with the predetermined portionality requirements, and in doing so we will have achieved the largest attainable increase.

This discussion brings out one rather curious element in the orientation of the turnpike analysis. It assumes that society suffers from a fixation on the output proportions and the total output in one particular year, h, and that to maximize output in that year, with no deviation from the preassigned proportions, it is prepared to undergo whatever indignities are necessary in the meantime. No matter how distasteful may be the output proportions required by the von Neumann path, it is assumed implicitly that society is willing to undertake the sacrifice. Like the driver who endures the dull stretches of the turnpike in order to get there quickly, our economy is taken in its collective will to choose whatever tedious consumption patterns the von Neumann path requires, but not just for a few hours as in the turnpike drive—perhaps for decades or even centuries.

In addition to monomania in society's goals, the turnpike theorem requires several other premises. One of the most obvious, when one thinks of it, is the requirement that the turnpike be accessible.

And as the road analogy suggests, this is not always a trivial matter. We all know of turnpike entrances about which it is most honest to confess that "you can't get there from here—you must start from somewhere else." The entrances and exits of the von Neumann path are all attainable, provided one simple condition—free disposal of excess outputs—is satisfied. That is to say, we must assume the validity of a premise that is implicit in much of mathematical programming which states that we are no worse off having 120 per cent of the desired output of some commodity than we would be if we had been given precisely the amount we desired. Of course, in practice this assumption simply is not true. Garbage removers must live too. But if, as an approximation, we are willing to accept this premise, a moment's thought will show us why it can guarantee entry to and egress from the von Neumann ray—indeed, why it gives us the ability to move from any one ray inside the diagram to any other. Suppose, for example, that the ray we wish to attain involves a 2 to 1 ratio between y_1 and y_2 but that we find ourselves with 30 units of y_1 and 20 units of y_2. We can then obviously achieve the desired proportion by throwing 5 units of y_2 onto the trash heap. That may or may not be the best way to obtain the desired result, but it certainly is guaranteed to do the trick!

Figure 58 shows what the path resulting from direct use of the disposal process might be like. From an initial point A we wish to proceed as far as possible along the desired output ray, OR'. To get there via the turnpike ray, OR, we decide to enter the turnpike by means of disposal. We therefore do so by getting rid of our excess y_2 output, i.e., by dropping straight down to point B, the point on optimal growth ray OR directly below our initial point A. We now proceed along the turnpike as far as we can before our terminal date, h periods hence. Suppose we arrive in this way at point C. Now we have too much of output y_1 for the proportions that characterize our target ray, OR'. We can, however, move directly leftward to point D on OR' simply by getting rid of DC, the excess quantity of x at point C.

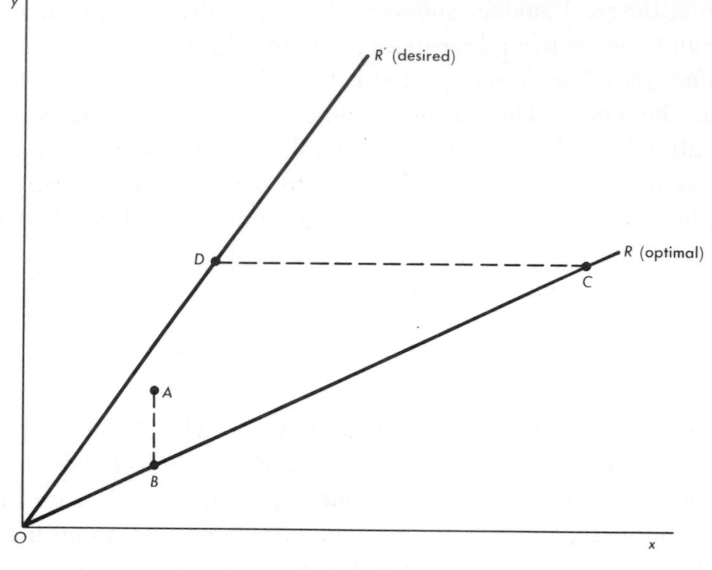

Figure 58

12. SKETCH OF THE PROOF AND DISCUSSION OF ITS PREMISES[27]

We can now outline a proof of the turnpike theorem, one put forth by Radner.[28] As we have seen, in the turnpike theorem the objective postulated for the economy is to move as far as possible along the desired output ray, meaning that we want its final outputs, $y_1^T, \cdots, y_n^T$, to have the same proportions as some prespecified bundle of outputs on that ray, $h_1, \cdots, h_n$. That is, we want to attain a set of outputs $y_1^T = kh_1, \cdots, y_n^T = kh_n$ in which the value of k is as large as possible. To measure our degree of achievement in

[27] Before starting on the next few pages, the reader may find it helpful to review Sections 8 and 9 of this chapter, especially the discussions of Figures 55 and 56.

[28] Roy Radner, "Prices and the Turnpike, III. Paths of Economic Growth that Are Optimal Only to Final States: A Turnpike Theorem," *Review of Economic Studies*, Vol. XXVIII, February 1961. See also Koopmans, *op. cit.*, for a very lucid discussion.

moving toward that objective at any intermediate period, it is convenient to begin by defining a measure of output growth.

Let $P_1, P_2, \cdots, P_n$, all positive numbers, be *any* set of output prices. Then let us define the value of output as

$$v = P_1y_1 + P_2y_2 + \cdots + P_ny_n.$$

It is clear that for any set of outputs lying on the desired ray, i.e., for any outputs proportionate to $h_1, \cdots, h_n$, whatever maximizes these outputs must maximize v and vice versa. For then v may be written as

$$v = P_1kh_1 + \cdots + P_nkh_n = k(P_1h_1 + \cdots + P_nh_n)$$

so that maximization of v and maximization of k are equivalent.

Now, while this holds for *any* set of prices, it is helpful for our purposes to select a particular set of prices—the von Neumann prices corresponding to the partial slopes of the hyperplane tangent to the von Neumann solution point (the plane $PR'P'R$ tangent to the production surface at solution point T in Figure 55). Using these price figures, we may now define the rate of growth in output value as the ratio of the output values in two succeeding periods

$$u = \frac{P_1y_1 + \cdots + P_ny_n}{P_1x_1 + \cdots + P_nx_n}.$$

In terms of the two-output world shown in our diagram this becomes $u = (P_1y_1 + P_2y_2)/(P_1x_1 + P_2x_2)$. Recall that at the x_1-origin point in the diagram we have $x_1 = y_1 = 0$ and $x_2 = 1$. Substituting these values into the growth ratio expression, we obtain

$$u = (P_1 \cdot 0 + P_2y_2)/(P_1 \cdot 0 + P_2 \cdot 1) = P_2y_2/P_2 = y_2.$$

In other words, u is ER, the height of the price plane at the point above the x_1-origin. That is, u is the rate of growth of output as we had defined it earlier in the chapter. By the tangency of our plane with the production locus we note that any parallel plane through any other feasible point must involve a growth rate u' (a y_2-intercept) which is less than u. u is therefore the maximum rate of growth in value attainable from any feasible point, so that u can be considered as the speed limit for the system. Moreover, because of the curvature of the production surface, we note that as our plane is moved in parallel shifts through points farther from von Neumann point T, the rate of growth of the system, as given by height ER, becomes smaller and smaller.

The argument behind the turnpike theorem can now be summarized briefly. Consider the optimal path whose rate of value growth during the relevant periods $1, 2, \cdots, h$ may respectively be denoted by $u_1', u_2', \cdots, u_h'$. As one alternative to this optimal path the economy has at its disposal the turnpike route $ABCD$ shown in Figure 58. Along this route segment AB can be traversed in one period (it simply involves getting rid of the excessive quantity AB of y_2). Similarly, the economy can get from point C to point D in one step by getting rid of its excessive y_1. Hence, of the h periods in which it seeks to maximize its output, the economy has $h - 2$ periods to travel along the turnpike, along trajectory BC. That means that along this turnpike route the economy will be traveling for $h - 2$ periods at the speed limit, u. Let us use this turnpike path $ABCD$ as a standard with which to compare the (as yet undetermined) optimal path. It is clear that if a large number of periods is involved (h is large), and the optimal path is to beat the alternative turnpike route that has just been described at its rates of growth, $u_1', \cdots, u_h'$, then most of these speeds must be very close to u, the speed limit on the turnpike. But we have seen from our discussion of Figure 55 that such rates of growth can be attained only at points very close to the von Neumann point, T, and so it follows that along most of its route the optimal path must coincide with or lie very close to the turnpike. This, then, is the essence of the Radner proof.

The reader may well feel that the argument is a bit too simple, that somehow it has sneaked something over on him. And to some extent this is true. We may see more clearly what is going on by reviewing briefly some of the premises that were implicit in the discussion. We shall focus on three assumptions that have played a critical role in the argument:

a. The convexity of the feasible production region
b. The choice of objective; maximization of a terminal bundle of preselected output proportions
c. Constant returns to scale.[29]

a. *Convexity*. The convexity of the shaded production possibility region in Figure 55 is, as we saw in Section 8 of this chapter, an assumption of diminishing returns in production in the substitution of one input for another and in the substitution of one output for another. That is, as we switch more and more resources, say from the production of y_1 to the production of y_2, convexity implies that $\partial y_2/\partial y_1$, the marginal rate of substitution, will diminish.

This premise is obviously necessary for our conclusion that the optimal point T is the only one that reaches the price plane $PR'P'R$ in Figure 55, and for the observation that as we move farther and farther from point T, diminishing returns slow down the economy's rate of growth. If convexity did not hold, it simply would not follow that all fast routes must lie near the turnpike.

b. *The choice of objective*. Our second critical premise is the assumption that the economy is concerned only with its terminal output bundle and does not care about the composition of its outputs in intermediate periods, the periods before h, the day of reckoning. This is obviously unrealistic and quite unreasonable. There is no one horizon date in terms of which we are prepared to evaluate the accomplishments of the economy and we certainly do care about the composition of the economy's output in each and every year—this year, next year, and the year after that. But under these circumstances the turnpike theorem becomes rather less plausible. Again the travel analogy from which the theorem derives its name

[29] Several other premises have in fact been implicit in the preceding discussion. These include the premise that the optimal prices are all positive (the von Neumann theorem only asserts that they are nonnegative) and the assumption of the disposal of excessive inputs and outputs that is necessary to get us from A to B and from C to D in Figure 55. For a discussion of these matters and generalizations of the result utilizing less demanding assumptions, see Koopmans, *op. cit.*

should make this clear. Traveling by turnpike can be recommended if we care only about getting as far as possible in a given time. But if we are concerned about the pleasure derived during the course of the trip, it may well be rational to take a slower, more scenic route, sacrificing ultimate achievement (distance covered) for utility derived in the interim.

c. *Linear homogeneity.* Finally, let us consider how constant returns to scale enter the matter. It is in part to this assumption that we may ascribe the fact that the turnpike turns out always to involve proportionate growth in all outputs—movement along a ray such as *OR* in Figures 57 and 58. The matter may be viewed as follows. It is certainly plausible that if speed is the sole objective and distances are sufficiently great, it will always pay to proceed to *some* turnpike. But why should that turnpike always be a ray through the origin—why should it not be, e.g., some sort of curved trajectory? It is like a theorem which implies that all U.S. turnpike roads must radiate from Dallas, and that there can be no turnpike heading straight across the United States from east to west, one which misses that city altogther.

To get an inkling of the reason the mathematics are in fact able to conclude that the turnpike must be a ray, let us contrast the consequences of optimal proportionate growth with some sort of optimal nonproportionate growth. If we choose to travel along the fastest of the proportionate growth paths (the von Neumann path), the inputs of period $t + 1$ will have the same relative magnitudes as those in period t. By constant returns to scale the rate of growth attainable in period $t + 1$ will be as great as that in period t. The path which starts off fastest continues to be fastest throughout the time periods involved. But suppose now that we decide to try instead a nonproportionate path which starts out growing rapidly; suppose it is initially the most rapid among some prespecified class of nonproportionate growth paths. However, as time passes, since growth is not proportionate, output (input) proportions must change. This means we must move farther and farther from our initial point in Figure 55. Convexity, the diminishing returns to substitution of one output for another, must then begin to cut down the rate of growth of the economy, and so, ultimately, the nonproportionate growth path, whatever its initial rate of growth, must lose steam because it moves away from whatever initial point was chosen for its high growth rate.[30]

13. CONCLUDING COMMENT

In this chapter we have seen reviewed several growth models of very great analytic power and considerable interest for theoretical investigation of the growth process. However, we have seen the price that has been paid for the depth to which they can be probed. They require highly restrictive assumptions which limit their applicability most severely, and this has, certainly up to this point, precluded their use as instruments of policy. Even the literature on the golden rule and the turnpike theorem which were designed to broaden the applicability of the analyses have admittedly represented only very limited steps in that direction. The premises underlying these two results also mean that they must be treated with utmost caution as tools to be used in the examination of reality.

To provide a contrast with these models, the next chapter reviews

[30] A further graphic discussion may perhaps make this point clearer. With constant returns to scale the production possibilities represented by Figure 55 will not change from period to period because the figure is represented in terms of relative inputs, just as was the case for the capital-labor ratio used as our horizontal axis in the earlier diagram of this chapter. Now the reader may note that a tangent plane can be chosen for any point on the production surface, not just that for the von Neumann point T. Suppose we select the plane tangent to point C. Call this new plane C^*. Let C^{**} be any plane parallel to C^* but going through any point other than C in the production possibility region. Then it is clear that C^{**} must lie below C^*. That is, if we take the prices P_{1c}, P_{2c} to be those corresponding to point C, it is clear that at these prices point C will in some sense be the output of greatest value, $v_c = P_{1c}y_1 + P_{2c}y_2$. But because at point C, $y_2/y_1 \neq x_2/x_1$, in the next period the input proportions will have changed from those at point A and the economy will no longer be able to get to point C. Its output point in the next period must therefore lie below plane C^*. With constant returns to scale, only by producing at a point such as T, where outputs are proportionate to inputs, can the economy continue for period after period on the highest attainable growth plane corresponding to some fixed set of prices.

two very simple constructs designed to offer some bits of illumination on policy matters. It will be seen that those models are considerably more limited in subtlety and analytic depth. But, even so, the conclusions which can be drawn from them must be hedged with care.

Chapter Eighteen

TWO MODELS WITH POLICY IMPLICATIONS *

After the discussion of the sophisticated growth models that occupies the preceding chapter, the very elementary analyses which are about to be described may appear inappropriate, particularly since they are the work of the author of this volume. However, they illustrate the degree of simplification which at this stage seems to be required to draw any implications for decision making from theoretical work in economic dynamics. Their inclusion therefore seems desirable as an illustration of the present state of the art.

1. UNBALANCED GROWTH AND RISING SERVICE COSTS: PREMISES

The model to which we turn now is designed to help us understand the financial problems of a wide variety of economic services: municipal government, education, the performing arts, restaurants, and leisure time activity. It will be argued that inherent in the technological structure of each of these activities are forces working almost unavoidably for progressive and cumulative increases in the real costs incurred in supplying them. As a consequence, efforts to offset these cost increases, while they may succeed temporarily, in

* Portions of this chapter are reprinted from articles in the *American Economic Review*, and *The Review of Economics and Statistics*, by permission of the editors.

the long run are merely palliatives which can have no significant effect on the underlying trends.

Our model uses several assumptions, only one of which is really essential. This basic premise asserts that economic activities can, not entirely arbitrarily, be grouped into two types: technologically progressive activities in which innovations, capital accumulation, and economies of large scale all make for a cumulative rise in output per man hour and activities which, by their very nature, permit only sporadic increases in productivity.

Of course, productivity does not grow at a uniform rate throughout the economy, so it is hardly surprising that, given any arbitrarily chosen dividing line, one can fit all goods and services into one or the other of two such categories. I am, however, making a much stronger assertion: that the place of any particular activity in this classification is not primarily a fortuitous matter, but rather that it is a manifestation of the activity's technological structure, which determines, with a considerable degree of likelihood, whether the productivity of its labor inputs will grow slowly or rapidly.[1]

The basic source of differentiation resides in the role played by labor in the activity. In some cases labor is primarily an instrument for the attainment of the final product, while in other fields of endeavor for all practical purposes the labor is itself the end product. Manufacturing gives us the most obvious examples of the former type of activity. When someone purchases an air conditioner, he neither knows nor cares how much labor went into it. Thus, it has been possible to effect successive and cumulative decreases in the labor input coefficient for most manufactured goods, often along with some degree of improvement in the quality of the product.

[1] One point must be made clear at once—nothing in the following discussion is to be taken to imply that any particular activity is incapable of profiting from significant technological changes. The great increases in productivity that arose out of the agricultural revolution, the mechanization of the kitchen, and the really spectacular productivity increases in the performing arts made possible by the electronic media all have belied arguments which purported to show that there was little room for innovation in these fields. I fully expect that the future will provide other technological revolutions in areas in which we do not anticipate them.

On the other hand, there are a number of services in which the labor is an end in itself, in which quality is judged directly in terms of amount of labor. Teaching is a clear-cut example, where class size (number of teaching hours expended per student) is often taken as a critical index of quality. Here, despite the invention of teaching machines, the use of closed circuit television, and a variety of other innovations, there still seem to be fairly firm limits to class size. We are concerned when elementary school classes grow to 50 pupils and are disquieted by the idea of college lectures attended by 2000 underclassmen. Without a complete revolution in our approach to teaching, there is no prospect that we can ever go beyond these levels (or even up to them) with any degree of equanimity. A more striking example is one I have offered in another context: live performance. A half hour horn quintet calls for the expenditure of 2½ man hours in its performance, and any attempt to increase productivity here is likely to be viewed with concern by critics and audience alike.

The difference between the two types of activity in the flexibility of their productivity levels should not be exaggerated. It is a matter of degree rather than an absolute dichotomy. There are all sorts of intermediate activities which fall between the two more extreme varieties. Yet, the distinction between the relatively constant productivity industries and those in which productivity can more easily rise is a very real one.

In addition to the separability of activities into our two basic categories I shall utilize three other assumptions, two of them primarily for ease of exposition. The first of these premises asserts that all outlays other than labor costs can be ignored. This is patently unrealistic but it simplifies greatly our mathematical model. A second, more important, and more realistic assumption is that wages in the two sectors of the economy go up and down together. In the long run there is some degree of mobility in all labor markets, and consequently, while wages in one activity can lag behind those in another, unless the former is in the process of disappearing altogether, we cannot expect the disparity to continue indefinitely. For simplicity in the next section I shall take hourly wages to be precisely the same in both sectors, but the model is easily complicated to allow for some diversity in wage levels and their movements.

A final inessential assumption, which is, however, not altogether unrealistic, asserts that money wages will rise as rapidly as output per man hour in the sector where productivity is increasing. Since organized labor is not slow to learn of increases in its productivity, it is likely to adjust its wage demands accordingly. This premise affects only the magnitude of the absolute price level in our model and does not influence the relative costs and prices that are the critical elements in the analysis.

2. A MODEL OF UNBALANCED EXPANSION

As just mentioned, we assume that the economy is divided into two sectors, sector 1, in which the productivity of labor is constant, and sector 2, in which output per man hour grows cumulatively at a constant compounded rate, *r*. Thus we have for the respective values of outputs Y_{1t} and Y_{2t} in the two sectors at time *t:*

$$Y_{1t} = aL_{1t}$$

$$Y_{2t} = bL_{2t}e^{rt}$$

where L_{1t} and L_{2t} are the quantities of labor employed in the two sectors and a and b are constants.

We suppose wages are equal in the two sectors and are fixed at W_t dollars per unit of labor, where W_t itself grows in accord with the productivity of sector 2, our "progressive" sector, so that

$$W_t = We^{rt} \qquad (W = \text{some constant}). \qquad (161)$$

We may now derive several properties of such a system. First and most fundamental is:

PROPOSITION ONE: The cost per unit of output of sector 1, C_1, will rise without limit, while C_2, the unit cost of sector 2, will remain constant. *Proof:*

$$C_1 = W_t L_{1t}/Y_{1t} = We^{rt}L_{1t}/aL_{1t} = We^{rt}/a$$

$$C_2 = W_t L_{2t}/Y_{2t} = We^{rt}L_{2t}/bL_{2t}e^{rt} = W/b.$$

Note that the *relative* costs will behave in this manner whether or not wages increase in accord with (161), for we have

$$C_1/C_2 = (L_{1t}/Y_{1t})/(L_{2t}/Y_{2t}) = be^{rt}/a.$$

In practice, it is plausible in these circumstances that market demand for the output of sector 1 would decline. Suppose, for example, the elasticity of demand for the two outputs were unity in terms of prices which were proportionate to costs. Then relative outlays on the two commodities would remain constant; i.e., we would have

$$\frac{C_1Y_1}{C_2Y_2} = \frac{We^{rt}L_{1t}}{We^{rt}L_{2t}} = \frac{L_{1t}}{L_{2t}} = A(\text{constant}). \qquad (162)$$

Hence the output ratio of the two sectors would be given by

$$Y_1/Y_2 = aL_{1t}/bL_{2t}e^{rt} = aA/be^{rt},$$

which declines toward zero with the passage of time. Thus we have:

PROPOSITION TWO: In the model of unbalanced productivity there is a tendency for the outputs of the "nonprogressive" sector whose demands are not highly price inelastic and not very income elastic to decline and perhaps, ultimately, to vanish.[2] We may inquire, however, what would happen if despite the change in their relative costs and prices the magnitude of the relative outputs of the two sectors were maintained, perhaps with the aid of govern-

[2] Note that with the elasticities posited and with a constant labor force the output of the nonprogressive sector would not decline; it would remain absolutely constant. For by (162) $L_{1t}/L_{2t} = A$; so with total labor supply fixed, i.e., $L_{1t} + L_{2t}$ constant, it follows that L_{1t} and therefore Y_{1t} will not vary with time. However, if expenditures on Y_{1t} rise at a rate an iota slower (demand slightly elastic), Y_{1t} will, indeed, fall over time.

ment subsidy, or if demand for the product in question were sufficiently price inelastic or income elastic. Then we would have

$$(b/a)Y_1/Y_2 = L_1/L_2e^{rt} = K.$$

That is

$$L_1/L_2 = Ke^{rt}. \tag{163}$$

Thus we have:

PROPOSITION THREE: In the unbalanced productivity model, if the ratio of the outputs of the two sectors is held constant, more and more of the total labor force must be transferred to the nonprogressive sector and the relative amount of labor in the other sector will tend to approach zero.

We may also show that a determination to retain a fixed ratio between the outputs of the progressive and nonprogressive sectors can act as a drag on economic growth, causing it to level off over time (unless one revalues sufficiently the outputs of the nonprogressive sector whose increasing absorption of the labor force is, of course, the source of the difficulty).

To prove the growth proposition, form the following index of output of the two sectors, with constant weights B_1 and B_2:

$$I = B_1Y_1 + B_2Y_2 = B_1aL_1 + B_2bL_2e^{rt}.$$

Now from (163) note that

$$L_2 = VL_1e^{-rt}, \tag{164}$$

where $V = 1/K$. Substituting this into I, we obtain

$$I = (B_1a + B_2bV)L_1 = RL_1, \tag{165}$$

where the expression in parentheses, which we have called R, is a constant.

Now let us take as our (rather usual) measure of growth the output per capita. Assuming population to be proportionate to the total labor supply, $L_1 + L_2 = L_1(1 + Ve^{-rt})$ [by (164) and (165)], our total measure of growth becomes

$$I/(L_1 + L_2) = RL_1/L_1(1 + Ve^{-rt}) = R/(1 + Ve^{-rt}),$$

which clearly increases with t but at a declining rate as it approaches the value R asymptotically. We have, then, arrived at:

PROPOSITION FOUR: An attempt to achieve balanced growth in a world of unbalanced productivity must lead to a declining rate of growth relative to the rate of growth of the labor force. In particular, if productivity in one sector and the total labor force remain constant, the growth rate of the economy will asymptotically approach zero.

3. *A DIAGRAMMATIC RESTATEMENT*

A number of commentators have found it convenient to restate the preceding argument in geometric terms.[3] Assuming a fixed labor force, the division of the economy into a progressive and nonprogressive sector can be described by a sequence of production possibility loci with Y_1 and Y_2 on the two axes of the diagram. Using slightly more general assumptions than were employed in the algebraic argument, this production possibility curve need not be linear. Now, as the productivity of labor in industry 2 increases, the leftward end of the production possibility locus will, with the passage of time, shift farther and farther from the origin. The right-hand end, representing full utilization of the labor force by the nonprogressive sector alone, will not change its position. Thus, in Figure 59 the production possibility curve shifts from an initial

[3] The diagram used in this section was first constructed by David Bradford, and the discussion follows his work. Other diagrammatic translations of the argument have been provided by L. K. Lynch and E. L. Redman and by D. A. Worcester, Jr. Only the last of these has so far been published, though it is my impression that the other authors developed their graphic constructs a bit earlier. See "Macroeconomics of Unbalanced Growth: Comment," *American Economic Review*, Vol. LVIII, September 1968.

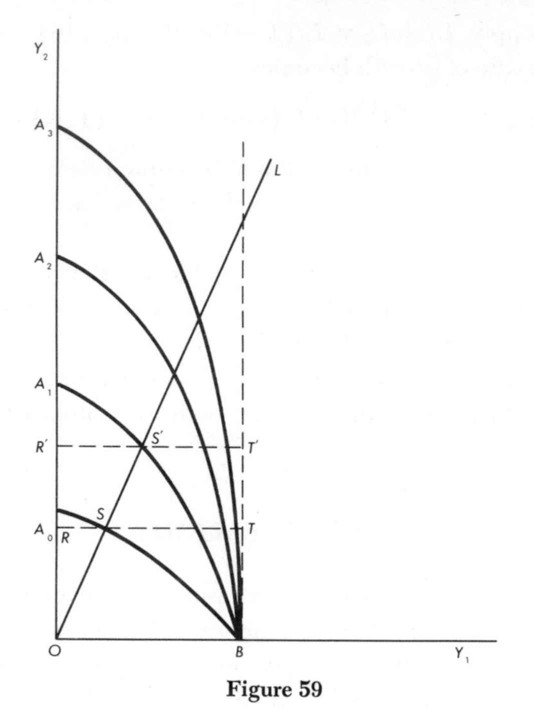

Figure 59

position A_0B, after some time has elapsed, to A_1B and then to A_2B, etc.

All our propositions can be derived with the aid of the figure. Only two of these derivations will be described because these two can be explained briefly. Proposition One, the rising relative cost of Y_1, is obvious on inspection, since the opportunity cost of Y_2 in terms of Y_1 is given by the (absolute value of the) slope of the production possibility locus ($\Delta Y_2/\Delta Y_1$). If the outward shift of the production curve involves no change in its shape, this slope must increase without limit with the passage of time, and we have our result at once.[4]

[4] In particular, the result must hold if the production loci are straight lines, as assumed implicitly in the mathematics. But as Bradford points out, the proposition can break down if the curves change shape sufficiently as they shift.

Proposition Three, the growing proportion of the labor force involved in Y_1 required to maintain a constant output ratio, is also derived without difficulty. A constant ratio between Y_1 and Y_2 has as its locus a ray (straight line) through the origin such as OL, for the equation of the required locus is $Y_2 = kY_1$. Now, by its production function $Y_1 = aL_1$, output Y_1 is strictly proportionate to the labor employed in its production. OB is the maximum output of Y_1, the amount which would be produced if the entire labor force, L, were in the nonprogressive sector. Therefore at any lower output level of Y_1, say RS, we have $L_1/L =$ (Output of Y_1)/(Maximum output of Y_1) $= RS/RT$. We now see that in the next period, with proportionate growth in the two sectors, L_1/L will have risen to $R'S'/R'T'$. Proceeding in this way we arrive at Proposition Three, the constantly rising proportion of the labor force in the nonprogressive sector.

4. DISCUSSION OF THE PROPOSITIONS

The logic of the entire analysis can be restated rather simply in intuitive terms. If productivity per man hour rises cumulatively in one sector relative to its rate of growth elsewhere in the economy while wages rise commensurately in all areas, then relative costs in the nonprogressive sectors must inevitably rise; *and these costs will rise cumulatively and without limit*, for while in the progressive sector productivity increases will serve as an offset to rising wages, this offset must be smaller in the nonprogressive sectors. For example (ignoring nonwage costs), if wages and productivity in the progressive sector both go up 2 per cent per year, costs there will not rise at all. On the other hand, if in the nonprogressive sector productivity is constant, every rise in wages must yield a corresponding addition to costs—a 2 per cent cumulative rise in wages means that, year in year out, costs must be 2 per cent above those of the preceding year. Thus, the very progress of the technologically progressive sectors inevitably adds to the costs of the technologically unchanging sectors of the economy, unless somehow the labor markets in these areas can be sealed off and wages held absolutely constant, a most unlikely possibility.

We see then that costs in many sectors of the economy will rise relentlessly and will do so for reasons that for all practical purposes are beyond the control of those involved. The consequence is that *some* of the outputs of these sectors may tend to be driven from the market. On the other hand, for those goods whose relative outputs are maintained, an ever-increasing proportion of the labor force must be channeled into their production and the rate of growth of the economy will tend to be slowed correspondingly.

5. *SOME APPLICATIONS*

The preceding observations can be used at once to explain a number of observed phenomena.

The demand for the product of higher education seems to be relatively income elastic and price inelastic. Higher tuition charges undoubtedly impose serious hardships on lower-income students. But, because a college degree seems increasingly to be a necessary condition for employment in a variety of attractive occupations, most families have apparently been prepared to pay the ever larger fees instituted in recent years. As a result higher education has been absorbing a constantly increasing proportion of per capita income. And the relatively constant productivity of college teaching leads our model to predict that rising educational costs are no temporary phenomenon—that they are not a resultant of wartime inflation which will vanish once faculty salaries are restored to their prewar levels. Rather, it suggests that, as productivity in the remainder of the economy continues to increase, costs of running the educational organizations will mount correspondingly, so that whatever the magnitude of the funds they need today, we can be reasonably certain that they will require more tomorrow, and even more on the day after that.

But not all services in the relatively constant productivity sector of the economy face price inelastic and income elastic demands.

Many of them are more readily dispensable than education as far as individual consumers are concerned. As their costs increase, their utilization tends therefore to decrease and they retreat into the category of luxury goods with very limited markets or disappear almost completely. Fine pottery and glassware produced by the careful labor of skilled craftsmen sell at astronomical prices, fine restaurants and theaters are forced to keep raising their prices, and at least in the case of the latter we know that volume is dwindling while it becomes ever more difficult for suppliers (the producers) to make ends meet.

An extreme example of an activity that has virtually disappeared is the construction (and, indeed, the utilization) of the large and stately houses whose operation even more than their construction allows for little in the way of enhanced productivity, and whose rising costs of operation have apparently decreased their salability even to the wealthy.

Our analysis also has direct implications for the financial problem of the cities. More than one reform mayor has taken office determined to undertake a radical program to deal with the city's difficulties and found himself baffled by the deficit which before taking office he had ascribed largely to inefficiency and corruption. There seems in these cases to be no obvious explanation for the growth in the city's financial needs—for the fact that a municipal budget far above that which was roughly adequate a decade earlier threatens to be inadequate to prevent serious disruption of the city's most vital services today.

A critical element in the explanation becomes clear when we recognize how large a proportion of the services provided by the city are activities falling in the relatively nonprogressive sector of the economy. The bulk of our municipal expenditures is devoted to education, which, as we have already seen, offers very limited scope for cumulative increases in productivity. The same is true of police, of hospitals, of social services, and of a variety of inspection services. Despite the use of the computer in medicine and in traffic planning, despite the use of closed circuit television and a variety of other devices, there is no substitute for the personal attention of a physician or the presence of a police patrol in a crime-ridden neighborhood. The bulk of municipal services is, in fact, of this general stamp and our model tells us clearly what can be expected as a result. Since there is no reason to anticipate a cessation of capital accumulation or innovation in the progressive sectors of the economy, the upward trend in the real costs of municipal services cannot be expected to halt; inexorably and cumulatively, whether or not there is inflation, administrative mismanagement or malfeasance, municipal budgets will almost certainly continue to mount in the future, just as they have been doing in the past. This is a trend for which no man and no group should be blamed, for there is nothing that can be done to stop it.

6. IMPLICATIONS FOR SOCIAL WELFARE [5]

The analysis which has just been presented may seem rather gloomy in its implications, and so it is for those concerned with the financing of the nonproductive areas of activity. The mayor of a city, the president of a university, or the seller of handicraft services can take little comfort from learning that his rapidly mounting costs are, to a considerable extent, part of the price of progress in the economy as a whole.

But to the general public, matters are quite different. From its point of view the model records the behavior of an economy whose income constantly rises as its productive capacity grows cumulatively. True, the *relative* costs of services rise relentlessly in the process. But that is only another way of saying that the *relative* prices of manufactured goods fall correspondingly. It is also true, as Proposition Three implies, that if overall goods and service output demands retain, approximately, their relative magnitudes, then the services must absorb a greater and greater proportion of the

[5] This section draws heavily on comments by David Bradford in his unpublished paper, "Balance on Unbalanced Growth," with Professor Bradford's permission.

total labor force. Undoubtedly, this phenomenon already manifests itself in practice. But the increasing absorption of labor by the service activities is, again, only the obverse of a declining demand for labor per unit of output in manufacturing.

From the point of view of society, then, the only danger in the process is that significant external benefits will be lost when some of the nonprogressive outputs are held back by consumers' or taxpayers' or philanthropists' unwillingness to bear their rising costs. For example, if, as we flatter ourselves, higher education does offer substantial external benefits, then nigardliness in its funding will damage interests of society well beyond the interests of those immediately affected. It is primarily for this reason that the phenomenon described in the preceding model should be of concern for policy. And though the issues involved are very serious, as we have seen, it should be recognized that the process automatically provides the means necessary to deal with the problems it creates, for the difficulties stem ultimately from a growth in productivity in our economy which can *automatically* provide the resources needed to pay for higher service costs should society decide to do so.

7. SECOND MODEL: SOME PITFALLS IN CONTRACYCLICAL POLICIES

It is not generally recognized by economists that where governmental contracyclical policies are concerned common sense is a particularly dangerous tool. Policies—automatic or not—which appear to be properly designed may very well turn out to aggravate fluctuations.[6]

To illustrate this point, we shall describe two rather plausible types of contracyclical fiscal policy and show that they can lead to some rather surprising results. Our discussion assumes that we

[6] Several warnings on this problem have already appeared in the literature. See Milton Friedman, "The Effects of a Full-Employment Policy on Economic Stability: A Formal Analysis," *Essays in Positive Economics* (Chicago: University of Chicago Press, 1953); and A. W. Phillips, "Stabilization Policy in a Closed Economy," *Economic Journal*, Vol. LXIV, June 1954.

are living in the world of the Samuelson accelerator-multiplier model.[7] It will be recalled that the time path of national income, Y_t, in that model is described by the second-order linear difference equation

$$\begin{aligned} Y_t &= \text{Consumption} + \text{Acceleration investment} \\ &\quad + \text{Autonomous investment} \\ &\quad + \text{Net government outlay} \\ &= kY_{t-1} + c(Y_{t-1} - Y_{t-2}) + A + G_t, \end{aligned}$$

where k is the marginal propensity to consume and c is the "relation" of the acceleration principle. In other words, we have

$$Y_t - (k + c)Y_{t-1} + cY_{t-2} - A - G_t = 0 \qquad (166)$$

or, writing $b = -(k + c)$,

$$Y_t + bY_{t-1} + cY_{t-2} - A - G_t = 0. \qquad (167)$$

Let us now suppose that the government determines to regulate its net outlays, G_t, in a way which reduces the severity of the cycle in income generated by (166). Let us consider several possibilities.

a. *A policy to offset income trends.* Suppose the government decides to offset income trends by deficit spending $(G_t > 0)$ when income has just been falling $[(Y_{t-1} - Y_{t-2}) < 0]$ and by collecting a budget surplus when income has been rising, and that the magnitude of this action is proportioned to the size of the change in income. This policy, which is designed to offset income trends, is described algebraically by

$$G_{t,1} = -a(Y_{t-1} - Y_{t-2}), \qquad (168)$$

where a is a positive constant.

Substituting from (168) into (167) and collecting terms, we obtain

$$Y_t + (b + a)Y_{t-1} + (c - a)Y_{t-2} - A = 0. \qquad (169)$$

[7] P. A. Samuelson, "Interactions Between the Multiplier Analysis and the Principle of Acceleration," *op. cit.*

b. *A policy to adjust income levels.* Suppose the government determines always to compensate for the difference between effective demand, Y, and some desired (near full employment) level, E. That is, it seeks to move effective demand toward the full employment level. If there is no lag in government response, this yields

$$G_{t,2} = w(E - Y_t), \tag{170}$$

where w is some positive constant. If there are one- and two-period delays in government reactions, we have, respectively,

$$G_{t,3} = w(E - Y_{t-1}) \tag{171}$$

$$\text{and } G_{t,4} = w(E - Y_{t-2}). \tag{172}$$

Substituting these expressions into (167), our basic income equation, we obtain, respectively, for the zero, one-period, and two-period lag cases

$$Y_t + \left(\frac{b}{1+w}\right)Y_{t-1} + \left(\frac{c}{1+w}\right)Y_{t-2} - \frac{A+wE}{1+w} = 0 \tag{173}$$

$$Y_t + (b+w)Y_{t-1} + cY_{t-2} - A - wE = 0 \tag{174}$$

$$\text{and } Y_t + bY_{t-1} + (c+w)Y_{t-2} - A - wE = 0. \tag{175}$$

It should be noted that equations (169) and (173)–(175) may be considered to approximate the much-discussed built-in stabilizers in our economy. For example, the fact that the government surplus tends automatically to rise (the deficit to fall) because tax payments as a proportion of income automatically go up when money incomes rise, and fall when money incomes decline, can be expressed by these relationships. Thus, our analysis of (169) and (173)–(175) should shed some light on the contribution which these automatic stabilizers really make.

8. *ANALYTIC TOOLS: ISO-STABILITY CURVES*

Let us now develop some tools to help us analyze the effects of these policies on the stability of our model's behavior.

In Figure 60 the axes represent the coefficients b and c, of the difference equation

$$Y_t + bY_{t-1} + cY_{t-2} + r = 0.$$

Ignoring the nonhomogeneous term, r, every such equation can thus be represented by some point in the diagram and vice versa.

As is shown in the Appendix to Chapter Eighteen, triangle UVW is the locus of all points representing difference equations whose

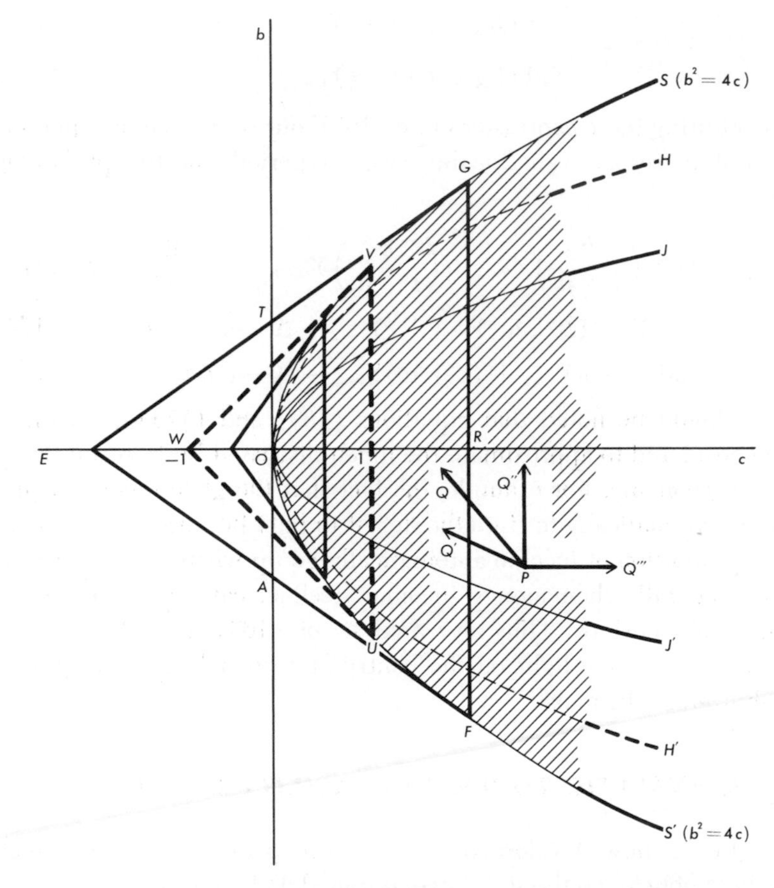

Figure 60

characteristic root of largest absolute value is of modulus unity.[8] Hence, these are the equations on the borderline between damping and explosion, i.e., stability and instability. The smaller triangles nested within *UVW* represent equations with stable solutions; the smaller the triangle, the smaller the absolute value of its dominant root and hence the less explosive its time path. Similarly, the larger triangles outside *UVW* represent equations with unstable solutions; the larger the triangle, the larger the modulus of the dominant root.[9] These triangles, then, constitute the family of second-order difference equation iso-stability curves. It is clear that any change in the coefficients of a difference equation which is represented by a move in the direction of the origin must represent an increase in stability. In particular, stability must be increased by any leftward move inside the region bounded by the parabola *SOS'* (marked $b^2 = 4c$).

9. *ISO-FREQUENCY CURVES*

Parabola *SOS'* is the locus of all points which represent equations with multiple characteristic roots. All points inside this parabola involve complex roots and, hence, fluctuations. The family of iso-frequency curves, i.e., the loci of equations of which all yield a time path involving cycles of the same duration, must all lie within this shaded region. These iso-frequency curves are the parabolas such as *HOH'* and *JOJ'* which lie in this region. All of them are tangent to the *b*-axis at the origin of the diagram, and they satisfy the equations $b^2 = 4k^2c$, where k is a number between zero and unity.[10]

In particular, the portion of the horizontal axis which lies to the right of the origin represents all equations whose cycles are four

[8] In particular, *UV* represents complex root equations, *WU* represents equations with dominant unit root, and *WV* equations with dominant root $= -1$. All propositions given in this section are demonstrated in the appendix to this chapter.

[9] Specifically, if triangle *EFG* is the locus of equations whose dominant root has modulus k, then we have $EO = OR = k^2$ and $AO = OT = k$.

[10] More specifically, if a cycle is of duration $2\pi/\theta$, we have $k = \cos\theta$.

periods long. Points below the c-axis represent cycles which are less frequent than this, up to the limiting case of lower arc OS' of the outermost parabola, $b^2 = 4c$. As we approach this arc, the cycles become longer and longer, without limit, and their frequency approaches zero. Similarly, moving in the upward direction, we go toward arc OS and cycles whose length approaches two periods.[11]

In sum, any downward move within the shaded complex roots region reduces the frequency of cycles and is, in that sense, stabilizing.

10. EVALUATION OF STABILIZATION POLICIES

The preceding diagrams now permit a simple and quick analysis of the stabilization effects of the policies which were described earlier.

First let us look at the trend-offsetting policy (168). For this purpose we compare (169), the income difference equation in the presence of such a policy, with equation (167) in which G is now taken to be a constant. We note that in (167) the first coefficient, $b = -(k + c)$, is negative, and the second coefficient, c, is positive. Hence this equation is represented by a point in the southeast quadrant of Figure 60. I assume also that (167) generates a cyclical time path so that it must be represented by a point, say P, within the lower half of the area bounded by the parabola $b^2 = 4c$.

Now, in equation (169) coefficient b has been increased to $(b + a)$, and c has been decreased to $(c - a)$.[12] This means, in terms of Figure 60 that the point representing our difference equation has moved upward and to the left by the same amount, a. It

[11] In the case of a difference equation it should be noted that a cycle less than two periods long is undefinable, since such an equation refers only to values of the variables at discrete points in time—one value per period—and since a cycle must have at least a high point and a low point, it must take on at least two such values; that is, it must occupy at least two time periods.

[12] This discussion ignores the effect of the various policy measures on the equilibrium income level via changes in the constant term of the equation. It is easy to add a constant amount of government expenditure to each of the policy equations to offset any effect on this constant term.

has moved from P to, say, Q. The leftward move is, as we have seen, definitely stabilizing; any such move must increase the rate of damping of the cycle. But the upward move is very likely [13] to involve an increase in frequency—that is, we are now likely to have more cycles in any given period of time than we would have in the absence of the trend-offsetting policy. Thus, such a measure may well turn out to be a mixed blessing.[14]

Let us see if our other policy alternative will do better. First comparing (173), our income equation in the case of a policy with zero lag in income adjustment, with the basic equation (167), we see that both b and c have been decreased in absolute value by the same proportion, $1/(1+w)$. That is, b will have been *increased* from its initial negative value, whereas c will have fallen. The net result will thus be similar to that of the trend-offsetting policy, a northwestward move in Figure 60—increased damping but more frequent cycles. Only in this case the unfortunate increase in cycle frequency will *always* result, despite the zero lag in government response! [15]

In practice, of course, there are likely to be lags in government

[13] The only possible exception is the case where the iso-frequency curve rises more sharply toward the left than does the vector PQ, whose slope is, of course, -1. This will only occur toward the extreme left of the shaded region. Specifically, since the equation of an iso-frequency curve is $b^2 = 4k^2c$, its slope is $db/dc = +kc^{-1/2}$, or, since $k = b/2c^{1/2}$, we have $db/dc = b/2c$, which is less than unity only to the left of the lines $b = +2c$. This is the portion of the shaded region in Figure 60 to the left of lines OV and UO, the only region in which policy (168) does not increase the frequency of fluctuations.

[14] It will be noted that nothing is being said about the effect of these policies on the amplitude of the cycle in the short run. That is because this amplitude in a linear model is so much a matter of initial conditions. It is, at any rate, possible to show that the policies cannot be depended upon to reduce cycle amplitude except through their effects on dampening of oscillations. In the long run, of course, a more damped time path will eventually have a smaller amplitude.

[15] The effect will not be quite the same as that of the trend-offsetting policy because the move will no longer be represented by a line, PQ, of slope -1. Since both coordinates are reduced proportionately, in the present case the change will be represented by a vector, PQ', which is pointed *directly toward the origin*. We know in the present case that frequency will always be increased because the absolute value of the slope of vector PQ' is b/c, while, as shown in footnote 13, that of the iso-frequency curves is $b/2c$.

response to changes in economic data. As we shall now see, this is only likely to make things worse. Comparing (174) with (167) we see that a one-period lag in an income adjustment policy results in a rise in b to $(b+w)$ and no change in c. There is thus a move due north from P to Q'' in the point representing our equation in Figure 60—the policy now serves only to increase frequency of fluctuations without any compensating increase in cycle damping such as accompanies the two measures which we examined previously!

A two-period lag can perhaps be considered as making things worse still, for it leaves b unchanged and *increases* c to $(c+w)$. The net result is a move directly to the right in Figure 60 from P to Q'''. There is an increase in explosiveness of the cycle and no change in frequency!

11. CONCLUSION

The results of this discussion may reasonably be considered somewhat frightening. Plausible and reasonable contracyclical policies turn out to be capable of increasing the explosiveness and frequency of economic fluctuations. In fact, none of the possibilities examined proved to be entirely harmless in these respects, even in the highly simplified world of the multiplier-accelerator model. There would, therefore, seem to be little ground for confidence in such measures in the far more complex and unpredictable world of reality.

This, of course, is not meant to imply that good automatic stabilizers cannot be invented.[16] The analysis only shows that the design of an automatic stabilization policy is a dangerous game which requires careful calculation and testing.

[16] But common sense remains a dangerous ally. In the present model, for example, a good stabilization policy is one which has effects opposite from those of (172); i.e., it moves us directly leftward from a point like Q''' in the direction of P in Figure 60. But such a policy $[G_t = -w(E - Y_{t-2})]$ calls for a government deficit exactly two periods after every inflationary occurrence (and the reverse in the wake of periods of depression) no matter what the length of the cycle, and even if the inflationary pressure has not yet disappeared!

Appendix to Chapter Eighteen

DERIVATION OF THE ISO-STABILITY LOCI

1. ISO-MAXIMAL ROOT LOCI: SECOND-ORDER LINEAR DIFFERENCE AND DIFFERENTIAL EQUATIONS

Real Roots

Let r_1 and r_2 be the roots of the characteristic equation

$$x^2 + bx + c = 0.$$

Set

$$r_1 = k,\ r_2 = \begin{cases} k - \epsilon \text{ for } k > 0 \\ k + \epsilon \text{ for } k < 0 \end{cases}. \tag{i}$$

Then

$$b = -(r_1 + r_2) = -2k \pm \epsilon,\ c = r_1 r_2 = k^2 \mp k\epsilon. \tag{ii}$$

Thus, eliminating ϵ, we have the equation of the straight-line iso root ($r_1 = k$) locus

$$c = k^2 - k(b + 2k) = k^2 - bk - 2k^2 = -k^2 - bk$$

or

$$b = -k - \frac{c}{k}. \tag{iii}$$

The intercepts of the equation are obtained by noting that

$$\text{When } b = 0,\ c = -k^2 \quad \text{and when } c = 0,\ b = -k. \tag{iv}$$

Let r_1 be the root of largest absolute value. We must therefore have

$$0 \leqq \epsilon \leqq 2|k|$$

because then and only then is r_1 the dominant root. Specifically, at the end points of this interval, if $\epsilon = 0$, $r_1 = r_2 = k$; and if $\epsilon = 2|k|$, $r_2 = (k - 2k) = -k = -r_1$. Hence, by (ii), the iso-maximal root locus (iii) has the end points

$$c = k^2, b = -2k \tag{v}$$

and

$$c = -k^2, b = 0. \tag{vi}$$

To summarize, the iso-maximal root locus consists of two straight-line segments, (iii). For $k > 0$ this has negative slope $-1/k$, and the end point (v) lies below the c-axis. Similarly, for $k < 0$ it has a positive slope, and end point (v) lies above the c-axis. The two segments meet on the c-axis at point (vi).

Comment. Points (v) lie on the parabola $b^2 = 4c$ since these are the cases $\epsilon = 0$, so that $r_1 = r_2$ (double roots). Moreover, at these points (iii) is tangent to that parabola, whose slope is $db/dc = 1/\sqrt{c} = 1/k$.

Complex Roots

Let the complex roots be $(v + wi)$ and $(v - wi)$ whose absolute value is $k = \sqrt{v^2 + w^2}$. Then we have $c = (v + wi)(v - wi) = v^2 + w^2 = k^2$ as the equation of the iso-maximal root locus. This is the vertical line which joins (iii) at points (v).

2. *ISO-FREQUENCY LOCI*

Let r_1 and r_2 be the complex conjugate roots

$$-b/2 \pm i\sqrt{(4c - b^2)}/2 = v \pm wi$$

The solution is $R^t(c' \cos \theta t + u' \sin \theta t) = y(t)$. By appropriate choice of the constants c' and u', we can take [17] $0 \leqq \theta \leqq \pi$. Then θ is a single-valued function of $\cos\theta$. But

$$\cos\theta = v/\sqrt{v^2+w^2} = -\frac{b}{2}\Big/\sqrt{\frac{b^2}{4}+c-\frac{b^2}{4}} = -\frac{b}{2}/\sqrt{c},$$

where we always take the absolute value of the complex root, $\sqrt{v^2+w^2} = \sqrt{c}$, to be positive. Hence an iso-frequency curve has the equation $-b/2\sqrt{c} = k$

or $$b^2 = 4k^2c. \qquad \text{(vii)}$$

This is a family of parabolas all lying within the half plane $c \geqq 0$ and symmetric about the c-axis. Since $k = \cos\theta \leqq 1$, the outermost parabola is the borderline of the complex region $b^2 = 4c$. For $k = 0$ the parabola degenerates into the nonnegative portion of the c-axis.

For $b \leqq 0$ we have $\cos\theta = -b/2\sqrt{c} \geqq 0$ so that $0 \leqq \theta \leqq \pi/2$; cycles will be at least $\dfrac{2\pi}{\pi/2} = 4$ periods long. For $b > 0$ the cycles will be less than four periods long. Hence the branch of a parabola (vii) which lies below the c-axis is a different iso-frequency curve from that which lies above that axis. In particular, the lower branch of the outer parabola $b^2 = 4c$ is the case $\cos\theta = 1$ or $\theta = 0$, that is, of "cycles of infinite duration." The in-between case $b = 0$ (the c-axis degenerate parabola) is $k = \cos\theta = 0$ or $\theta = \pi/2$: the four-period cycle. Finally, the upper branch of the outer parabola $b^2 = 4c$ involves cycles of two-period duration.

[17] For if θ lies outside this interval, we can set $\theta = m\pi + Q$, where m is some (positive or negative) integer and $0 < Q < \pi$. Then we have

$$\begin{aligned} y(t) &= R'[c'\cos(m\pi t + Qt) + u'\sin(m\pi t + Qt)] \\ &= R'[c'\cos m\pi t\cos Qt - c'\sin m\pi t\sin Qt + u'\cos m\pi t\sin Qt \\ &\qquad + u'\sin m\pi t\cos Qt] \end{aligned}$$

and since $\sin m\pi t = 0$, $\cos m\pi t = (-1)^{mt}$

$$y(t) = R'[(-1)^{mt}c'\cos Qt + (-1)^{mt}u'\sin Qt]$$

which differs at most by a factor of (-1) from the original solution in θ.

A SHORT READING LIST[1]

INTRODUCTION

Cassel, Gustav: *Fundamental Thoughts in Economics,* Chap. I (Ernest Benn Ltd., London, 1929).

Clark, J. B.: *The Distribution of Wealth* (The Macmillan Company, New York, 1938).

Frisch, Ragnar: "On the Notion of Equilibrium and Disequilibrium," *Review of Economic Studies,* 1935–1936.

Knight, Frank H.: "Statics and Dynamics," *The Ethics of Competition* (Harper, New York, 1935).

Robbins, Lionel: "On a Certain Ambiguity in the Conception of Stationary Equilibrium," *Economic Journal,* 1930; reprinted in *Readings in Economic Analysis*, Vol. I, R. V. Clemence, editor (Addison-Wesley Press, Cambridge, Mass., 1950).

Samuelson, Paul A.: "Dynamics, Statics, and the Stationary State," *Review of Economic Statistics,* 1943; reprinted in *Readings in Economic Analysis, ibid.*

Veblen, Thorstein: "Why Is Economics Not an Evolutionary Science?" in *The Place of Science in Modern Civilization* (B. W. Huebsch, New York, 1919).

PART ONE

Alexander, S. S.: "Mr. Harrod's Dynamic Model," *Economic Journal,* 1950.

Allen, R. G. D.: *Mathematical Economics* (Macmillan & Co., Ltd., London, 1956).

[1] We have sought to make our selection primarily on the basis of comprehensibility. As a result many fine but highly mathematical or foreign language publications have been omitted. Where it seemed convenient a descriptive phrase has been inserted in parentheses at the end of the reference; this is meant to indicate the most relevant aspect of the book or article and does not always suggest its main subject.

Domar, Evsey D.: *Essays in the Theory of Economic Growth* (Oxford University Press, New York, 1957).

Haberler, Gottfried: *Prosperity and Depression,* 3rd Ed. (United Nations, New York, 1946).

Hahn, F. H., and Matthews, R. C. O.: "The Theory of Economic Growth: A Survey," *The Economic Journal,* 1964.

Hamberg, D.: *Economic Growth and Instability* (W. W. Norton, New York, 1956).

Hansen, Alvin, "Economic Progress and Declining Population Growth," *The American Economic Review,* 1939; reprinted in *Readings in Business Cycle Theory* (The Blakiston Company, Philadelphia, 1944). (The stagnation thesis.)

Harrod, Roy F.: *Towards a Dynamic Economics* (Macmillan & Co., Ltd., London, 1948).

———: "An Essay in Dynamic Theory," *Economic Journal,* 1939.

Keirstead, B. S.: *The Theory of Economic Change* (The Macmillan Company of Canada, Ltd., Toronto, 1948).

Knox, A. D.: "The Acceleration Principle and the Theory of Investment: A Survey," *Economica,* 1952.

Lancaster, Kelvin: *Mathematical Economics* (The Macmillan Company, New York, 1968).

Lenin, V. I.: *Imperialism: The Highest Stage of Capitalism* (International Publishers, New York, 1939).

Meade, James E.: *A Neo-classical Theory of Economic Growth* (Allen, London, 1961).

Mikiado, Hukukane: *Convex Structures and Economic Theory* (Academic Press, New York, 1968).

Mill, J. S.: *Principles of Political Economy.* Book IV (Ashley, ed., Longmans, Green & Co., London and New York, 1926).

Ricardo, David: *On the Principles of Political Economy and Taxation,* esp. Chapter XXI (E. P. Dutton and Co., New York, 1911).

Robinson, Joan: *An Essay on Marxian Economics* (Macmillan and Co., Ltd., London, 1942).

———: *The Accumulation of Capital* (Richard D. Irwin, Chicago, 1956).

Samuelson, Paul A.: "A Modern Treatment of the Ricardian Economy," *Quarterly Journal of Economics,* 1959.

Schumpeter, Joseph: *The Theory of Economic Development* (Harvard University Press, Cambridge, Mass., 1934).

———: *Business Cycles* (McGraw-Hill Book Co., New York, 1939).

———: *Capitalism, Socialism and Democracy* (Harper and Brothers, New York and London, 1947).

Senior, Nassau: *An Outline of the Science of Political Economy* (George Allen and Unwin, London, 1938).

Solow, Robert: "A Contribution to the Theory of Economic Growth," *Quarterly Journal of Economics,* 1956.

———: *Capital Theory and the Rate of Return* (North-Holland, Amsterdam, 1963).

Sweezy, Paul M.: *The Theory of Capitalist Development* (Oxford University Press, New York, 1942 and Dennis Dobson Ltd., London, 1946). (Marxian dynamics.)

Veblen, Thorstein: *The Theory of Business Enterprise* (Charles Scribner's Sons, New York, 1904). (Business cycles; magnificent dynamics.)

PART TWO

Buchanan, N. S.: "A Reconsideration of the Cobweb Theorem," *Journal of Political Economy,* 1939; reprinted in *Readings in Economic Analysis,* Vol. I, *op. cit.*

Collery, A. P.: "Expected Price and the Cobweb Theorem," *Quarterly Journal of Economics,* 1955.

Ezekiel, Mordecai: "The Cobweb Theorem," *Quarterly Journal of Economics,* 1938; reprinted in *Readings in Business Cycle Theory, op. cit.*

Fisher, Irving: *The Nature of Capital and Income* (The Macmillan Company, New York, 1906). Appendix to Chap. XVI. (Risk and uncertainty.)

Hart, A. G.: *Anticipations, Uncertainty and Dynamic Planning, Journal of Business,* Oct. 1940, *Studies in Business Administration,* Vol. 11, No. 1, University of Chicago Press, Chicago, Ill.

———:"Risk, Uncertainty and the Unprofitability of Compounding Probabilities," *Studies in Mathematical Economics and Econometrics* (University of Chicago Press, Chicago, 1942).

Hicks, J. R.: "The Theory of Uncertainty and Profit," *Economica,* 1931.

———:"Recent Contributions to General Equilibrium Economics," *Economica,* 1945. (On the Lange analysis.)

———: *Value and Capital,* 2nd ed., Clarendon Press, Oxford, 1946.

Knight, Frank H.: *Risk, Uncertainty and Profit,* especially Parts I and III (Houghton Mifflin Co., Boston and New York, 1921. Reprinted by The London School of Economics, London, 1931).

Lachmann, L. M.: "A Note on the Elasticity of Expectations," *Economica,* 1945.

Lange, Oscar: *Price Flexibility and Employment* (The Principia Press, Bloomington, Indiana, 1944).

Makower, H., and Marshak, J.: "Assets, Prices and Monetary Theory," *Economica,* 1938. (Risk and uncertainty.)

Muth, John F.: "Rational Expectations and the Theory of Price Movements," *Econometrica,* 1961.

Nerlove, Marc.: "Adaptive Expectations and Cobweb Phenomena," *Quarterly Journal of Economics,* 1958.

Pashagian, Peter B.: "Rational Expectations and the Cobweb Theory," Report 6804 (Center for Mathematical Studies in Business and Economics, University of Chicago, Chicago, 1968).

Patinkin, Don: *Money, Interest, and Prices* (Row, Peterson and Co., Evanston, Illinois, 1956).

Reder, Melvin: *Studies in the Theory of Welfare Economics,* Part II (Columbia University Press, New York, 1947). (Stability, comparative statics, and dynamics.)

Shackle, G. L. S.: *Expectation in Economics* (Cambridge University Press, Cambridge, England, 2nd ed., 1952). (Risk and uncertainty.)

PART THREE

Allen, R. G. D.: *Macroeconomic Theory: A Mathematical Treatment* (St. Martin's Press, New York and Macmillan & Co., Ltd., London, 1967).

Leontief, Wassily: "Econometrics" in *A Survey of Contemporary Economics,* H. S. Ellis, editor (The Blakiston Company, Philadelphia and Toronto, 1948). (The problem of aggregation.)

Lindahl, Erik: *Studies in the Theory of Money and Capital,* Part I (George Allen and Unwin, London and New York, 1939). (Period analysis.)

May, Kenneth: "Technological Change and Aggregation," Sec. III, *Econometrica,* 1947.

Metzler, L. A.: "Three Lags in the Circular Flow of Income," in *Income, Employment and Public Policy* (W. W. Norton & Co., New York, 1948).

Ohlin, Bertil: "Some Notes on the Stockholm Theory of Saving and Investment," *Economic Journal,* 1937; reprinted in *Readings in Business Cycle Theory, op. cit.* (The *ex ante-ex post* approach.)

PART FOUR

Allen, R. G. D.: *Mathematical Economics* (St. Martins Press, New York, 1956), Chapters 1–9. (A superb exposition of the mathematical techniques.)

———: "The Engineer's Approach to Economic Models," *Economica,* 1955.

Baumol, William J.: "Topology of Second Order Linear Difference Equations with Constant Coefficients," *Econometrica,* 1958.

Beach, E. F.: *Economic Models: An Exposition* (John Wiley, New York, 1957), Chapters 5 and 6. (A good elementary introduction to the mathematics.)

Bushaw, D. W., and Clower, R. W.: *Introduction to Mathematical Economics* (Richard D. Irwin, Homewood, Ill., 1957), Chapters 3, 4, and 12.

Butenin, N. V.: *Elements of the Theory of Nonlinear Oscillations,* trans. by Scripta Technica (Blaisdell Publishing Company, New York, 1965).

Samuelson, Paul A.: "Dynamic Process Analysis," in *A Survey of Contemporary Economics, op. cit.* (An introduction to difference and differential equations.)

Tinbergen, Jan: "Econometric Business Cycle Research," *Review of Economic Studies,* 1940; reprinted in *Readings in Business Cycle Theory, op. cit.* (Use of difference equations in econometrics.)

Tustin, Arnold: *The Mechanism of Economic Systems* (Harvard University Press, Cambridge, Mass., 1953). (Explains how the engineer's techniques can be used in dynamic economics.)

The following articles and books contain various macroeconomic dynamic models which should be of interest both for their own sake and for the method of construction.

Baumol, William J.: "Notes on Some Dynamic Models," *Economic Journal,* 1948.

———: "Formalization of Mr. Harrod's Model," *Economic Journal,* 1949.

———: "Speculation, Profitability and Stability," *Review of Economics and Statistics,* 1957.

Bennion, E. G.: "The Multiplier, the Acceleration Principle, and Fluctuating Autonomous Investment," *Review of Economic Statistics,* 1945.

Domar, Evsey D.: *Essays in the Theory of Economic Growth* (Oxford University Press, New York, 1957).

Frisch, Ragnar: "Propagation Problems and Impulse Problems in Dynamic Economics" in *Economic Essays in Honour of Gustav Cassel* (George Allen and Unwin, London, 1933).

Goodwin, R. M.: "Innovations and the Irregularity of Economic Cycles," *Review of Economic Statistics,* 1946.

Hansen, Bent: *A Study in the Theory of Inflation* (Allen and Unwin, London, 1951), Chapters VII and VIII. (The latter giving a simultaneous equation system.)

Hicks, J. R.: "Mr. Harrod's Dynamic Theory," *Economica,* 1949.

———: *The Trade Cycle* (Oxford University Press, London, 1950).

Kalecki, M.: "A Macrodynamic Theory of Business Cycles," *Econometrica,* 1935.

Koopmans, T.: "The Dynamics of Inflation," *Review of Economic Statistics,* 1942.

Lundberg, Erik: *Studies in the Theory of Economic Expansion* (P. S. King & Son, Ltd., London, 1937).

Metzler, L. A.: "The Nature and Stability of Inventory Cycles," *Review of Economic Statistics,* 1941.

Palander, T.: "On the Concepts and Methods of the Stockholm School," *International Economic Papers* No. 3.

Phillips, A. W.: "Stabilization Policy in a Closed Economy," *Economic Journal,* 1954.

Samuelson, Paul A.: "Interactions between the Multiplier Analysis and the Principle of Acceleration," *Review of Economic Statistics,* 1939; reprinted in *Readings in Business Cycle Theory, op. cit.*

Smithies, Arthur: "Process Analysis and Equilibrium Analysis," *Econometrica,* 1942.

Tinbergen, J.: "Suggestions on Quantitative Business Cycle Theory," *Econometrica,* 1935.

———: *Statistical Testing of Business-Cycle Theories* (League of Nations, Geneva, 1934).

Turvey, Ralph: "Period Analysis and Inflation," *Economica,* 1949.

———: "Some Notes on Multiplier Theory," *American Economic Review,* 1953, esp. Section III.

NONLINEAR MODELS

Baumol, William J.: "Interaction Between Successive Polling Results and Voting Intentions," *Public Opinion Quarterly,* 1957.

Goodwin, R. M.: "The Nonlinear Accelerator and the Persistence of Business Cycles," *Econometrica,* 1951.

Hicks, J. R.: *A Contribution to the Theory of the Trade Cycle* (Oxford University Press, New York, 1950).

Ichimura, Shin-ichi: *The Historical Development of Economic Dynamics* (The Science Council of Japan, Division of Economics and Commerce, Economic Series No. 4, Tokyo, 1955), Part III.

———: "Notes on Non-Linear Business Cycle Theories," *Osaka Economic Papers,* 1955.

PART FIVE

Almon, Clopper: *Matrix Methods in Economics* (Addison-Wesley Publishing Company, Reading, Mass., 1967).
Bellman, Richard E.: *Introduction to Matrix Analysis* (McGraw-Hill Book Company, New York, 1960).
Brems, Hans: "How Induced is Induced Investment?" *Review of Economics and Statistics,* 1955.
Chipman, John: *The Theory of Inter-Sectoral Money Flows and Income Formation* (Johns Hopkins Press, Baltimore, 1951).
Foote, R.: "A Four-Equation Model of the Feed-Livestock Economy and Its Endogenous Mechanism," *Journal of Farm Economics,* 1953.
Goodwin, R. M.: "The Multiplier as Matrix," *Economic Journal,* 1949.
Leontief, Wassily: *Studies in the Structure of the American Economy* (Oxford University Press, New York, 1953), Chapter 3.
Metzler, L. A.: "Stability of Multiple Markets: The Hicks Conditions," *Econometrica,* 1945.
———: "A Multiple-Region Theory of Income and Trade," *Econometrica,* 1950.
Patinkin, *op. cit.,* Mathematical Appendices 8–10.
Samuelson, P. A.: *Foundations of Economic Analysis* (Harvard University Press, Cambridge, Mass., 1947), Chapter IX and Appendix B.
Solow, Robert: "On the Structure of Linear Models," *Econometrica,* 1952.
———, and Samuelson, P. A.: "Balanced Growth Under Constant Returns to Scale," *Econometrica,* 1953.
Tintner, Gerhard: "A 'Simple' Theory of Business Fluctuations," *Econometrica,* 1942.

PART SIX

Dorfman, Robert, Samuelson, P. A., and Solow, R. M.: *Linear Programming and Economic Analysis* (McGraw-Hill, New York, 1958), Chapter 12.
Gale, David: *The Theory of Linear Economic Models* (McGraw-Hill, New York, 1960).
Hahn, F. H., and Matthews, R. C. O.: "The Theory of Economic Growth: A Survey," *Economic Journal,* 1964; reprinted in *Survey of Economic Theory,* Vol. II (St. Martin's Press, New York, 1965).
Hanson, J. A., and Neher, P. A.: "The Neoclassical Theorem Once Again," *American Economic Review,* 1967.

Johnson, Harry G.: "The Neoclassical One-Sector Growth Model," *Economica,* 1966.

Kemeny, J. G., Morgenstern, O., and Thompson, G. L.: "A Generalization of the von Neumann Model of an Expanding Economy," *Econometrica,* 1956.

Koopmans, T. C.: "Economic Growth at a Maximal Rate," in *Activity Analysis in the Theory of Growth and Planning,* E. Malinvaud and M. O. L. Bacharach, editors (St. Martin's Press, New York, 1967).

———: "Objectives, Constraints and Outcomes in Optimal Growth Models," *Econometrica,* 1967.

Marty, A. L.: "The Neoclassical Theorem," *American Economic Review,* 1964.

Meade, J. E.: *A Neo-Classical Theory of Economic Growth* (Allen, London, 1961).

Phelps, E. S.: *Golden Rules of Economic Growth* (Norton, New York, 1966).

Ramsey, F. P.: "A Mathematical Theory of Saving," *Economic Journal,* 1928; reprinted in *Precursors in Mathematical Economics,* W. J. Baumol and S. M. Goldfeld, editors (The London School of Economics, London, 1968).

Robinson, Joan: *Essays in the Theory of Economic Growth* (St. Martin's Press, New York, 1962).

Solow, Robert M.: "A Contribution to the Theory of Economic Growth," *Quarterly Journal of Economics,* 1956.

Swan, T. W.: "Economic Growth and Capital Accumulation," *Economic Record,* 1956.

Tobin, James: "Money and Economic Growth," *Econometrica,* 1965.

von Neumann, J.: "A Model of General Economic Equilibrium," *Review of Economic Studies,* 1945–1946 (G. Morton, trans.); reprinted in *Precursors in Mathematical Economics, op. cit.*

ANSWERS

CHAPTER 9

Sect. 1

1. a) 3 b) 2 c) 2 d) 2 e) 3 f) 503 g) *n*;
2. same as 1
3. a) $y(1) = 2, y(2) = 4, y(3) = 8, y(4) = 16, y(5) = 32$
   b) $y(1) = -2, y(2) = 4, y(3) = -8, y(4) = 16, y(5) = -32$
   c) $y(2) = 3, y(3) = 4, y(4) = 5, y(5) = 6, y(6) = 7$
   d) $y(2) = 2, y(3) = 4, y(4) = 4, y(5) = 8, y(6) = 8$
   e) $y(2) = 2, y(4) = 4, y(6) = 8, y(8) = 16$, etc.
4. a) $y(2) = 5, y(3) = 12, y(4) = 29, y(5) = 70$
   b) $y(3) = 12, y(4) = 29, y(5) = 70, y(6) = 169$
   c) $y(3) = 5, y(4) = 12, y(5) = 29, y(6) = 70$

Sect. 2

1. a) $y(t) = 3(5)^t$
   b) $y(t) = 5(-2)^t$
   c) $y(t) = -4$
   d) $y(t) = M(L)^t$
   e) $y(t) = 3(5)^t$
   f) $P(t) = 3(5)^t$

Sect. 3

a) Stationary
b) Decreases to nothing without oscillation
c) Explodes with oscillation
d) Explodes without oscillation

Sect. 5

Demand equation: $D_t = a - bP_t$, supply equation: $S_t = w + vP_{t-1}$ where a, b, w, and v are constants and P is price. Then set supply equal to demand.

CHAPTER 10

Sect. 2

1. a) $y(t) = 3^t + 1$
   b) $y(t) = 3 \cdot 4^t + 5 \cdot 2^t$
   c) $y(t) = 2 \cdot 3^t - 5 \cdot 2^t$
   d) $y(t) = 2(5)^t + 6(-2)^t$
   e) $y(t) = 55 \cdot 6^t + 2^{t+1}$
   f) $y(t) = 3 \cdot 2^t + 5(-2)^t$

Sect. 4

1. a) $y(t) = 3(5)^t + 2$
   b) $y(t) = 3 \cdot 4^t + 5 \cdot 2^t - 3$
   c) $y(t) = 2(5)^t + 6(-2)^t + 1$
   d) $y(t) = 3 \cdot 2^t - 5(-2)^t - 30$

Sect. 5

1. a) $Z(t) = -\frac{5}{2}t$
   b) $Z(t) = -\frac{1}{3}t$
   c) $Z(t) = -\frac{3}{16}$
   d) $Z = t^3$

Sect. 6

1. a) $y(t) = a(-3)^t + bt(-3)^t$
   b) $y(t) = a(5)^t + bt(5)^t$

Sect. 7

1. a) $(10^t)[2 \cos(126.9°t) + 3 \sin(126.9°t)] + 2$
   b) $(15^t)[5 \cos(36.9°t) + \sin(36.9°t)]$
   c) $(10^t)[2 \cos(53.1°t) + 3 \sin(53.1°t)] + 1$
   d) $(15^t)[5 \cos(143.1°t) - \sin(143.1°t)]$
   e) $16 \cos(90°t) - 7 \sin(90°t)$
   f) $[-2.444] \cdot 10^{10} + 2$; $[-1.506] \cdot 10^{10} + 1$; -16

CHAPTER 11

Sect. 3

4. VII $r_1 < -1, r_2 < -1$, VIII $r_1 < -1, -1 < r_2 < 0$
   IX $r_1 > |r_2|, 0 < r_1 < 1, -1 < r_2 < 0$, X $r_1 > 1, -1 < r_2 < 0$
   XI $r_1 > |r_2|, r_1 > 1, r_2 < -1$, XII $|r_2| > r_1, 0 < r_1 < 1,$
   $-1 < r_2 < 0$
   XIII $0 < r_1 < 1, r_2 < -1$, XIV $|r_2| > r_1, r_1 > 1, r_2 < -1$

CHAPTER 12

Sect. 3

1. $V(-2) = 3$
   $V(-1) = 2$
   $V(+2) = 1$
2. The positive root is larger in absolute value since it is greater than 2 while the negative root lies between -2 and 0.

3a) $f_1 = 3x^2 - 6x - 3$
   $f_2 = 4x + 2$
   $f_3 = -.75$

 b) $f_1 = 3x^2 - 3$
   $f_2 = 2x - 1$
   $f_3 = 2\frac{1}{4}$

Sect. 5

1. a) $f_1 = 3x^2 - 6x + 3$
      $f_2 = 0$
   b) $f_1 = 3x^2 - 6x + 6$
      $f_2 = -2x + 2$
      $f_3 = -3$
2. a) 1b has 2 complex roots
   b) 1 a has the triple roots $x = 1$

Sect. 7

1. $x_2 = 64/117$
2. $x_1 = 2/5$

CHAPTER 13

Sect. 3

2. $y_{t+1} = ay_t + b$, case ii $a > 1$, case iii $0 > a > -1$, case iv $-1 > a$.

Sect. 5

1. *B* and *D*
2. Limit cycle *C*
3. a) $S = 1 \quad U = 12$
   b) $S = 2 \quad U = 15$

CHAPTER 14

Sect. 2

1. a) $y = 4e^{-3t}$
   b) $y = e^{17t}$
   c) $y = 5$
   d) $y = 0$

Sect. 3

1. a) $y = e^{3t} + e^{t}$
   b) $y = 3e^{4t} + 5e^{2t}$
   c) $y = 2e^{5t} + 6e^{-2t}$
   d) $y = 3e^{2t} + 5e^{-2t}$

Sect. 4

1. a) $y = -\frac{25}{8}e^{4t} + \frac{29}{4}e^{2t} - \frac{9}{8}$
   b) $y = fe^{2t} + ge^{-2t} - 25$
   c) $y = f + ge^{-3t} + 3t$

Sect. 5

1. a) $y = e^{-3t} + 5te^{-3t}$
   b) $y = fe^{5t} + gte^{5t}$
   c) $y = f + gt + 5t^2$

Sect. 6

1. a) $y = e^{-6t}(h \cos 8t + j \sin 8t) + \frac{226}{100}$
   b) $y = e^{3t}(h \cos 2t + j \sin 2t)$
   c) $y = h \cos t + j \sin t$

Sect. 7

Unstable regions III, IV, and V
Stable regions, VI, VII, and VIII
Ultimately explosive (one root positive) the remainder of the diagram.

Sect. 8

1. a) $y = e^{t}(h \cos t + j \sin t) + \frac{1}{2}(t + 1)$
   b) $y = e^{t}(h \cos t + j \sin t) + e^{t}$
   c) $y = e^{t}(h \cos t + j \sin t) + e^{t} + \frac{1}{2}(t + 1)$
   d) $y = fe^{t} + gte^{t} + \frac{1}{4}t^2e^{3t} - \frac{1}{2}te^{3t} + \frac{3}{8}e^{3t}$

CHAPTER 15

Sect. 2

1. $y_{1t} = 4(2)^t + 8(-2)^t + 5$
   $y_{2t} = 2^t - 2(-2)^t + 2$
2. $y_{1t} = 10(5)^t - 12(-2)^t + 1$
   $y_{2t} = 2(5)^t + 6(-2)^t + 1$

Sect. 3

3. $y_{2t+1} - 2y_{1t+1} + 3y_{1t} + y_t - 3x_t = 5$ etc.

Sect. 5

1. a) $2^t/18$
   b) $3(4)^t/5$
   c) $e^{15t}/3$

CHAPTER 16

Sect. 4

1. a) It is unstable and has negative or complex roots: trace $= -3$.
   b) It is unstable: $|A(0)| = 1.45$
   c) Unstable: $|A(1)| = -\frac{1}{4}$
   d) Unstable: the trace is positive $= +3$ and the determinant is negative $= -2$.

INDEX

E

F

G

H

I

J

K

L

M

U

V

W